# POPULAR CUL
# EDUCATIONAL DI
# AND MATHEM

SUNY Series, Education and Culture: Critical Factors in the Formation
of Character and Community in American Life

Eugene F. Provenzo, Jr. and Paul Farber, editors

# POPULAR CULTURE, EDUCATIONAL DISCOURSE, AND MATHEMATICS

Peter M. Appelbaum

State University of New York Press

Published by
State University of New York Press, Albany

For information, address State University of New York Press,
State University Plaza, Albany, N.Y., 12246

Production by Dana Foote
Marketing by Dana E. Yanulavich

**Library of Congress Cataloging-in-Publication Data**

Appelbaum, Peter Michael.
    Popular culture, educational discourse, and mathematics / Peter M.
Appelbaum.
        p.   cm. — (SUNY series, education and culture)
    Includes bibliographical references and index.
    ISBN 0–7914–2269–0 (alk. paper). — ISBN 0–7914–2270–4 (pbk. :
alk. paper)
        1. Mathematics—Study and teaching.   2. Mathematics—Psychological
aspects.   3. Popular culture.   I. Title.   II. Series.
QA11.A64   1995
510'.7—dc20                                              94–46206
                                                            CIP

10  9  8  7  6  5  4  3  2  1

For Belinda, Noah, and Sophia

# CONTENTS

# ACKNOWLEDGMENTS

I thank Fred Goodman, for personifying the ideal 'superteacher', trusting me, inspiring me, and pushing me to do what I believe in. Thanks also go to the members of my dissertation committee at The University of Michigan, for their emotional support, intellectual advice, and patient flexibility: Terrence Tice, Malcolm Lowther, Helen Harrington, and Frank Beaver. Special appreciation goes as well to Eugene Provenzo and Paul Farber for their encouragement.

A number of people have read various drafts of this book, and their insights have been essential to its evolution. These include: Jane Anderson, Mary Antony, Doug Campbell, Stella Clark, Suzanne Damarin, Belinda Davis, Don Dippo, Ernestine Enomoto, Michael Goldenberg, Esther Gottlieb, Anne Herrmann, Christine Keitel, Thomas Popkewitz, Damon Scott, Cho-Yee To, and Jeffrey Weeks. Research was undertaken with the generous support of The University of Michigan Rackham School of Graduate Studies and School of Education. I especially thank The University of Michigan Institute for the Humanities, its staff and fellows, for a year of financial support and an enriching atmosphere. And I extend my warm appreciation to Thelma Tate of the Douglass Library of Rutgers University and Doug Ross of the American Federation of Teachers, who were tremendous help in the climactic rush to verify quotes and references. Finally, my love to Belinda, Noah, and Sophia, just because; and also for watching *Donald Duck* and *Square One* so many times with me.

# 0
# Introduction

I made the final decisions about the manuscript for this book one year after a presidential election that ushered in a new debate regarding politics as well as government and social policy. The new administration has popularized and problematized a "politics of meaning," along with a "compromise" style of leadership. The presidential election itself was noteworthy because the nature of media coverage of that political process was scrutinized by the media itself.

> Washington—Convinced that something is wrong with politics and stirred by the sense that they bear part of the blame, some of the nation's biggest news organizations are vowing to change the way they cover the 1992 presidential campaign. If they succeed, it could put the press on a collision course with the candidates and mark the first major change in political journalism in decades.[1]

Jay Rosen used the above quote to introduce an article in *Tikkun* about the failure of the media to live up to its declared agenda. He argued that journalists need a new ethic as political actors, so that political processes such as elections could become discussion and debate about the production of 'meaning'.

A connection to current politics is apt here. I argue similarly that educators in a broad sense (because I am part of a movement to remove distinctions such as researcher/practitioner, teacher/student) should comprehend their life as political, and hence that they need to begin thinking cogently about a political philosophy: what Rosen calls a set of beliefs about what politics (and education) is all about.

Journalists "get the story" and "cover the campaign." Educational researchers likewise strive to "get the story." News broadcasts "bring you the world," equate the news with a totality of events, and in this way construct myths which in turn convert culture (a

1

socially constructed collection of phenomena) into nature ("the way things are"). Journalism thus constructs "the world." Educational researchers similarly attempt to be "unbiased" in representing the reality of educational practice, and hence construct the world. Like the media that creates presidential elections as a narrative about a contest that produces a winner, educational research "writes" a story about objective observations of current practice that compete with each other for the honor of "best" or "most accurate," through which policy and subsequent theory should be further constructed.

Is winning the election what a presidential contest should be about? Rosen argued no. The media should not create the election as such. Rather, "the task of the press should be to construct the world in such a way that we can become what we are—a democracy." The assumption, he wrote, is that "democracy is an unmet ideal: a way of life we have claimed as our own, but still need to invent."[2] What democracy requires is public debate, not just information. I argue that educational research follows a parallel course: We need debate, not information. I attempt to introduce a shift in the way we talk about education that I believe holds promise for the production of such debate. As Christopher Lasch notes, we need to construct the political universe in such a way that the activity that is most visible is discussion and debate. I do not want what you are about to read to close off discussion through a well-presented argument that convinces you of some facts. Instead, I intend my writing to encourage a different way of talking about the facts, and what a fact might be.

I begin work with this book on the project of critically examining the way in which educational discourse constructs the world of education. I take as a particular theme the topic of mathematics education, mainly because mathematics is the one subject that most of us can imagine as far removed from issues of politics, value, professional ethics, and democracy. Hence, if I can keep your interest to the end, and if you enjoy what I am doing, it should be very difficult for you not to believe that the same thing could and should be done for any discipline that might be constructed by educators as part of the world.

Rosen suggested that the business of the media is to make politics "go well." They should produce a better portrait of the political community than would otherwise exist.

In this portrait we should be able to recognize ourselves, but also the others with whom we share the same political world. We should be able to see candidates for public office engaging in principled argument, in a setting where they can display their full humanity. We should see journalists, if we see them at all, behaving as exemplary listeners and questioners, asking what needs to be asked if politics is to "go well," and refusing the impulses that must be refused if the political sphere is to have meaning.[3]

As you read my book, I invite you to imagine what the parallel might be for educational researchers. In the process, I ask your patience, because I am trying to do something I have never done before, and which you likely have never read before. First of all, my writing becomes less of an argument designed to win you over and more of a request that you consider new options. Therefore, the standard signposts guiding you through the outline of an argument will not necessarily be found. Second, I am trying, in Rosen's words, to "back out of the frame more often and refuse the predictable urge to dominate the discussion." My work is an attempt to engage my audience as a public, in order that my readers become participants in a healthy public space. In the end, I hope to promote a "politics of meaning."

What about the charge that scholarship is not synonymous with journalism? Should I not be doing something different from a television reporter? Another aspect of my project is the examination of popular culture as if there were no such distinctions. My premise is that these boundaries are part of the story that is told, and that we need to challenge even these most basic presumptions. In doing so, it is possible to reconsider fundamental aspects of educational practice, such as the power relationships among teachers and students. Current theorizations about popular culture studies point to a destabilization of these relationships when the student becomes the "expert" about popular culture. Such considerations are for me basic to the emerging debate about education as a cultural politics.

## Opening

For those of you who need to jump to the end of a book to identify the author's conclusion, I provide the convenience of typing it right here:

Mathematics education research has tended to focus on classroom activities, optimal sequence of topics, or individual cognitive development. It has therefore inadvertently tended to construct a stark, unsustainable distinction between school mathematics and the world outside of schools. In doing so, the typical literature has displaced popular and mass culture, the public space, and related categories of power and politics, or has excluded them altogether.

Of course, I might be lying. That is, this might not be the conclusion I reach, but rather a statement I want you, the reader, to have in mind as you enter my book. The above 'conclusion' might merely be a tentative summary statement serving to generate questions. Pretheoretical questions can often direct curiosity. I invite you to join me in my inquiry into what are at once philosophical and cultural aspects of mathematics education. To locate a conclusion, you may need to skip to my last chapter after all, begin with that one, and come back here later. But if I say something is my conclusion, it certainly should be so.

Another fiction: After numerous years teaching mathematics and studying mathematics education, I jumped to the above determination not on the basis of empirical evidence entered into a database, but through my own personal, idiosyncratic experiences, in which questions I often asked seemed to have been provided with axiomatic answers masquerading as 'reality', in turn relegating questions about themselves to being irrelevant. Through dogged, naive persistence, I have failed to understand why these axiomatic, transparently obvious facts about reality should not be understood as socially constructed cultural symbols. In this story, I have repeatedly asked myself and others why, for example, we believe that there exists a discipline called mathematics, which, oddly enough, deserves a particularly central role in planned objectives for learning, which in turn is to take place in a specific way within localized sites called schools. Such reflection has led me, the protagonist of this story, to conceive of a purposeful book on education: to explore how culturally available symbolic representations of mathematics and the politics of education generate normative concepts that foster or repress certain forms of educational practice.

## Why is this Chapter 0?

Zero is to number signs, as the vanishing point is to perspective images, as imaginary money is to money signs.
In all three codes the sign introduced is a sign about
signs, a meta-sign, whose meaning is to indicate, via a
syntax which arrives with it, the absence of certain other
signs.[4]

But zero also demands a primary status, a "privileged claim to
attention," continues Brian Rotman, pointing to the way in which
this chapter bears certain expectations for the reader. It will be read
before the others (unless you choose to leap around and come back
to this chapter later, as you have already been given 'permission' to
do), and so it will be relatively pure. Here you demand perhaps a
layout of the research question, a comfortable mapping of the relevant literature, and a short outline of the argument to follow,
untainted by the complicated nuances of detail and elaboration to
arise in later chapters. Further chapters should be responses to the
epistemologically rudimentary content of this one. And so the
organization of my book becomes in a way a representation of my
subject matter itself, the representation of the representation of
mathematics.[5] That is, the organization of the book, and the symbols used to convey that organization, are an example of the extent
to which mathematics permeates and mediates our notions of
knowledge, scholarship, and argument. As Rotman writes,

Zero is epistemologically rudimentary . . . not only in
the sense that mathematics claims to provide an objective, historically invariant, empirically unfalsifiable
'truth', thus making its signs more culturally and logi-
cally naked, transparent, and parsimonious than other
signs, but in the immediately practical sense that counting is a simpler more primitive semiotic activity.[6]

Maybe this should really be chapter 4 or chapter 5. Feel free to rip
the binding and reorganize the chapters as you wish.

Actually, I prefer Rotman's third basis for the privileging of
zero: "Its connection, obscure but undeniable, to the much older
and more deeply embedded idea of 'nothing' indicates that questions about its introduction be phrased in very general terms." Is

this the one chapter which, by its signification, is its own introduction? Is it void of research content? Is this simply the chapter that denotes the absence of all others? Or is this the chapter which, through the agency of its sign, states what could not be written without its presence?

How about, this is the chapter that states what the author cannot write: what the author does not write; what the reader imagines (or, what I imagine you imagine?). Imagine you are on a quest to explore how culturally available symbolic representations of mathematics and the politics of education generate normative concepts that, in turn, foster or repress particular forms of educational practice. You have before you a number of doors, each labeled with a cryptic message and offering an attractive complimentary guidebook. Each entrance claims to take you to the same destination:

> How do such normative concepts contribute to the establishment of the forms and content of debate over contested issues? How, indeed, are these concepts and symbolic representations constructed through ongoing mathematics education practice? And how is their construction mediated by the interaction of expert and public discourse?[7]

You glance quickly at the various doors in front of you. One boldly proclaims PERSPECTIVE:[8] its guidebook claims you will learn how to identify 'perspectives', frames of reference or series of working rules by which a person is able to make sense of complex and puzzling phenomena (i.e., social life). Expose yourself to dazzlingly interesting artifacts from public debates over the purposes and materials of mathematics education, and, with these tools, you will soon be able to identify how each person's 'perspective' contains a set of assumptions falling under six categories: (1) about being human (what distinguishes humans from other species); (2) about society (a picture of structural features that emerge, develop, persist, and change as a consequence of people acting in association with other people); (3) about the relationship between individual humans and society (1 and 2); (4) about what should be taken as crucial properties or fundamental factors that condition human conduct and experience in a social order; (5) about what it is to know or understand properties or aspects of social life under investigation; and (6) about academic explanations of social life and how they may or may not relate to policies that can be used to direct the everyday affairs of the members of society. By applying this template to a variety of materials, you can piece together the multiple perspectives on mathematics education of a particular historical time period.

A second door declares IDEOLOGY OF EDUCATION:[9] its guidebook highlights seven points of touristic interest. Every construction of an argument about education, says this guide, is built on the foundation of an ideology of education, the basic substances of which are: (1) a theory of knowledge, its content and structure; (2) a theory of learning and the learner's role; (3) a theory of teaching and the teacher's role; (4) a notion about what resources are appropriate for learning and teaching; (5) a theory of assessment; (6) assumptions about the organization of learning situations; and (7) assumptions about the aims and objectives of education. Dissect rhetoric and policy to reveal the hidden ideology, says this book, and you will understand that which you seek.

A third door is adorned with an appealing calligrapher's script denoting SLOGANS.[10] The guidebook, allegedly written by Maxine Greene, a prominent philosopher of education, describes 'slogans' as unsystematic, popular ways of talking about education, and quotes another established philosopher, Israel Scheffler: "phrases repeated warmly or reassuringly rather than pondered gravely." Our terrain is filled with slogans, suggests this guidebook; and you may identify slogans by any combination of their characteristics. For example, they suggest answers already given. They also perform a magical function for people who need to believe that schools by definition promote both personal development and social adaptation. In Scheffler's words, they are "rallying symbols;" they in no sense describe what actually exists, yet they are taken—"wishfully or desperately" writes Greene—to be generalizations or statements of fact. More importantly, she continues, "slogans may have a particular appeal in the United States because of their association with the American Dream and all that it implies." Learn to recognize slogans, and you will discover how such expressions have reified the notion of the "mythic individual, man [sic] in his dignity and perfectibility crafted through generations of striving to achieve a glorified image especially contrived for the New World." Indeed, suspects the author (Greene?), the fundamental mythology of American education has had much to do with the ways in which schools serve to nurture perfectibility; and slogans are the key to unraveling that mythology.

Finally, you read that slogans are linked with a definition of "human essence." One aspect of this link is the interrelationship of human dignity, rationality, and self-sufficiency mired in the traditional image of a person honed and modified through eighteenth century experience; this was a function of an "age of reason" extending back to the classic past. Terms such as 'man' and 'democratic citizen' both refer to abstract qualities arbitrarily used to define the human essence. The irony of such a definition is that it purportedly captures universal characteristics, yet actually excludes more than it encompasses. Among other things, it excludes fallibility, ambivalence, passion, and most of instinctual life. Further, it gives rise to an inequitable standard of behavior by suggesting an idea so lofty and civilized that the ordinary person can scarcely aspire to it; by cultivating suspicions of spontaneity, enthusiasm and expressiveness; and by making it unimaginable to ascribe 'humanness' to people whose lifestyles veer from the 'norm'.[11]

You open this last door, and peek inside. Strange! All of these doors lead to the same road—a sort of cartoon version of what one would expect in a road—oddly crafted out of two brightly differentiated substances: individuals, and an amorphous substance called society. It is almost as if the very distinction in substance, while throwing all perception into stark relief, merely forces an implausible flatness. Even in those places where the lines between 'individual' and 'society' are blurred, so that the varying hues of each shade help in the definition of the other, the presence of the shades themselves serves to stop time in a moment distant from real-life experience. It might be fun to travel in such a fantasy land, you admit, but hardly appropriate for a book.

Across the way, however, you notice another bold sign, this one appearing to be a business shield. It reads, SOCIETY OF EPISTEMOLOGISTS AGAINST EPISTEMOLOGY. Intriguing? Go on in. Ah, greets an usher to what is probably an academic meeting. You must be the mathematics education person. A firm handshake tugs you toward a chair. Here's your copy; you're just in time. Your copy: it is a prospectus for a book, listing YOU as a member of the editorial board and assigning today's date as the date of a meeting to approve this prospectus. You panic, not having read it yet; what should you do? The meeting fades from sight as you begin reading the opening quote:

The Prospectus

All mathematical pedagogy, even if scarcely coherent, rests on a philosophy of mathematics.[12]

The above oft-quoted statement, seemingly so startling yet plausible, has provided the foundational argument for a great many valuable efforts. For example, Thomas Cooney[13] studied the ways in which a beginning teacher's professed view of mathematical knowledge can interact with his or her actual presentation of mathematics as a discipline, when confronting the practical aspects of classroom life, and the fears and fantasies of being a teacher. Stephen Lerman[14] has, on the other hand, investigated theories of knowledge and knowledge acquisition as formative frameworks for teaching styles and pedagogical assumptions. And Alba Gonzalez Thompson[15] interpreted teachers' beliefs, views, and preferences about mathematics and its teaching as playing a significant role in shaping their instructional behavior.

For many, it is crucial to determine the correct epistemological basis for mathematics: a philosophy that is either correct or most accurately describes mathematics as it now stands. Such an epistemology, by prescribing the nature of mathematical knowledge, would supply a stable source of criteria for the development and evaluation of educational programs and associated techniques. Thus Lerman writes:

One reads increasingly in mathematics education journals of the need to think of mathematics teaching as about processes rather than content, but, unless the epistemological sources and consequences of this are clarified and the wider implications for the teaching of mathematics examined, little will be achieved in terms of development and change in the mathematics classroom.[16]

Lerman further quotes Reuben Hersh:

The issue is, not what is the best way to teach, but what is mathematics really all about . . . controversies about high school teaching cannot be resolved without confronting problems about the nature of mathematics.

For those who find such arguments convincing, the issues of mathematics education have consistently boiled down to disagreements over the nature of the discipline's knowledge content, extracted from any notions of context (especially since Imré Lakatos' classic[17] description of mathematical epistemology as a two-party political contest: the Euclideans versus the Quasi-Empiricists). Unfortunately, however, such an approach and the research it encourages are bound to be inadequate. We will never be able to determine the simply correct, or the most accurate, philosophy of mathematics, for the very reason that underlies the maintenance of the field's epistemological debate: More than one philosophy is professed, and hence sustained, at the same time.

In particular, more than one epistemology exists. How can this be? I risk a rather crude empiricism to state the obvious: At base, there is no philosophical question here, simply a social situation.[18] The best course of action that I can determine, therefore, is to forego the argumentation undergirding one epistemology or another, or demonstrations of the superiority or priority of one or another view. Rather, if we can understand the relationship between theory and practice as less linear and as more intricately intertwined in the mutual production of both, we can interpret various epistemologies of mathematics as parts or aspects of mathematics; that is, they are parts of a woven fabric of truths, facts, fantasies, hopes, relationships of power, and practice. The point then will be to appreciate how such complexes of practice come to be, and how and through what relationships of power and identity fluctuation they are created by those involved in their maintenance and production.

What I am suggesting here is an approach not very familiar to educational literature but one increasingly adopted in current sociocultural theorizations. That is, I am proposing to interpret mathematical knowledge as inseparable from larger contexts of (educational) practice in which the nature of mathematical knowledge, what counts as 'doing mathematics', and what is conceived of as relevant to the content and context of mathematics, are all aspects of practices that are in many respects particular to their social and cultural setting.[19] In such settings, people actively maintain and/or transform these practices in an ongoing construction of meaning.

Often, when educators try to understand or describe the nature of learning and teaching, or of schooling and knowledge, their notions about categories of identity and understanding, whether explicitly theorized or simply taken as accurate descriptions of 'how things happen' (suggesting that these categories reflect objective experience), lead simply to the confirmation of prevailing views about education and schooling. A more reflective alternative would be to challenge those prevailing views. and to perpetually redefine such categories in and through practice. Nevertheless, visions of what constitute experiences in schools typically appeal to or incorporate widely held but unexamined normative definitions. Education research approached in this way, and the politics and practices that follow from it, wind up endorsing unalterable dichotomies and other conceptualizations used to justify or rationalize the maintenance of systems that professionals are presumably interested in changing for the better.

I want to start with the notion that social experience of any kind can be 'read' as the production of meaning, both in discourse and in action. Accordingly, I hold that finding ways to understand how such meaning is produced, and how our very categories of perception are constructed or legitimized, is a worthwhile academic task. My emphasis on how implies a focus on the study of processes rather than remote origins: on multiple rather than single causes; on rhetoric or discourse instead of reductive ideology or presumed consciousness. I further take culturally imbedded meanings as unstable, open to contest and redefinition, and requiring vigilant repetition, reassertion, and implementation by those who have endorsed one or another definition. In contrast to theorizations that focus on the relative stability of meanings as a major feature of culture, I seek here to avoid attributing an immediately transparent and shared meaning to cultural concepts. I argue instead that we should look at the conflicts within the processes that create even seemingly entrenched meanings as relatively 'established'. Power becomes a central conceptual tool in such work, as such conflicts imply relations of power.

"Meanings are not fixed in a culture's lexicon," Joan Wallach Scott has said, "but are rather dynamic, always potentially in flux."[20] How do concepts acquire the appearance of fixity, she asks, as she calls for attention to the challenges posed for normative social definitions and to the ways these challenges are met. I find Scott's program to be particularly apt and hope to apply it to the study of mathematics education. Hence I want to directly consider the interplay of forces involved in our society's construction and implementation of meanings that impinge on conceptions of mathematics and its practice. That is, I intend to "unsheathe the politics of the matter." Certain questions naturally arise, then, as to whose interest it is to control or contest meaning, what the nature of that interest is, and by what processes it is expressed. While I do not view particular answers to such questions as originating forces of social events, I do take them to be of central concern to the philosophy of mathematics education that I hope to develop.

My choosing mathematics as my focus is significant because of this discipline's consistent placement in an epistemology that provides answers to the above sorts of questions via (purportedly) objectively determined, absolute, and universal interests. I prefer to speak of discursively produced, relative, and socially contextual interests, by which I mean interests produced within and by means of a nexus of various discourses at once productive and determined. Here I directly refute the sort of separation of material conditions and human thoughts and actions that would be found in less useful theorizations, within which the material conditions are said to generate the latter, or within which a constructed dichotomy of conditions and human agents reifies rather than problematizes a nature/ culture dualism.

For example, I would immediately question a popular conception among mathematics educators that children develop mathematical notions subsequent to work and exploration with physical objects and experiments.[21] I ask instead how such theoretical constructs determine certain types of 'teachers', 'students', mathematical practice, and the like. Similarly, the quotes given at the beginning of this prospectus serve as excellent examples of how particular practices can force an artificial distance between power and knowledge, rather than as slogans that we might choose to adopt in a debate. I want to posit, then, that 'interests' are not found merely in actors or their structural positions, but are discursively produced as aspects of an elaborate and ongoing formulation of subjectivities: My 'objects' of study are dynamic epistemological phenomena.

Some key terms need to be reconsidered within such a theorization. For example, 'experience' can no longer be presumed to be the objective circumstances that condition 'identity', nor can 'identity' be seen as an objectively determined sense of 'self' defined by needs and interests. Indeed, what I hope to develop is a keener sense of the pertinent terms that such work requires. I expect a preliminary theory of power to be useful here and intend the refinement of that theory made possible by my project to be a particular contribution to such philosophical efforts. I begin by following Michel Foucault's 'physics of power,' in which power, as a property of all relationships and practices, structures the field of possibility for action.[22] But I problematize the ways in which such a conception of power can maintain weaknesses of traditional epistemologies. (Foucault has been faulted, for example, for not attending adequately to issues of gender.) One source of fertile ideas can be found in theorizations recently lumped under the rubric of "Identity Politics."[23] Such attempts to establish more appropriate ways of comprehending human consciousness deconstruct both 'the individual' and 'society' by emphasizing the fluidity of traditional categories of analysis (e.g., class, race, gender, ethnicity) within both groups and individuals. Identity is understood as multiply stranded and contradictory. Hence consciousness is found to be prescribed by various differences within the individual; it is as fixed as the culturally specific and evolving modes of discourse available, and as fluid as these discourses, themselves foci of collective struggle with implications for who we are and how we perceive the 'conditions' we face. It is necessary, therefore, to rethink politics, often conceived of as the collective interaction and consciousness of similarly situated individual subjects. I begin tentatively with a rather broad formulation, in which politics becomes a process by which plays of power and knowledge constitute identity and experience. Identities and experiences are then conceived of as variable phenomena, discursively organized in particular contexts or configurations.[24]

At stake in this kind of endeavor is, first, how we as researchers construct these meanings and, second, the ways in which they repudiate or confirm our notions of education, schooling, and mathematics, both within and external to education and schooling. Take, for example, the following question: Is the mathematics of a single, professional mathematician—what a mathematician does when 'doing mathematics'—synonymous with what a student does or should be doing when 'doing mathematics'? This question raises an important issue while simultaneously defining distinctions in meaning among mathematician, adult, student, child, etc.; these distinctions in turn incorporate paradigms of power and action as well as ideologies of practice and hierarchy. Here's another one: Should mathematics courses be aimed at specific groups of students with particular needs? Simply stating such questions may lead us to notice how often we create categories of meaning and analysis through our questions and practices. Not uncommon is an assumption about how an educational encounter takes place, through planning by adults who subject students to it. The ways in which we conceive mathematics as relevant or irrelevant to a student's concerns, to societal needs, to a coherent education, or to a pertinent aspect of training, as well as how we come to such conceptions, cannot help but affect our relationships with students, with teachers, with others, and the ways in which these relationships are structured by the discourses available to us. Similarly, the discourses we establish are mediated by these relationships and the processes by which they are themselves motivated or denied by discourse. The circularity of the discussion is inevitable but revealing nevertheless.

## Program of Inquiry

The plan of inquiry for my book has at its base the desire to probe the arbitrary notions of relevance structured by the very nature of mathematics education as it is commonly perceived. Because mathematics as a discipline and the teaching of mathematics are typically understood as apolitical, serving to reproduce philosophies of mathematics that presume the discipline's inherent nonhuman truth, I want to go directly to those realms most apparently extraneous to mathematics education and study how such categories of externality are produced, mediated, and interwoven with the political as well as the most personally human.

Moreover, because mathematics education research has focused primarily on classroom activities, optimal sequence of knowledge topics, and the cognitive development of individuals, it has implicitly constructed a stark distinction between school mathematics and the world outside of schools, placing popular and mass culture, the public sphere, and related issues of power and politics in the background. Unwittingly, academic work in mathematics education has tended to demand a barrier between individual and social constructions of knowledge. Attempts to address larger social concerns, such as gender differentiation with respect to mathematics, or the impact of technology on culture and identity, have likewise focused on school mathematics and on received notions of 'achievement' in mathematics. On the whole, such efforts have served merely to confirm received categories of gender and mathematical practice, or paradigms of technology as progress and opportunity, rather than enabling an understanding of how we come to concern ourselves in this field with some presumably 'external' issues and not others.

My primary strategy is thus to focus on the 'other' realms of discourse and knowledge, both to investigate what I perceive as arbitrarily lacking in mathematics education discussions, as well as to develop new insights into mathematics education from such 'other' perspectives. Hence I have chosen to study the following problem, generally stated:

> Within the decade of the 1980s, and into the 1990s, what interrelations may be found among mathematics, power, identity, and education in academic research, the public sphere, popular and mass culture, and school experience?

Prior investigation indicates possible perceptions of mathematics education that deny received categories of distinction.

I have chosen to explore recent discourse in the United States for two reasons: first, because education once more became a dominant theme in the public sphere during this period; future mathematics education discussion and research necessitates an adequate historical awareness; second, because the objects of my study, in being so close to current experience in time and place, force a form of contemporary critical reflection that has come to be central to 'Popular Culture Studies'. The approach thus supports a form of pedagogy so far rare if not nonexistent in mathematics education, a pedagogy that attempts directly to address issues of power, identity, and politics in relation to schooling.[25]

In pursuit of this inquiry, and to meet its associated aims, I focus on the following sources:

(a) Academic and media coverage of mathematics teaching and learning. My sources include extant academic literature as well as newspaper, magazine, and other media coverage of mathematics education.

(b) Academic and media coverage of how mathematics education can or should respond to technological

developments, ranging from debates over calculators and computers in the schools to discussions
concerning the simultaneous 'mathematization' of
society through technology and 'demathematization' of individuals via the use of technological gadgets.

(c) Responses to popular interest or lack of interest by
mathematicians and educators, including reports
and projects of the Mathematical Association of
America and the National Council of Teachers of
Mathematics.

(d) Sources associated with the presidential elections of
this period, in which 'becoming the education president' was a major moment in the public space. For
example, the 1984 candidacy of Jesse Jackson forced
explicit power arguments regarding education into
political discourse. My sources will include transcripts of campaign speeches, materials in clipping
files of media coverage and interpretation of cam-
paigns, transcripts of television reports, and party
platform documents.

(e) Popular films and prime-time television programs
that explicitly referred to education and schooling.

(f) A sample of popular periodicals and newspapers.

I will devote specific attention to both the literature on gender
and that on mathematics as forms of reflection on public/private
distinctions, reflection that utilizes types of discourse that construct notions of the 'other' in establishing social theories; and to
ways the theorization of identity politics has grown out of one of
these traditions of reflection. Of particular interest will be (1) feminist pedagogical responses to the problematic nature of power and
social change, and (2) popular culture pedagogies, which attempt
to link the public sphere with learning and schooling but which to
date have had little opportunity to be connected with mathematics
education.

One central concern will be the need to establish the relevance of such seemingly remote material to work in classrooms.
Such a concern is at the heart of popular culture studies today; I

hope my project will make a significant contribution to such efforts.

I am necessarily connected quite directly to issues of mathematics education, in that my work is that of a mathematics educator and thus should not be separated from my background and concerns for my classroom life as a teacher of mathematics. Furthermore, I intend to explicitly integrate my 'findings' with issues of instructional practice in mathematics. Therefore, one constellation of fundamental questions driving the inquiry is:

What constitutes mathematics and the doing of mathematics? Why does this question seem so often to be meaningful as one examines both theory and practice? And what does this have to do with arguments for mathematics' role in school curricula as a unique discipline?

Particularly at issue are (1) the ways in which we form and maintain understandings of the subjectivity of the student, and (2) the implications of such notions for relationships among students, between students and teachers, between students, teachers, and members of the larger community, and for claims about 'knowledge'. For example, we may think of mathematics as a received body of knowledge and skills imparted to the student by an omniscient teacher/ authority. In this case, students become independent spectators of society and culture, and their application of their knowledge and skills determines the value of received, purportedly neutral knowledge. They may become participants in a democratic society if they see such action as possible and important. However, we might also conceive of mathematics as a communicative discourse developed by groups of people working together to understand problematic situations. Here students are per fiat members of a community who must create forms of communication and critical reflection, and who must develop the technical abilities and skills to effect such participation. Because they are the creators of their own knowledge, such knowledge is inherently an element in the politics of which they are a part.

Since mathematics has been traditionally understood as a body of neutral technology slowly but surely progressing in the service of humanity, it has been difficult for us to probe how such mathematics is generated and why, who decides what is considered mathematics, and why, and the extent to which certain groups of people are disempowered through such mathematics rather than benefiting from its universal gifts. These issues are not only important to mathematics educators and to those interested in questions of educational policy. They are also part of mathematics itself and thus should be explicitly addressed in the mathematics classroom at all educational levels.

I seek to establish a base for developing notions of power and identity that speaks to how we produce culturally significant forms of mathematics and the doing of mathematics. No less important, I ask how people create what they perceive as constitutive of their relationships with others, and how they develop notions of self, both through what they produce as culturally meaningful forms of mathematical practice. I also investigate how school mathematics mediates the production of Platonic, rational meanings of quantification, pattern and spatial contexts in ongoing everyday practice, and how present noncritical assumptions about the neutrality of mathematics and school mathematics become through practice 'truths' that sustain conceptual schemes dividing power and knowledge. In doing so, I hope to underscore the importance of social experience in and out of schools as the production of meaning, hence the politics of power and knowledge.

Specific Strategies of Inquiry

*a. Toward a New Epistemological Theory*

> Our Western propensity to regard knowledge and power as separate 'things' is, for us, a governing epistemological assumption. It enables us to aim to expand or improve knowledge without necessarily worrying about how much power we thereby put into whose hands.[26]

Since beginning my graduate studies, my questions have progressed from those having to do with understanding 'what happens' in mathematics classrooms—focusing on how to describe and explain the experience—to those concerned with how and why we try to understand such experience. I am riding on a wave of rich descriptions of school life gathered in the last couple of decades and thus can benefit from research that has pointed to students as well as teachers as active agents in the formation of social experience. This research has emphasized the fundamental importance of the students, demonstrating their prominent participation in the actual events in schools, and has successfully challenged received interpretations of 'progress' and 'regress'. Likewise, new narrative descriptions of classroom life have suggested altered notions of lesson structure, causation, and collective interpretations of social definitions (e.g., of roles) in schools. By piling up evidence about students, networks of student friendship, and explanations of interpretations within terms of the 'student sphere' (and teachers and the 'teacher sphere'), this large body of research refutes a common blindness to the importance of individual subjectivity in the structuring of classroom experience, encourages attention to students and teachers in our stories of school policy, and shows that the personal, subjective experiences of both students and teachers matters as much as 'public policy', curriculum, or teaching strategies, and that the former influence the latter. Furthermore, such approaches to education have pointed to age/power patterns of differentiation, as well as other categories of social analysis, like race, class and gender, which must be adequately conceptualized in order to account for the experience described.[27]

However, we need to be aware that the simple valuation of a particularized student and teacher experience can be distinguished from a meaningful analysis of school events. For example, such research can tend to isolate students as a special topic, whether different questions are asked, different categories of analysis are used, or only if different actions or documents are examined. In the case of mathematics, for example, a focus on particularized research can and often does support cognitive psychological investigations of mathematics learning in some ways; yet it is possible that such popular and widespread theoretical foundations of educational theory could be marginalized as a distinct, almost irrelevant sphere of research and discourse. (Such is indeed the case with cognitive psychological theories that are not brought into comprehensive sociocultural theorizations; but it can be argued that such theories are not appropriate because they do not address minimal requirements of such theorizations. How these problems are ignored on both sides is an important question.) It is healthy to maintain a focus on groups customarily excluded from (political) study, but it is also important to make sure that particularized and pluralized subjects do not reduce human agency to the function of economic forces, or to other forces like cultural capital defined within a strictly economic model.

I have chosen 'gender' as a special topic because theorizations of gender have been particularly concerned with such issues and thus can help in the effort to work through the difficulties of applying categories of analysis to discourses that themselves employ similar categories of understanding. On the one hand, I am drawn to Levi-Strauss' notion of oppositions as a tool of social inquiry.[28] On the other hand, I recognize that such a template may be more a by-product of two-valued logic as a symbol of rationality than a useful metaphor for cultural concepts. Thus the recognition of polarity may tell us more about the ways in which mathematical formulations of the 'good' and the 'convincing' structure our actions as researchers than about the phenomena being studied. The fact that the applicability of certain categorizations can vary over time supports the critical stance more than the one of blind faith; nevertheless, people really do seem, to us, to express themselves in terms of such oppositions, so it appears at first that it should be useful to ask why in fact people construct discourses that necessitate these delineations. Education provides an outstanding focus for such an inquiry, entrenched as it is within the ageist dualism of child-adult and the related relationships of student-teacher, child-(female) caretaker, or even powerless-powerful and knowledge-lacking versus knowledge-full, which serve to define 'adult' as much through our notion of 'child' as they define 'teacher' through our notions of 'student', and vice-versa.

We can problematize such juxtapositions, as John Dewey suggested, by viewing things as processes rather than as frozen items. Thus, while gender is sometimes understood within traditional social scientific frameworks as one term in long-standing formulations that provide (universal) causal explanations, in the sense that the existence of phenomena or realities are explained, it is also possible to theorize about the nature of such phenomena as realities, seeking an understanding of how and why they take the form they do. In the second style, gender becomes 'cultural constructions'; in rejecting the biological (material) determinism implicit in 'sex', 'sexual difference', etc., gender becomes a social category imposed on a sexed body.[29]

The issues become even more interesting when we also consider the implications of categories like 'mathematical' and how they interact with 'gender'. Joan Wallach Scott draws an explicit, revealing connection to grammar: Looking at the grammar of discourse, we analyze the formal rules that follow from categorical designations; the grammar provides a way of classifying phenomena, a socially agreed upon system of inherent traits. Classifications suggest a relationship among the categories, which in turn make distinctions or separate groupings possible. There are some elements of this sort of analytical awareness in American pragmatism, for example in Dewey's reconstruction of school-society polarities. However, most recent developments in this direction stem from Continental post-Structuralism.

In the unraveling of hierarchies that are constructed through cultural oppositions, we are, I emphasize, quite concerned with power and politics. But, of course, power and politics, as concepts in social theories, are themselves caught up in the same processes of conflict and continuing redefinition, so that we need to be carefully self-referential in their use. Again, some theorizations of gender are particularly useful here, through their recognition of the need for newly conceived working definitions of 'equality' and 'difference'. In Western cultures, these categorical expressions are usually presented as opposites, forcing strategy for change to be couched in terms of achieving equality regardless of difference, or in terms of the importance of difference as a requisite feature of equality. The issue for me will be how to understand the establishment of conceptions of equality and difference, and the meaning of these conceptions for practice and change. For example, the presumption that certain people are successful in school mathematics automatically designates a form of difference, as does the argument for multiple curriculum tracks, distinct subject areas within curriculum, or the organization of mathematical education by age and grade.

How, then, can a successful exegesis of culturally laden concepts be accomplished? We can tease out significant categories of analysis that are implicitly common in discourse on education and mathematics education by looking for those concepts that are attributed to constitutive elements of social relationships based on perceived differences between groups, which themselves are classified by the binary opposition this category establishes. Culturally available symbols evoke multiple, and often contradictory, representations of the conceptual category. I ask which symbolic representations are involved, and in what contexts. There are normative concepts that set forth interpretations of the meanings of the symbols, limiting and containing their metaphoric possibilities (these typically take the form of a fixed binary opposition, categorically and unequivocally asserting the meaning of the opposition, e.g., male/female). The normative concepts depend on the refusal or repression of alternative possibilities, and sometimes overt contests about them take place. I ask at which moments and under what circumstances. The position that emerges as dominant is typically stated as the only possible one, and subsequent 'history' is written as if these normative positions were the product of consensus rather than conflict. The point, then, is to reexamine the nature of the conflict and the ways in which such 'consensus' is achieved. In doing so, the investigation disrupts the notion of fixity and searches for the nature of the debate or repression that leads to timeless permanence in binary representation. It is here that it is important to link the personal with politics and social institutions or organizations, to avoid restricting our gaze to some small focus. I ask how identities are substantively constructed and how this construction relates to a range of activities, social organizations, and historically specific cultural representations.

Categorical concepts are thus primary ways of signifying relationships of power; they are fields within which or by means of which power is articulated. Established as an objective set of references, such concepts structure perception and the concrete or symbolic organization of social life. To the extent that these references establish distributions of power, they become implicated in the conception and construction of power itself. Furthermore, such concepts allow us to decode meaning and to understand the complex connections among various forms of human interaction. By looking at the ways in which they legitimize and construct social relationships, we can develop insights into the reciprocal nature of conceptual discourse and social experience, as into the particular and contextually specific ways in which politics constructs a conceptual discourse, and vice-versa.[30]

Of course, politics is only one of many areas in which we could look at conceptual discourse. Because politics is usually construed as having to do with government or the 'nation-state', it becomes virtually unchartered territory, while mathematics is commonly perceived as independent of the business of politics. Furthermore, political analysis is a typical stronghold of resistance to the inclusion of material or even questions regarding the instability or nonneutrality of mathematics and mathematics education (other than to say that mathematics can support the technological and hence economic strength of a nation).

*b. Aspects of a Systemic Analysis*

Canonical writings speak, in particular, to those who can hear, that is, to the members of the community, who, on account of that perspicacity of hearing, constitute the social entity or systemic community. The community then comprises that social group the system of which is recapitulated by the selected canon. The group's exegesis of the canon in terms of the everyday imparts to the system the power to sustain the community in a reciprocal and self-nourishing process. The community through its exegesis then imposes continuity and unity on whatever is in the canon.[31]

The exegesis of mathematics education as a sociocultural phenomenon can be accomplished in another, related way: Social change comes to expression in symbol change, so that meaning can be understood as symbolic transaction. That is, symbol change occurs in the exegesis of a systemic canon, which constitutes the social entity's expression of itself. I search for the canonical texts of education and mathematics education in the 1980s and 1990s. The exegesis of the canon can then be interpreted as informing the ongoing social action that in turn sustains the whole. Similarly, I detect canonical themes and metaphors of mathematics and school mathematics in the popular culture of television and cinema. I then examine the ways in which a possible cogency or contested cogency is imputed to the relationships among these canonical concepts that the individual producers of this cultural material have not necessarily explicitly expressed in and through their material, but by means of which we can reveal multiple and possibly conflicting logics. As Jacob Neusner has put it, the 'cogency' "frames that just fit that joins system to circumstance."[32]

'Mathematics education', if there is such a 'whole', works its way out through the exegesis of its canon, and one of the histories of mathematics education is the history of its exegesis. To the participants in the mathematics education community, the whole seems sound and beyond argument: In the beginning are not words and intrinsic affinity, but 'the Word'. Thus the history is that of the perpetual present of mathematics education—the ways in which its exegesis speaks with a message of the 'is' and the 'ought', with meaning for the everyday—that is, the exegesis of the exegesis. (For example, in studying a particular text of the National Council of Teachers of Mathematics, I compare it with other similar texts and ask how recurring points of emphasis—critical issues and generative tensions—draw attention from the limits of the text to the social world that the text's author(s) proposed to address, that is, the move from text to context, and how this movement is accomplished.) By reading the canon as a response to critical and urgent questions, we gain insight into how the canon provides a coherent picture (for those who construct the canon) of how things are suitably sorted and fitted together, of why things are done in one way rather than in another, and of who they are who do and understand matters in this particular way.

## Mass Culture and Critical Pedagogy

> If writing is to become part of the critical process, deconstruction of mass culture is the first priority. We mean that writing could consist in the first place in analysis of TV shows of the most popular variety, critical interrogation of popular music, and close scrutiny of film genres that approximate mass culture, such as disaster films, horror shows, and adventures. In other words, the job of the teacher is to legitimate mass audience culture in order to criticize and transcend it, or to discover whether genuine expressive forms are repressed within it.[33]

What Aronowitz and Giroux declare for writing, I want to state just as emphatically for mathematics. Indeed, part of my reflection on mathematics will refer to how much mathematical expression has in common with other forms of communicative discourse, and thus to what extent it needs to be understood as one dimension of general literacy, including writing, reading, listening and speaking, representation, and depiction. In this view of mathematical education as the development of an evolving literacy, it becomes paramount to search out the ways in which literacy and communicative discourses mediate and are mediated by social contextual forces. More to the point here, little work, if any, has been done by mathematics educators to probe the efficacy of mass culture criticism for education in mathematics. For the most part, the styles of pedagogy required would necessitate complete abandonment of the mathematics curriculum as it has been established for the last few centuries. Furthermore, the analysis of mass culture seems to belong to 'other' disciplines. But if we are genuinely interested in examining the 'borders' of mathematical practice and disciplinary structure, we should attempt to understand how and why the demands of critical pedagogy appear so antithetical to mathematics education, and how and why we should or could respond to this appearance.

A discussion of power and education, moreover, requires such attention, because the critical interrogation of mass culture flies directly in the face of traditional notions of schooling and authority. In popular culture pedagogy, it is the student who is the 'expert'—who has the most direct experience with the subject matter—and it is the teacher who often must subject him or her self to this expertise. Together, students and teachers pursue the development of adequate discourses for the description, understanding, and critique of mass culture. Such educational encounters also necessitate reflection on identity and individuality, as the analysis of popular culture insists that one consider the reasons why he or she finds a particular TV show, film, magazine, or whatever, something that he or she 'enjoys' or has some use for.

I would expand Aronowitz and Giroux's list of mass culture artifacts to include technological gadgets that permeate contemporary society. Some of these artifacts, such as Nintendo games, fit within their general theme of entertainment. But others, such as pocket calculators or computerized cash registers, are equally important. Because mathematics is an essential tool for the creation of these technologies, mathematics education might be a particularly appropriate field for interrogating how and why they are produced and used.

Actually, after coming up with this extension of a critical literacy approach to mathematics and technology, I have found such a notion to be brewing within fringe groups of the mathematics education community. Christine Keitel, for example, has written of mathematics as technology, and artifacts such as calculators and computers as extensions of the humanly constructed tools of mathematics that simultaneously demathematize members of society (who no longer perform the actual mathematics), and mathematize society through making the implicit mathematics an integral part of the culture.[34] Philip Davis has, on the other hand, recently called for mathematics educators, at least at the college level, to introduce discussion of the ethical application of mathematics and its (technological) uses into the subject matter of their courses.[35] And ethical considerations have, of course, been common elements in the curricula of various schools of engineering for quite some time, albeit as a distinct topic independent of the science and mathematics the applications of which would then have ethical dimensions (hence separating knowledge and power, mathematics and politics). Thus, we can, if we wish, find a history of support for a contextual approach to mathematics education, one that recognizes the politics of the subject matter as inherent to the discipline, and hence can plausibly reconstruct these efforts.

In one sense, mathematics educators have had to reframe their notions of mathematics education to justify its dynamic place in the school curriculum, in light of recent threats to its importance from computer science and informatics. So it is not surprising to find some members of this community stretching the cloak of mathematics to cover these fields, hence subsuming the largest threat to the prominence and prestige of their own work. In another sense, it has been mostly mathematics teachers who have taken on the obligations and projects in these relatively new areas, so that it is equally pragmatic that they would do so in a way that interprets these areas as a form of mathematics, or that emphasizes their mathematical aspects. Yet this might be a good time to reassess how and why we seek to maintain or inject these disciplines into the school curriculum as such. Why do we not see informatics, for example, as a subdiscipline of linguistics or textual studies, and hence more appropriately taught within, say, English courses?[36] How, then, would these fields define each other?

## Relevant Literature

Ole Skovsmose[37] once characterized alternative approaches to mathematics education by their views of mathematics, and their conception of educational communication and transformation, in addition to their epistemology. In doing so, he was able to contrast common alternatives to a critical pedagogy. For example, he applied the label 'Structuralism' to those curricula characterized by a view of mathematics as determined by crystallizing fundamental concepts through logical analysis of existing mathematical theories (following Bourbaki), theories of learning promoted by Jerome Bruner, and Piagetian genetic epistemology. 'Pragmatic' curricula, according to Skovsmose, perceive mathematics as a science of hypothetical situations, use a pragmatic educational philosophy emphasizing problem solving (drawing from but not necessarily honestly adhering to John Dewey), and see the essence of knowledge to be found in its applications. For Skovsmose, 'Processing-Orientation' curricula highlight the processes of thought that have led to mathematical insights; the main concern of such an education is to give students opportunities for making reinventions of their own.[38]

Skovsmose's analytic philosophy enabled him to demonstrate simply that none of these three common alternatives can meet the two basic requirements of a critical pedagogy: (1) the students (and the teachers) are attributed a 'critical competence' (decisive and prescribing roles must be abandoned in favor of all participants having control of the educational process); and (2) the students and teachers together must establish a 'critical distance' (seemingly objective and value-free principles for the structuring of the curriculum are put into a new perspective, in which such principles are revealed as value loaded, necessitating critical consideration of contents and other subject matter aspects as part of the educational process). It would seem then, that Skovsmose abandoned all common curriculum alternatives in his own work. However, he did not offer a similarly formulated approach to curriculum, outlining a view of mathematics, a conception of educational communication and transformation, and an epistemology, all of which could meet the expectations of a critical pedagogy. It was not clear whether or not he saw this as possible or whether he believed such methods of curriculum construction were inherently contrary to the pedagogy he intended to achieve. He offered instead the curriculum strategies of 'thematization' (in which disciplinary demarcations are set in abeyance in order for educational groups to explore thematic topics) and 'project organization' (in which groups are provided resources for research work done independently).

In his more recent *Towards a Philosophy of Critical Mathematics Education,* Skovsmose demonstrates how the strategies of thematization and project organization are at once rich forms of educational practice and generative of theoretical reflection upon that practice. Narratives of particular curriculum projects are the sites of two necessary attributes: exemplarity and mathematics archaeology. With exemplarity Skovsmose is highlighting the possibility for a specific phenomenon to reflect a totality, so that one may come to understand a whole complexity by concentrating on a specific aspect of that complexity. Archaeology becomes important, however, when mathematics is integrated within a project or theme to such a degree that it disappears for both the students and teachers. Projects should not end when the most visible parts of them are produced and the results exhibited, but must include a means for identifying where and how the mathematics is imbedded in social structures and routines.

> If bringing about a discussion of the power of mathematics is to make sense, then we have to be able to identify examples of mathematics in use. Therefore, a mathematical archaeology can make sense both when directed towards activities in a classroom and towards social pheomena. The problem is the same: applications of mathematics are difficult to observe and therefore to express an opinion on. If they stay invisible and beneath the technological surface of society, they get out of control. When the children fail to realise that mathematics is in action, they do not have any chance to question their opinions about it. When they do not realise that they are using mathematics, their image of the subject as belonging only to a textbook is not challenged.[38]

My own work pursues, along with Skovsmose, questions regarding whether or not exemplarity and archeology are sufficient as well as necessary. I also seek the possibility for proactive creation of new forms of mathematical meaning as well as the analysis and critique of current social structures and routines.

Stieg Mellin-Olsen, another Scandinavian, chose instead to build fresh theories of learning and theories on the nature of mathematics and pedagogical practice that speak to the inherently political aspects of schooling and knowledge.[40] He draws on those existing disciplinary approaches to educational issues that he believes sufficiently address such political concerns. In psychology, he emphasizes the work of Soviet activity theorists (e.g., Vygotsky); in sociology, he highlights symbolic-interactionist perspectives (e.g., Mead). Furthermore, anthropological studies of local mathematical forms of communication incompatible with Western European mathematics as commonly perceived (i.e., in Skovsmose's terms, typically conceiving of mathematics as a collection of Platonic truths) lead him to the importance of language and the social context of educational encounters. This theoretical tack is certainly of ironic value for the theorist. For example, I can now argue that Mellin-Olsen's work is outdated and that it could not take advantage of recent sociocultural theory.

Mellin-Olsen's *The Politics of Mathematics Education* is indeed the book that I associate most closely with my own project. This pioneering exposition portrayed students as the products of their own mathematical knowledge. By locating them within a symbolic interactionist framework, Mellin-Olsen was able to infer the possibility of politically charged learners and to interpret their learning within a larger social context, as that of members of their community. However, his emphasis on the psychological theory of 'activity' did not satisfactorily treat the troublesome theoretical individual/society duality. Likewise, his presentation of 'activity', which stressed its ability to address the future-orientation of much schooling, required a de-emphasis on the actual practices of mathematics education. But recent ethnographic research has suggested instead that such a future-orientation, while reasonable given the explicable role of schooling as preparing people for the future, is not all that useful if we wish to understand schooling, classroom lessons, and other educational encounters as cultural events that mediate and produce semiotic meaning.[41] My project speaks directly to the difference between such approaches to educational discourse.

As well, Mellin-Olsen's particular interpretation of mathematics as a 'language' demanded that he focus on the relationship between mathematical knowledge as experienced by the pupils and their possible 'activities'. This meant that he could not adequately consider the mathematics as itself potentially fluid, and he was forced into a standard 'conservative schooling for radical ends' perspective on education. His developments led almost exclusively to statistical and Euclidean-geometrical analyses of social problems, in which reified mathematics (e.g., Platonic conceptualizations of mathematical meaning) is fostered by groups of students, themselves under the guidance of a traditionally omniscient mathematician-teacher sympathetic to student concerns. There was little discussion of alternative educational arrangements or of evolving, different conceptions of what it means to 'do mathematics'.

As Mellin-Olsen himself worried, his development of what it means to 'do mathematics' had no direct connection to his students actually being political actors in their community, despite his own demonstration that all activity is political activity in a social context. In fact, his suggestions for curriculum could actually 'teach' students that they have absolutely no ability to produce such an effect, acting either individually or cooperatively.

I believe, at this stage, that conceptualizations of power and identity politics found in recent social theory can use the work of Mellin-Olsen as a springboard for a vibrant contemporary philosophy of mathematics education. For example, an examination of power, which can be understood as a major feature of experience structuring the field of possibility for action, can help educators form a more careful treatment of practice that is not limited by psychological emphases on the individual and individual rationality. Thus, using the concept of power will help to situate mathematics education within a larger social and cultural framework. Schooling and other educational encounters will accordingly be acknowledged as precariously placed within a social fabric that includes such aspects of the public sphere as popular culture and the simultaneous processes of mathematization and demathematization of society via technologies. (To show that power is an important concept is necessarily a major introductory goal of my book. That mathematics educators have not made even minimal use of the concept in any form is made more shameful by Skovsmose, who, via Jacques Ellul's thesis regarding technology as the dominating feature of contemporary civilization—human beings thus being completely immersed in technology—noted that power and power relations are central to pedagogies that recognize technology, because technology is typically a vehicle of the establishment and is used for the adjustment of power relations.[42] Moreover, much literature is available that does attempt the explication of power relations embedded in specific curriculum organization.)

Similarly, theorizations collectively known as 'identity politics' contribute significantly toward a comprehensive method of analysis that deconstructs both commonly held notions of 'the individual' and 'society' by showing the fluidity of traditional categories of analysis (e.g., class, gender, ethnicity, race) within both groups and individuals. Furthermore, identity politics constructs a sensitivity to the importance of particular practices within particular locations. Discourse analysis is used directly to address the links between being a political being 'qua being' and 'being political' in practice.

A reconstructed philosophy of mathematics education that attends to such issues can offer a valuable contribution to understanding the relationships of power, politics, conceptions of public schooling, and the public sphere. Such a project can also produce a framework for the development of a discourse of mathematics education in which 'mathematics' is viewed as an evolving literacy only artificially distinguishable from other disciplines, rather than as a received body of Platonic truths.

## Concluding Remarks

My project is inherently multidisciplinary. It intends to bring ideas usually found in anthropological or sociological endeavors to bear directly on forming a philosophical approach to mathematics education. Philosophical studies themselves are few in this area, and they are heavily dominated by considerations of mathematical subject topics and their logical sequence in curriculum or by 'micro' psychological learning theories. Hence, a careful introduction of commonly neglected 'macro' sociocultural theorizations will, it is hoped, bring new fertility to traditional educational research on these matters. As well, such a pedagogical investigation has much to offer those efforts to grasp significant aspects of action and social change, since educators have devoted centuries of reflection to the interrelated dynamics of these processes. The ways in which teachers have developed the pedagogical metaphors of journey, or growth, for example, still have great untapped potential. More recently, pedagogues have written of transformation—of awareness and the democratic nature of society, or of the power relations between nature and cultural forms. For identity politics, this would be viewed as enabling fluid tendencies to come to fruition. This process would be manifested in the ways that culturally specific modes of discourse allow an understanding of the role material conditions have had in the formation of identity, hence necessarily changing identity. Thereby it would also be indicated how stability itself appears as a dynamic process of preservation through the structuration of power, power manifested in the production of discourses. Finally, the process would also be evident in the ways both transformation and reproduction are at once suppressions of 'difference' and 'other'. Increasingly, as such matters have come to be taken seriously by researchers, disciplinary and professional boundaries have become necessarily blurred. For example, the anthropology, sociology, and philosophy of education have become the pedagogy of anthropology, sociology, and philosophy.[43]

My questions, then, are always phrasable in both educational and sociocultural terms. For example, it is as important to inquire about the relations of power in education, how they are portrayed in the public sphere, and the impact of this portrayal on the relations of power among public philosophy or expert discourse, as it is to ask what aspects of power relations are pedagogical. My study, besides enriching our approach to educational questions, can aid our understanding of how a social concept such as power, and the attempts to define it, are themselves constructs of relations of power, of the power and identity politics involved in the structuration of the discourse of power itself.

What I want to emphasize, however, is the development of analytic notions of power and identity politics that provide insight into the production of culturally significant forms of mathematics and the 'doing' of mathematics. This creates the opportunity to link mathematical pedagogy with forms of 'popular culture studies', an opportunity heretofore unavailable to mathematics educators. No less important, it will be possible fruitfully to investigate how people create what they constitute as their relationships with others, and how they construct their own identities, through what they produce and construe as culturally meaningful forms of mathematical practice, without neglecting the realms of fantasy and the 'private' as well as the 'public'. Finally, a self-referential inquiry into school mathematics as a technique of power/knowledge places this particular form of educational encounter within a theory of relations among practices-in-setting, ideologies of practice, and institutional arenas. I ask how school mathematics mediates the production of Platonic, rational meanings of quantification and spatial contexts in ongoing everyday practice in all settings; how present noncritical assumptions about the neutrality of mathematics and school mathematics become through practice 'truths' that sustain conceptual schemes dividing power and knowledge; and how academic theorizing based on 'good practice', while increasingly popular, may thus have little hope of providing the 'solutions' many researchers expect. In doing so, my project celebrates the sort of reflective practitioners that are willing to go beyond their own practice to the identity politics they are themselves a part of.

. . . You are startled to attention. The author has presented his prospectus presentation, and the other members of the board are hurling judgmental questions, clothed in disapproval. . . . But "the interrogative text enlists the reader in contradiction while classic realism does its best to efface contradiction," the author strains to interject;

> I do not mean to suggest that the interrogative text is therefore 'good' and classic realism ideological, misleading, and therefore 'bad'. But if we are not simply to subject ourselves (in every sense) to ideology, we need a new way of approaching classic realism.[44]

A hoarse whisper: I still don't see the data here. A slow, controlled temper:

> When you study a very new subject, it very often happens that you are not able to understand the line of thought of the author. Must your conclusion be that you are too stupid to understand the material, or may you hope for the possibility that the author has not given careful arguments?[45]

You notice everyone has turned to you. Apparently, you are not only a member of this committee, but the designated chair, and it will be your decision, in the end, whether or not to approve the prospectus. You consider, is this a hurdle or a learning experience? You say, let's go ahead with it. It's a long prospectus; but we'll make him pare it down to a decent literature review in the introductory chapter of the book.

## Introduction

The issues mentioned regarding the 'doors to knowledge'—of perspective, ideology, and slogans—both as subjects of study and as methods of inquiry, are indeed important. For example, it is possible to trace a genealogy from my present project to early attempts in the sociology of education that attended to curricular issues by way of connecting particular curricular perspectives to larger contextual (economic, political, and cultural) factors. I am referring here, for example, to the work of Michael Young, Geoff Whitty, and Rachel Sharp in Britain, and Michael Apple, Henry Giroux, Maxine Greene, Herbert Kliebard, and Thomas Popkewitz in the United States.

The insight of these thinkers that I identify as crucial to the conception of my own work is that many of us tend to perceive knowledge as a relatively neutral 'artifact'. Indeed, the idea of a school seems most suited to the transmission of such 'knowledge'. By pointing out this rather banal 'reality', it is possible to ask, as did Michael Apple, whether we have made of 'knowledge' "a psychological 'object' or a psychological 'process'," thereby almost totally depoliticizing the culture that schools distribute. Whose culture is being distributed, these people began asking. Are there particular social subgroups related to kinds of knowledge and power? "In whose interest is certain knowledge (facts, skills, propensities, and dispositions) taught in cultural institutions like schools?"[46] By switching the field of curriculum debate from optimal techniques and subject matter selections for appropriate schooling outcomes, to relationships among various social perspectives on schooling and society, such questions opened up an entirely new 'sociocultural' rather than 'psychological' and 'administrative' perspective on curriculum itself.

Questions such as these are especially significant when applied to mathematics in schools; here the subject matter and the teaching of that subject matter are so easily and often accepted as a special case and understood as apolitical. By 'zeroing in' on this particular discipline, I am able, on the one hand, to be explicit in my analysis of the relationship between power, identity, politics, and knowledge. But on the other hand, it may be possible partially to dispel myths of speciality regarding mathematics itself. Perhaps, if the conceptual applications of power and identity politics can be demonstrated to have specific efficacy for discussions of mathematics, it might be arguable that they apply to education involving any subject matter. Considering the relative dearth of such applications in contemporaneous public discourse today as compared to professional publications during the decade of the 1980s, such an argument may have some impact on the strategies I and other researchers select in the late 1990s, as we seek to have some semblance of influence on educational policy and practice.

The issue of ideology is equally significant, because it is within a discourse that makes extensive use of this concept that most of the subsequent work was based. What ideology actually 'means' in this literature varied somewhat; but the range of definitions had in common the attempt to make direct connections between an idealist realm of ideas and powerful symbols within knowledge and language, and the material world of 'things' and everyday life.

When educators discovered the writings of Antonio Gramsci, they found within them a powerful cultural conception of ideology that went beyond the notion of values and beliefs that guide thought and action.[47] Instead, they found ideology immersed in something so completely total—not secondary or foundational to human action, but lived at such a depth that it saturates society to such an extent—that, as Gramsci put it, it constitutes the limit of common sense for most people. Gramsci used the word 'hegemony' to identify the way in which people's common sense corresponds for them to the reality of social experience. Consciousness is in some way 'saturated': The educational, economic and social world we see and interact with, and the commonsense interpretations we put on it, become 'the world'—the only world. As Raymond Williams wrote in his explication of Gramsci:

> [Hegemony] is a whole body of practices and expectations; our assignments of energy, our ordinary understanding of man [sic] and his world. It is a set of meanings and values which as they are experienced as practices appear as reciprocally confirming. It thus constitutes a sense of reality for most people in the society, a sense of absolute because experienced [as a] reality beyond which it is very difficult for most members of a society to move in most areas of their lives.[48]

Schools as educational institutions thus act as processors of knowledge as well as of people, as agents of cultural and ideological hegemony. They are not only "one of the main agencies of distributing an effective dominant culture," wrote Michael Apple; "they help create people (with the appropriate meanings and values) who see no other serious possibility to the economic and cultural assemblage now extant." Again, Raymond Williams is helpful on this point:

> The process of education; the processes of a much wider social training within institutions like the family; the

practical definitions and organization of work; the selec-
tive tradition at an intellectual and organizational level:
all these forces are involved in a continual making and
remaking of an effective dominant culture, and on them,
as experienced, as built into our living, reality depends.[49]

This largely social reworking of ideology was balanced by a
focus on individuals within social structures by Louis Althusser.[50]
Educators who read the recent translations from the French began
conceiving of individuals "interpellated" by ideology. That is, it is
through ideology that an a person identifies him or her self as who
they are. Althusser also described schools as 'industrial state apparati'—institutions by which the state wields power over the inter-
pellating role of ideology.

The issues around ideology, hegemony, and interpellation are
important for a study of mathematics education because they
demand reflection on how the designation of mathematics as a key
discipline within the school curriculum, and how the selection of
particular knowledge as 'mathematics' or not, mediate and are
mediated by these larger impacts of schooling and learning on individuals, culture, and hegemony themselves. It becomes crucial to
examine the roles of dominant models of management, evaluation,
and research, which seem to contribute to the meaning of, and
help organize, our practice as educators. Often, we think our activity is essentially neutral (both in an economic sense and in a cultural sense), and indeed, a positive contribution to society; we
rarely explore how our "models [and metaphors] serve rhetorical
functions by giving funding agencies and 'the public' a vision of
our seeming sophistication, and . . . how these simultaneously disguise the . . . values, interests, and social functioning which under-
pin them."[51]

Educational slogans float on the 'common sense' of the these
models, reifying them as the reality of experience. We need to go
beyond how a student acquires more knowledge to ask why and
how particular aspects of our collective and varied—indeed often
contested—culture are presented in school as objective or factual
knowledge. We need also to ask how the kinds of symbols that
schools organize are related to how different kinds of students are
organized and ultimately stratified (e.g., economically and culturally), largely thanks to schools as ideological state apparati.

## Power!

It can be depressing to dwell on the reciprocal confirmation of hegemony. What is required is a method of studying the processes of confirmation and transformation of both ideology and practice. One way to go about this is to inject 'power', as the energy behind social, economic, and cultural movement, into theory. Early attempts to do this within educational theory often conceived of power as a scarce commodity, like money or cultural capital, which people 'have' in relative amounts.[52] The metaphor employed in this scheme is one of distribution: Knowledge is held in unequal amounts by different social and economic classes, age groups, and members of different races or genders that have differing power within society; likewise, the ability to brand something as 'knowledge' or not is related to the amount of power one 'has'.

An alternative conception of power, made fashionable following the translations of another Frenchman, Michel Foucault,[53] understands it as a property of relationships, similar to gravity in physics. This shift from an economics to a physics of power avoids the hypostasizing of power that makes it an object for examination rather than allowing us to appreciate it as an indicator about relationships. The shift also leaves behind notions of ideology and hegemony, making these theoretical concepts studyable as theories themselves. The role of theorizing becomes just another part of a complex of practices. Foucault's remarkable maneuver was to collapse the distinction between power and knowledge, that is, to begin with a single category of power/knowledge.

Within this scheme, all practices are understood as 'discursive', as readable and criticizable in terms of providing clues to the meanings upon which they are based.[54] Practices themselves become 'technologies of the social', sites through which power/knowledge relations are produced; and they are part of the apparati of government (as in Althusser) and means for regulating the population. But they are also historically constituted rather than being the product of universal and transhistorical structures (echoing in a way the work of Gramsci). The implications of this approach for mathematics education is that it becomes imperative to trace the history of particular forms of discursive practices so that we can examine how the present 'truths' are constructed, and the effectivity of those truths in the government and regulation of the population.

The mythic individual behind so many educational slogans turns out to be an example of how practices become sites for the production, or creation, of 'subjects', of how practices define for themselves what it means to be a particular kind of person. Valerie Walkerdine[55] has posited the "rational unitary subject" as the key to the history of twentieth-century mathematics education practice; she links this subject with the idea of mathematics as 'reason' and the goal of mathematics education as reasoning:

> Reasoning was to become the goal of a technology designed to provide reasoners who could govern and those who might, at least, be hoped to be reasonable, not pushed to rebellion by a repressive and coercive pedagogy.[56]

The practices of mathematics education, according to Walkerdine, became sites for the production of the self-regulated child, at once a 'subject' and a 'discursive position' in the practices themselves. 'Reason' governs, suggests Walkerdine, because 'reasoning is natural', while some sections of the population are labeled profoundly 'unnatural'; the stereotypes of this unnatural 'other' are proved over and over again in the practice of regulation as if to make them 'true'. Actually, she claims, the truths are not based on certainty but on fear, phobia, and fetish, like any form of racism or regulation.

Theories influenced by the concepts of ideology and hegemony gave rise to arguments about how the language and world view of science, efficiency, 'helping', and the abstracted individual performed ideological functions for the curriculum field.[57] Theories of power would later describe these as discursive 'signifiers', mutually defining and defined by educational practice. In this way power is directly linked with knowledge and the capability of a profession such as teaching to construct a discourse that produces and legitimizes knowledge. 'Signifiers' denote the locations at which practitioners identify knowledge to be acquired or constructed by their clients (the students? the community?); they also organize and define the reality of educational practice itself, that is, the knowledge the practitioners themselves have or wield. Hence power is specifically linked to what is and what is not definable as knowledge, even as knowledge indicates the presence of power. Thus power becomes a useful conceptual tool in the self-analysis and critique of our educational practice.

In Foucault's formulation, however, power is not just a 'negative' concept (e.g., antisocial, violent, restrictive); it is 'productive': It makes things possible. Thus power is valuable in an analysis both of how people are able to accomplish certain things and of what it is possible for them to do (Foucault calls this the 'field of possibilities'). Here power becomes a useful conceptual tool in the formulation of a philosophy of education oriented toward practice, that is, one that carries a concern for how to effect outcomes within institutional settings. The Foucauldian notion of power is consonant with the objectives of educators such as David Nyberg and Maxine Greene, who are concerned with the efficacy of educational theory for enabling educational encounters to take place successfully.[58]

Nyberg starts from the premise that 'consent holds power together', arguing against the traditional juxtaposition of culture/education versus power. He encourages us to emphasize the positive, productive aspects of power as well as those typically identified with the antisocial wielding of force, and to construct from this more complete conceptualization an applicable and teachable democratic comprehension of power and freedom. Nyberg expresses himself in the tradition of Hannah Arendt, who wrote of power as corresponding to the human ability to act 'in concert'.[59] For Arendt, as for Foucault, power can never be the property of an individual; but (and perhaps she meant this solely in a political context) it can be 'owned' by a group and remains in existence only as long as the group stays together. (One might want to extend her notion of group to include general 'social configurations'; otherwise, her conception of ownable power is much too narrow.) A close associate of Arendt, J. Glenn Gray, later wrote of a sense of community that can give to each of us an access to power, a feeling of importance and self-worth. He contrasted the weakness of an isolated individual with the power of the cooperative individual. This emphasis on groups and social context of power may be useful in extending Mellin-Olsen's use of Soviet activity theory within a theorization of power.[60]

Maxine Greene, a more recent admirer of Hannah Arendt who writes on education, has called for the opening of public spaces "where freedom is the mainspring where people create themselves by acting in concert."[61] She points out that because freedom has most often had to do with private existence in contemporary parlance, associated efforts have been viewed as means of attaining private ends, which were themselves conceived of as means of resisting power (i.e., manipulation, a form of hegemony, or a ruler's sword).[62] But, by using Foucault's subtle distinction between manipulation and force on the one hand, and the exercise of power (as actions that structure the field of possible actions[63]) on the other, she is able to apply Foucault's dictum that power is exercised only over free individuals and only insofar as they are free. This effectively restricts the concept of power to avoid manipulation and force, as in slavery, but allows a more developed notion of freedom. Greene ends up emphasizing the ways in which individual or group conduct can be directed (in schools, communities, etc.). For her, Foucault's open field of possibilities is a political space for possible action, a public space of possibilities.

Nevertheless, if Maxine Greene and others are able to make such elegant links between power as a conceptual tool and public action, why then do we not see 'power' entering recent public discourse on education? Is it because power has few uses other than as a handy metaconcept that academicians find appropriate for retroactive description of public action? This subsequent question will need to be answered. At this point, however, I think we can safely say no, based on the extensive and meaningful contribution power has made to the study of education and schooling.

One possible explanation for the public silence about power is that most educators who have made substantial use of the concept are liberal or left-leaning academicians who are closed off by a conservative public philosophy. We might suspect, then, that concepts like power will gain prominence in the public space of the 1990s now that the 'New Right' has become the 'Old Right'. This explanation is weak because it ignores the question of why the New Right was able to control the public sphere in general and discussions of education in particular. First, it was a so-called 'public wisdom' that declared the New Right ideological grip on America: We should ask whether such a grip really was the case. This is especially apt for education, which has repeatedly been a twentieth-century stronghold for liberal and reconstructionist conceptions of democracy and schooling. Second, we should probe why and how conservative discourses on education have been so successfully and quickly integrated into public discussions of education. It is one thing to blame ineffectuality on the impenetrability of 'the system' but another to ask why 'the system' is suddenly so impenetrable (witness the impact of radical philosophies of education on schooling in the

1960s and early 1970s), and to ask what can be done to regain an influence on public policy.

Two thinkers of the 1980s who gave a great deal of thought to these questions were Henry Giroux and Svi Shapiro. Giroux faulted 'progressive' educators for wallowing in a language of critique and the pessimistic theory of reproduction (those aspects of schooling that tend to reinforce preservation of inequality and oppression within certain groups in society). He called for a 'language of possibility', mainly based on a theorization of resistance to cultural and political hegemony. Unfortunately, I have not been able to grasp how resistance can be used effectively, despite Giroux's enthusiasm: I lean toward Foucault's assessment of resistance as necessary fuel for the maintenance and concretization of existing power relations; and I sympathize with Philip Wexler, who described much resistance theory as inappropriate romanticization of the working class.[64] But we might nonetheless ask how power (particularly its positive and productive aspects) can contribute to the construction of a discourse of possibility.

Shapiro demonstrated that 'leftist' interpretations of education and schooling actually were not completely absent from the ongoing public discourse in the 1980s.[65] In some cases, such as the 1984 presidential campaign appearance of Jesse Jackson, liberal to left analyses of education were quite explicit. Jackson, in fact, spoke specifically of power and its role in mediating the nexus of education and social responsibility. In this campaign, Jackson addressed himself to a concern or problematic distinct from those of the other candidates; but in doing so, he opened the discourse of education in the public sphere. We shall note as well that "mathematical empowerment" was common professional jargon promoted by the National Council of Teachers of Mathematics (NCTM) by the late 1980s. Shapiro argued against an 'impervious public discourse' orientation in favor of a 'pervasive but by no means impenetrable power of hegemonic domination'. He suggested that the right had been able to be the dominant voice in the public sphere because it spoke to the interrelated social and educational crises of the time— the disintegration of culture and the erosion of morals.

Despite the fact that the concerns Shapiro identifies were a genuine expression of the social and cultural anxieties of middle class existence in the 1970s and 1980s, he pointed out that such a moral and cultural crisis was rooted in more fundamental causes than those selected by conservatives (e.g., moral and political excesses of the 1960s, profligate 'liberal' government, irresponsible and permissive sexuality). Motivation and need-dispositions of our ubiquitously consumptive society, with its "incessant demands for novelty, innovation, spectacle, youthful vitality, and so forth,"[66] produced a world that knew increasingly little of human values that were not marketable, or of meanings that did not express a cash value or an exchange relationship. This explained the ideological encirclement of both Jackson, who espoused a 'conservative schooling for radical ends'[67] use of education as cultural capital, and his fellow democratic candidates' use of discourse steeped in the implicit assumptions of discrete competencies, technical knowledge, and empirically verifiable abilities. We heard nothing of alternative visions of pedagogy (critical and reflexive, aesthetic and imaginative, democratic and empowering), and were left with "the pervasive valorization of positivist values in the statements of these political leaders," which "reif[ied] this view of education— that is, [made] it 'natural' and the only possible version of educational practice."[68] It is important to contrast the uniqueness of Jackson, who was alone in asserting a distinctly social purpose for education, talking explicitly of schooling and power, community and responsibility, with the centrality of such concerns in the pronouncements and rhetoric of rightist politicians.[69]

Can educators use their conceptualizations of power to speak to 'the moral and cultural crises' of our time? Can they use 'power' to successfully appropriate the classification and description of these crises? Shapiro suggested that it is not only possible, but probable that such an undertaking would be worthwhile. For example, he suggested that progressive educators join with the larger progressive educative movements[70] in abandoning 'inequality' and 'equity', with all of their particular assumptions and associations, in favor of 'social justice'; he posited that curricula constructed out of social justice themes could easily address contemporary crises in ways quite different from those put forth by the rightists.

Giroux was a little more threatened by the new right public philosophy than Shapiro.[71] He agreed that the New Right managed to resonate with the desires and experiences of many people in the United States. But he suggested that, more than selecting the discourse, the public philosophy distorted the desires and experience themselves, thus becoming more entrenched, while systematically ignoring major social problems and promoting hazardous levels of militarism. According to Giroux, what was absent in the 1980s was a public struggle over both redefining the meaning of patriotism and constructing a notion of citizenship that would be consistent with the tenets of critical democracy. Furthermore, popular culture presentations of public philosophy enabled the production of an historical amnesia regarding the ongoing struggles that had been waged over the meaning and unrealized potentialities that underlie different conceptions of citizenship. "Celluloid patriotism" in Hollywood films and TV programming spoke to the need for reaffirmation, to the need to have a voice and to create larger-than-life figures who articulated the frustrations and despair experienced by many people. Citizenship in this case combined an appeal to 'traditional values' with an ideology that legitimated 'hypernationalism'; this ideology reinforced forms of institutional authority that refused to tolerate dissent while promoting social relations in which chauvinism and modern forms of neosexism together redefined the meaning of masculinity and power.

Accordingly it seems that a pedagogy that makes use of mass culture criticism will be a fundamental component of alternative representations of power and education in the public sphere. Thus, as a final question, we should ask if power can be appropriated as a useful concept by educators concerned with the relevance of popular culture studies. If education is to demystify, liberate, and empower, and to construct models of power substantially different from free-market competition, it must deal with the culture of the marketplace. As Richard Ohmann wrote, "Soap operas and shopping malls and super bowls dwell in and form consciousness, defining the real and the possible, and channeling the life energies of Americans, with a power matched only by that of family and job."[72]

## Reading Popular Culture

Carlos Cortes articulates a useful connection between pedagogy and popular culture in an article, "Empowerment through Media Literacy: A Multicultural Approach."[73] Because he argues that schools play a critical role in creating opportunities for or obstacles to student empowerment, he suggests that this role should include helping them to become more empowered through media literacy, both as analytical consumers and as participants in collective action. Cortes also raises the maxim that teachers should continually be cognizant of the content of the 'media curriculum':

> They can bring it into their classrooms to enrich, motivate, provide social context, and heighten the significance of school subjects. They can prepare students to be more enlightened learners and influencers within the media curriculum.[74]

I expand 'media' to incorporate all artifacts of popular culture. This includes what Cortes and others study—television, film, radio, recorded music, newspapers, and magazines—but also computer games, puzzle toys, and technological gadgets such as supermarket scantrons. I join Cortes in resurrecting sociological work of the 1960s, such as that of Herbert Gans, who argued that

> Almost all TV programs and magazine fiction teach something about American society. For example, Batman is, from this vantage point, a course in criminology that describes how a superhuman aristocrat does a better job eradicating crime than do public officials. Similarly, the Beverly Hillbillies offers a course in social stratification and applied economics, teaching that with money, uneducated and uncultured people can do pretty well in American society and can easily outwit more sophisticated and more powerful middle-class types. . . . Although the schools argue that they are the major transmitter of society's moral values, the mass media offer a great deal more content on this topic.[75]

To take a more specific example relevant to this investigation, I can pretty much trace my enthusiasm for mathematics back to my elementary school years. I remember vividly the yearly ritual in which my teacher announced that we would watch a fun film, turned off the lights, and, after many attempts to start the film projector, aimed *Donald Duck in Mathmagic Land* at a grayish "screen" that hung only through its own magic from the top of the classroom blackboard. A generation of future mathematicians, mathematics teachers, educators, and others were awed by the "spirit—the true spirit of adventure." We learned how one finds mathematics "in the darndest places," and, following Gallileo, that "mathematics is the alphabet with which God created the universe." Today, *Donald* is available for purchase in any shopping mall video store, is often advertised at special sale prices by large discount stores, and is available for overnight entertainment at most chain video rental outlets across the country. What I learned in once-a-year thrills my three-year-old son absorbs through viewing the video version more than a dozen times in one day.

The Platonic vision of mathematics offered in Donald's "adventure through the wonderland of mathematics" differed more than agreed with the "practical mathematics" depicted in a typical episode of *The Donna Reed Show*, a television situation comedy I and most of my peers watched in syndicated reruns daily after school, a series which many continue to watch "nitely" on cable's Nickelodeon channel. Like innumerable episodes, this typical plot involved a 'battle of the sexes' in which Donna and her daughter Mary are involved in a subplot paralleling one focusing on Dr. Stone (Donna's husband) and their son Jeff. Jeff, the scientific male, schemes with the aid of Dad to build a 'hi-fi'; Donna and Mary are incapable of understanding the mathematics involved, but they do solve the economic and logistic dilemmas of Jeff's project. The men end up 'superior', while the women know better but still do not know the math.

How, then, are we to comprehend the confrontation of these illustrations of mathematics regarded as a body of knowledge and as an applied process with the notions of mathematics prevalent in contemporary discourse? During the 1980s, mathematics became identified, as in the Sputnik crisis of the fifties, with national industrial and military competitiveness. Hence, the television program *A Different World* portrayed calculus as very difficult yet also central to engineering and ROTC scholarship students. This at once constructed an image of ROTC programs at predominantly Black colleges as prestigious (because they are associated with difficult subjects mastered only by the best students) and an image of mathematics as integrally linked with the military and industry (through engineering). The construction also fostered mathematics and military officer training as common conduits to a new form of African-American success in the eighties. In the 1990s, media attention to Bob Moses and his "Alegbra Project" perpetuated this link between mathematics as a symbol of success and potential social mobility.[76]

Alan Bishop would include such media examples within a general scheme of "mathematical enculturation."[77] He outlines five significant levels of scale involved in an anthropological interpretation of mathematics education: cultural, societal, institutional, pedagogical, and individual. Like most mathematics educators interested in extrapsychological orientations, Bishop presumes an entity identifiable as 'mathematics', which he then fits into a social template. I argue in this book that we need to take a more contingent approach to the mathematics itself, building our definition of mathematical practices out of a body of research that emphasizes the extent to which mathematics takes place within socially and culturally constructed practices.[78] In this respect, our notions of what makes something cultural, societal, institutional, pedagogical, or individual would be influenced to some degree by our mathematics. Bishop is useful here nevertheless, because his global, cultural approach, relatively unique within mathematics education, enables him to entertain mathematics as a cultural phenomenon, and the political nature of mathematics education within cultural constraints. At Bishop's "societal level," mathematics is mediated by the various institutions in society and is subject to the political and ideological forces in that society. At the "institutional level," the internal structure and politics of the school affect how a particular constellation of events is grouped and organized under the rubric of mathematics education.

The present study examines the liminal terrain between Bishop's societal and institutional levels: It searches for a way in which educators—both those mainly engaged in K–12 teaching and those primarily focused on research and theorizing about such practice—can comprehend this confusing region of schooling as cultural politics. I study the professional and public discourse of mathematics education because discourse is a potent entry point into the identification of the cultural resources available to and produced by the ideological functions of language itself. I have chosen popular culture sources for the reasons discussed above: to begin a collection of popular culture from which mathematics educators can cull potential curriculum materials in the future; to begin understanding how my students can develop the capacity to deal with the implications of popular culture; to help myself and others become cognizant of the ongoing popular culture 'curriculum'; and to comprehend the relevance of public and professional discourse for mathematics education as an ongoing practice in and out of schools.

The influence of the public media on education is something mathematics educators need to seize as a tool rather than accept as an encroachment on their individual authority. This realization by the professional community emerged in the 1980s by, for example, the establishment of a lobbying branch of the Mathematical Association of America (MAA). Reports of federal attention to mathematics education issues and the role of this lobbying arm were regularly reported in *Focus*, the MAA newsletter. Public interest in the quality of school mathematics was seen as a positive step toward both the politicization of mathematics educators, who should demand more support for innovation and educational resources, and the potential willingness on the part of state and federal government to legislate money for such programs.

As evidenced by the Summer 1987 issue of *Action in Teacher Education*,[79] the Association for Teacher Educators (who publish *Action*) was equally aware of the importance of public discourse for professional practice. The entire issue was devoted to the influence of the news media on education. A bitter Martin Haberman wrote of how the print and electronic media approach the reporting of educational issues with a negative simplicity, depicting those in charge as unethical, incompetent, and engaged in some form of cover-up. John Condry reminded his audience that school is only one form of educator in the United States and that television is a powerful and harmful teacher; he called for a "know your enemy" approach, so that teachers could understand what they were fighting when "some things are so hard to teach." D. F. Gunderson and Nancy Haas noted that television stereotypes play a tremendous part in teacher role definition. Meanwhile, Robert Ciscell had studied how erroneous beliefs about the realities of the classroom are telegraphed by the media, so that media myths and faulty expectations were a major source of reasons for becoming a teacher.

George and Lynn Rhoades also wrote of concerns for teacher education in this Summer 1987 issue. They reported on the "agenda-setting" techniques of news reporting and the implications for teacher education. What the news media choose to report greatly affects public awareness of issues, they found. Indeed, those issues frequently and prominently covered by the news media are regarded as important by news consumers. My own survey of *The New York Times*, *The Los Angeles Times*, *The Detroit News*, and a compilation of African-American newspapers for the 1980s indicated five primary groups of mathematics education issues, as I discuss below. Furthermore, my survey provided additional evidence for the Rhoades' conclusion. Two large waves of concern about mathematics education generated by extensive media reporting led to subsequently large articles on government and individual 'solutions' to the earlier reported 'problems'. Sharon Van Oteghen and Nardine Aquadro developed this theme further. They commended the media for contributing to public awareness for educational reform, which they, like many professional educators, perceived as sorely needed. However, they were concerned that the media over-emphasized the disadvantages of a teaching career and deserved some of the blame for the prevalent teacher shortage.

In my own study of public rhetoric and discourse around mathematics education, I used three separate data sources. First, I undertook an exhaustive analysis of popular culture periodicals that mentioned mathematics, its teaching and learning, and related themes. Articles from the focal period of the 1980s and early 1990s were identified through a search of *The Reader's Guide to Periodical Literature*, the Wilson Database basket of periodical indexes, and the Public Affairs database, under for example the subject headings mathematics—study and teaching, mathematics—ability, and mathematics—numeracy. This generated a survey base of approximately 600 individual articles or news reports in a diverse set of publications (including, e.g., *Glamour, People Weekly, Newsweek, Time, The Congressional Quarterly Weekly, Readers' Digest, Phi Delta Kappan, Mother Jones*). Each article or news report was analyzed using a classification scheme of eight sets of curriculum deliberations originally suggested by Michael Young,[80] but recently reemphasized by Landon Beyer and Michael Apple.[81] Notes were taken for each item in the database regarding if and how it attended to these eight sets of questions.

Second, a similar collection was performed for *The New York Times, The Los Angeles Times,* and *The Detroit News,* and a compilation of African-American newspapers. Inductive categorization of these news stories generated five fields of 'crises' and their potential 'solutions': (1) tests, student performance, national achievement trends; (2) sex differences in performance, participation, and ability in mathematics; (3) incompetent teachers and an associated shortage of mathematics and science teachers; (4) the mediocrity of U.S. mathematics on an international level and the implications for the economy, the workforce, military superiority and industrial innovation; and (5) novel pedagogical and curricular experiments, which suggested ideal goals for mathematics education via a utopian vision. These categories of public concern about mathematics education should be kept in mind throughout this book, as they suggest key areas of popular interest in the importance of school mathematics.

As was mentioned above, two waves of public discussion of mathematics education were evident in this period. In the early part of decade, the 'news' of poor American performance on standardized tests, interpreted as indicating problems in the achievement of students in mathematics, led to a public interest in explanations and implications. Explanations were reported mainly through news items focusing on teacher shortages in mathematics and science and weak curricula. Implications were noted in reports about declining American prowess in an increasingly competitive international market and about the need for more curricular innovations such as the few models highlighted in occasional feature articles. The pattern was repeated in the later half of the decade. Resurgent reporting on test performance was followed by a large increase in the number of articles on improvements in mathematics curricula and the increasing fears about declining economic and military strength. Growing out of the 1970s, this decade witnessed prominent debates regarding the nature of gender differences in mathematics participation and performance, which were often reported as indicating gendered characteristics in ability. This peaked in 1984, with the startling report of scientific evidence for biological explanations of the differences. However, by the end of the decade, gender was mainly located in professional discourse alone. The importance of school mathematics for the workforce and subsequently for state economic interests, however, re-entered the public discourse and continued to rise in frequency of coverage into the nineties.

Preliminary analysis suggested several discursive patterns as crucial to this study. The decision was made to organize chapters by these themes rather than by a chronological series of events. The themes include:

(a) The tendency for public discourse to construct the isolated teacher in the classroom as determining the character and success of education.

(b) The tendency for professional discourse to construct the subject matter as the determining factor in education while denigrating popular culture as an educative public institution.

(c) The tendency for educational practice to construct for itself a constellation of "social problems" that then need to be administered to, thus perpetuating practice. An example is the notion of gender differentiation in performance or ability in mathematics.

I note here that the general themes seem to echo three of Schwab's four dimensions of curriculum theorizing: the teacher, the curriculum, the student, and the social milieu.[82] In a sense, Schwab's view can be seen as an outgrowth of the commonsense discourse I have identified. What is more immediately important, however, is the details of how, and where within the discourse, the different dimensions become prominent, and for whom and why. The explication of this phenomenon is a main goal of this book.

Finally, I have identified 'key cultural texts' as illustrative of the dominant themes of the discourse in the database. They serve as organizational structures for a discussion of the contemporaneous discourse. In the first chapter, the popular film *Stand and Deliver*, which was based on the story of Jaime Escalante, is used to unravel the discursive focus on the individual teacher in the classroom. Escalante is a mathematics teacher in East Los Angeles who was noted as having tremendous success with "difficult" Latino students. The *Wheel of Fortune* television game show, featured in the second chapter, enables an analysis of the discursive construction of mathematics as a subject matter centered in problem solving. *Wheel of Fortune* was the vanguard of a programming upheaval in television, renewing the popularity of game shows and redefining the nature of intelligence and knowledge in the process. In the third chapter, there is no single dominant "text"; instead, I assemble a variety of professional and popular representations of sex, gender, and mathematics. I deliberately avoid a single key text in order to examine more thoroughly the interaction of popular and expert discourse across multiple terrains of power and identity.

One interpretation of the structure of this work lies within Schwab's four dimensions. The first chapter is about the teacher of mathematics; the second is about the subject matter; the third is about the attribution of specific features to the student of mathematics. This seems 'reasonable'. The focal discourse on education depicted a teacher, teaching a subject, to students. However, each chapter strives to explode the compactness of these dimensions, encouraging each vertex of the teacher-subject-student triangle to be comprehended as socially constructed. In order to do so, I introduce a series of theoretical shifts from traditional theorizing on mathematics education.

The 'final' chapter (-1) is an integration of the former chapters in both content and theoretical context. As I have introduced crucial theoretical tools, which I believe can be introduced usefully and successfully into our present language about mathematics education, I feel I owe my reader a closer examination of them. Each builds on the previous theoretical components so that the final chapter can make an argument for a discursive shift in mathematics education discourse itself. In the first chapter, I offer a 'discourse' orientation to mathematics education 'practice'; here language is understood as socially constructed and ideological in function, while practice is a political and cultural constellation of discourse and behavior modes. In the second chapter, I begin to develop notions of power and knowledge and the theoretical advantages offered by blurring the distinction between the two. In the third chapter I suggest that mathematics education can be conceived as a woven tapestry of practices that incorporate power/knowledge implications understood through discursive analysis. In the 'final' chapter, I offer possible implications of this theoretical shift. By moving away from the usual (psychological) developmental approaches to mathematics learning and teaching, we can begin to form a more sociological and political construction of mathematics education as a cultural politics. To do this, it will be necessary to further develop our notions of power and the politics of identity within such a cultural politics. Finally, we can build a new discursive construction of mathematics education as a practice by integrating within this discourse the notions of power and identity politics.

In general, my book serves as a contribution to the sixth standard of the Mathematical Association of America's recommendations for the preparation of teachers, *Developing Perspectives*:

> The mathematics preparation of teachers must include experiences in which they:

explore the dynamic nature of mathematics and its increasingly significant role in social, cultural, and economic development;

develop an appreciation of the contributions made by various cultures to the growth and development of mathematical ideas;

investigate the contributions made by individuals, both female and male, and from a variety of cultures, in the development of ancient, modern, and current mathematical topics;

gain an understanding of the historical development of major mathematics concepts.[83]

However, my approach is slightly more 'critical'; like Alan Bishop,[84] I want to help create the kind of mathematical education that will enable mathematics to be recognized as a cultural force, absorbed, and appreciated, but also, more crucially, evaluated. It is therefore important to be self-referential to an even greater degree and ask why it seems important at this time for such a standard to be promoted by a professional organization of teachers of mathematics. It should also be emphasized, I believe, that such questions need to be responded to within a field of inquiry greater than that traditionally encouraged by mathematics educators. Tradition has been characterized by a technique-oriented curriculum, impersonal learning, text teaching, and narrowly conceived epistemologies of mathematics that ignore its features as a social process.[85]

To radically paraphrase Rachel Sharp, what needs to be developed for mathematics education is a holistic conceptual structure, one that may have little readily apparent relation to what present theorists believe should be explained. "Those who wish to understand education should, if necessary, forget about it for a number of years and concentrate their attention instead on more significant issues concerning the nature and dynamics of capitalist societies," she says. Such a project necessitates, at least initially, the suspension of one's specialized identity within education, for only then can one begin to penetrate the fetishized nature of social relations and the ideological content of current social thought.[86]

# 1

# The Best Teacher
# in America

America's dissatisfaction with its schools has become
chronic and epidemic. Teachers have long been at the center of the debates, and they still are today. Many commentators admit that no simple remedy can correct the problems of public education, yet simple remedies abound. Most
are aimed at teachers: Institute merit pay; eliminate teacher
education; test teachers to make sure they know eighth
grade facts. Paradoxically, teachers are the butt of the most
criticism, yet singled out as the one best hope for reform.[1]

The *Professional Standards for Teaching Mathematics* rests on
the following two assumptions:

Teachers are key figures in changing the ways in which
mathematics is taught and learned in schools.

Such changes require that teachers have long-term
support and adequate resources.[2]

## Everything Depends on the Teacher

The National Science Foundation (NSF) commissioned three separate studies of mathematics and science education in the late 1970s.
The first was a review of academic literature about curriculum and
instruction and teacher education between 1955 and 1975. The second was a survey of teachers, administrators, parents, and students
in kindergarten through 12th grade. The third was a case study collection with questionnaires used to confirm generalizations established through the first two studies. When the findings were
reported, setting the agenda for public policy and further debate to
come in the new decade, the common thread revealed was the "crucial role of teachers in determining the character and effectiveness
of mathematics education."[3] The limits of teachers' knowledge
about mathematics or about the ways young people learn were seen

to place predictable restraints on what the teacher could offer and accomplish in the classroom. And teachers' beliefs about the nature of mathematics or "the important goals of schooling" were interpreted as more subtle but equally important influences on their impact on students.

Teachers at all grade levels, the reports indicated, had applauded the return to traditional content ('back-to-basics'), instructional methods, and higher standards of student performance common in public discussion of education in the seventies. This suggested that teachers were the major obstacle to changes recommended by research, supervisors, and professional organizations, because these suggested changes were generally in opposition to traditional educational practice. Indeed, the mood of educational activity in mathematics, as reflected in the NSF studies, was summarized as "a search for stability, choosing from topics and techniques with which teachers [had] long experience and comfortable familiarity."[4]

By 1984, when the U.S. Senate passed House Bill 1310, designed to solve the current "crisis" in mathematics and science education, "the crucial role of the teacher" had become a central feature of commonsense understandings of the way education works successfully. The NSF studies had concluded that individual teachers were the pivotal force behind the mechanisms of educational change. Positing two levels for policy making—professional judgments based on information, and political or reactive decisions responding to prevailing societal attitudes or beliefs—the NSF reports made teachers the key to connecting the two levels. If teachers sense agreement between the levels, it was suggested, change takes place; if not, they are dissatisfied and no change can occur. H.R. 1310 allocated $350 million in 1984 and $400 million in 1985 for state grants for teacher training; NSF itself received an additional $45 million in 1984 and $80 million in 1985 for grants for teacher training institutes and development of instructional materials for teachers to use, awards to recognize outstanding teachers, and merit scholarships for college students who planned to become mathematics or science teachers. Such a focus on seed money to establish programs implies that Congress assumed that the best federal action to improve mathematics, science, and engineering education in the United States would be to provide federal money for programs, rather than, for example, becoming directly involved in these programs. Moreover, the emphasis on programs to improve teachers' knowledge and the cultivation of model teachers highlights the significance that teachers played in congressional perceptions of American schooling. The congressional bill was so popular that, despite an appended controversial school prayer amendment, it still passed 377 to 77.[5]

Teachers moreover were located at the center of a number of national mathematics education crises throughout the decade. One concern was an identified shortage of mathematics teachers, sometimes linked to the perilously declining appeal of a teaching career;[6] otherwise the problem was phrased as a shortage not of teachers, but of teachers qualified to teach mathematics.[7] Earlier interest in differential performance in mathematics by gender, argued as attributable to the students themselves, was later blamed on the unwitting behavior of teachers.[8] Good teaching of mathematics concepts was noted as essential to increasing minority participation in advanced mathematics and science, in particular to raising the test achievement of African-American children.[9] And teachers were routinely slapped for their students' relatively poor performance on standardized tests when compared with students in other countries.[10]

At the same time, however, a series of exemplary 'good teachers' were paraded before the public in books, films, journals, television, and other media, helping to construct the perception that the bureaucratic and jealous prevented such outstanding teachers access to the necessary freedom to teach in the ways they saw fit. Of particular interest here are the mathematics teachers Harold Finkelstein, John Saxon, Bruce Brombacher, John Paulos, and Jaime Escalante. Harold Finkelstein formed his own nonprofit consulting firm in Atlanta, Georgia. "His mission [was] to bring the joys of discovery learning into the schools, especially by reaching and training teachers."[11] A teacher himself, Finkelstein would enter inner-city junior high school classrooms and perform exemplary lessons; students from "disadvantaged backgrounds," typically described as displaying poor behavior, short attention spans, poor academic performance, and low motivation, would engage in lively dialogue and "warm to the challenge."[12]

John Saxon was forced to write his own algebra textbooks after discovering that two decades of "New Math and its, er, exponents"[13] had "crippled"[14] the nation's children in mathematics. Yet, turned down by "the major publishing houses because [he] was not a committee of experts,"[15] he went on to start his own company. After contacting William F. Buckley, he wrote a series of articles in the *National Review*; traveling across his home state of Oklahoma, he peddled his approach and convinced a cadre of schools to test his new book; later, he expanded his approach to mathematics education, wrote a full school curriculum, advertised extensively in professional journals, and became a millionaire. Saxon successfully fought the education establishment in the interest of his students. ("The blame rests squarely on those mathematics experts themselves, and on the book companies that employ them and the mathematics hierarchies in the school systems that have encouraged them."[16]) But he also helped parents reclaim a right to decide how and with which textbooks their children would learn, by rallying them into action. ("You can do your part by ensuring that your school checks out this report and acts. A few administrators will vote to sacrifice another year of their students' time and effort. . . . Your job is to see that this does not happen. Pick up the phone and call your school."[17])

Bruce Brombacher, 1982 Teacher of the Year, was heralded as "The Man Who Loves Junior High."[18] He was commended for his development of a new mathematics curriculum for his students in Ohio and for his innovative teaching style. Of particular significance was that he had chosen teaching mathematics over scientific research (he had been a graduate student in physics) and never regretted his decision. John Paulos, a college mathematics professor, captured the entire country as his 'class' in writing a book, *Innumeracy: Mathematical Illiteracy and Its Consequences*.[19] In the process, he established the image of a mathematics teacher able to present profoundly serious topics in a witty and understandable style.[20] Marketing his book on the talk show circuit, his new celebrity status helped him simultaneously personify the ideal, if quirky, mathematics teacher, while placing him as the figurehead of an emerging social movement fighting against mathematical illiteracy.[21]

But by far one of the most glorified and charismatic mathematics teachers of the 1980s was Jaime Escalante, a Bolivian American who taught at Garfield High School in East Los Angeles.

> From his very first day . . . Jaime Escalante knew his students were in trouble. "They were using their fingers adding stuff at the board. . . . They came in without supplies, with nothing. Total chaos." A no-nonsense kind of guy, Escalante skipped the lecturing and brought in his meat cleaver. He set an apple on his desk, donned an apron and

a chef's hat, and brandishing his weapon like some fiend-
ish butcher chopped the apple swiftly in two. "Let's talk
about percentages," he said. No one in the room said a
word. That was in 1974. Since then Escalante, 57, has startled hundreds of students, most of them poor Hispanics.[22]

Escalante's work "in the barrio" captured the fascination of an
enraptured public soon after a controversy between Garfield High
and the Educational Testing Service was reported in the *Los Angeles
Times*: 14 STUDENTS RETAKE TEST AFTER SCORES ARE DIS-
PUTED—PRINCIPAL CHARGES MINORITY BIAS.[23] Eighteen students had taken the Advanced Placement (AP) calculus examination, and 14 of them (later reported as 12) had been accused of
copying. As Jay Matthews—Escalante's first biographer—noted, it
was not the cheating or bias charges that were surprising. The startling point of the story was that a school like Garfield could even
find as many as 18 students willing to take the AP calculus test at
all, given the difficulties that schools with sufficient resources in
'advantaged' neighborhoods have collecting enough students to
form even one calculus class.[24] This became the core myth of the
Jaime Escalante legend, around which a feature film, a successful
book, numerous articles in newspapers and periodicals, and finally
a daytime program on public television saturated public discourse[25]
with the story of a genuine American hero dragging achievement
out of the urban jungle.[26] Escalante was not only a superb mathematics teacher, but a model for teachers of all disciplines.

I want to suggest that the development of particular individuals as the main characters of public mythology has much in common with what literary theorists describe as the ideological function of characters in realist fiction. The experience of consuming a
film about Jaime Escalante, or a story about John Saxon in *Reader's
Digest*, or a reference to such a story about a particular superteacher
within a congressional debate about funding allocations for mathematics education, is ultimately reassuring. However harrowing the
events of the story or the circumstances of its featured characters,
the world evoked in the 'fiction' and its patterns of cause and effect,
social relationships, and moral values largely confirm the patterns
of the world we seem to know. The myths of Harold Finkelstein,
John Saxon, Bruce Brombacher, John Paulos, and Jaime Escalante
are part of a larger discourse about how education, when it comes
down to it, depends entirely on the individual teacher in the class-

room. The 'fact' that these are 'true stories', rather than fabrications (such as Rousseau in his *Emile*, or Pestalozzi's Gertrude) is relevant only in that the 'truth' is part of the story itself, ideologically masking its mythical and ideological features.

In contemporaneous academic literature, such as Sarah Lawrence Lightfoot's *The Good High School*, the notion was that excellence could be achieved in a variety of educational environments, in locally appropriate ways, via the work of "excellent" teachers.[27] Quick adoption of such a perception of education as depending so crucially on the teacher by teacher-educators in schools of education was not surprising.[28] In some ways, placing an emphasis on the teacher helps practitioners identify ways in which they can make an impact and find satisfaction through their work. But this location of both inertia and potential within the teacher was a significant change from an earlier emphasis on social and structural constraints on teaching, or curriculum projects. Placing the focus on the teacher can also relieve all others of responsibility. In policy and funding decisions, the attention to teachers as the direction of effort was continually evident throughout the decade.[29]

When 'Business' was applied as the metaphor for tackling educational policy, the previously identified 'discrete problem', the math teacher shortage, was accepted without challenge.[30] Innovative solutions were proposed, such as differential pay scales to lure mathematicians into teaching and alteration of the mix of real versus psychic income. But the attack on "deans and professors of education, well-meaning but poorly informed members of congress, and state legislators and their staffs, almost all of whom embrace more-of-the-same solutions"[31] (the "education establishment"), was just as blind to the fact that the problem as received was equally "more of the same." Business might have provided a genuine alternative; yet corporate interest in education continued instead to echo the fixation on teachers as the focus of change efforts throughout the decade. In 1990, for example, *Fortune* magazine quoted a prominent executive vice-president's summary of how business was "turning students on to science." The boldface subtitle of its "Special Education Issue" article on mathematics and science education again reaffirmed the superteacher as the corporate agent of innovation:

> Want to help the dismal math and science skills of Amer-
> ican kids? Just tuck away the textbooks, open up the labs,
> add an inspired teacher—and stand back.[32]

The new twist was the avoidance of faulting the teachers themselves. By blaming unsatisfactory student performance on the sys-
tematic barriers to individual action, corporate participation in
change efforts further enhanced the rugged individualism of the
specific teacher as central to the understanding of current and possible educational organization.

## The Teacher as Myth

If Plato taught us anything, it is to recognize the rhetorical power
of the superteacher myth in arguments for particular educational
practice. Yet, as Deborah Britzman has suggested, cultural myths in
the making of a teacher can serve ideological interests in key
ways.[33] She noted three recurring cultural myths about teachers:
everything depends on the teacher; the teacher is the expert; and
teachers are self-made. Each myth is stated and understood in
highly individualistic terms, thereby valorizing the individual and
making 'inconsequential' the institutional and social constraints
that frame the teacher's work.

The acclaimed mathematics teachers of the 1980s can be used
to illustrate Britzman's framework. Despite the particular social
environment of inner-city Atlanta, Finkelstein drew his students
into discovery learning "because he [knew] well the subject matter
they [were] studying and [had] carefully prepared his strategy."[34]
Discovery learning is "initiated, monitored and controlled" by the
teacher.[35] Finkelstein himself, a former professor of mathematics,
founded his own nonprofit corporation in order to devote himself
to convincing others of the efficacy of his approach. John Saxon, a
graduate of West Point and former army test pilot, personally drove
across the state of Oklahoma to convince schools to try his textbooks. When publishers refused to consider his ideas, he borrowed
money from his son and published the books out of his own home.
He personally promoted his books first through polemical articles
in the *National Review* and later in controversial advertisements in
professional journals.[36] Jaime Escalante spent years going to school
at night to obtain teaching credentials. At Garfield High, he estab-

lished his own calculus-oriented curriculum in a former music room, independently seeking funding for innovative programs that brought his students to weekend and summer institutes. By placing the teacher in a self-contained world, these myths transformed the teacher's actual isolation into a valued autonomy which, in turn, promoted the larger social value of rugged individualism.

## Teacher as Signifier

During the 1980s such superteacher myths also helped establish the mathematics teacher as the nexus of a web of discourse about current social crises. Rather than searching for the reasons people did not find mathematics interesting and why students did not select more advanced mathematics courses, the dominant focus of discussion was on the failures of teachers to inspire students in mathematics; ill-prepared or unqualified teachers thus became responsible for an inadequate supply of newly qualified and enthusiastic colleagues. As well, they were blamed for a fundamental shortage of experts in mathematics and science and an impending slide in the country's military superiority and technological leadership. Similarly, the prominence of standardized test scores in policy decisions obscured debate over the appropriateness of such tests or subject matter tested in favor of the teachers' failure to teach properly or to teach the right material for the tests. The individual teacher became, then, the key, on the one hand, to maintaining a 'knowledge advantage' over other countries (leading to technological and economic dominance), and, on the other, to providing business with a workforce of adequate mathematical aptitude (linked to market production, the balance of trade, and production levels).

To be an excellent teacher was a patriotic calling, an effort to support 'national interests' as articulated by the political 'New Right'. But the telescoped attention on the individual teacher was most blatantly ideological in its reduction of structural inequalities by race, class, and gender to the notion of individual achievement and participation. By not adequately teaching children—all of whom can learn, within the dominant ideology—the teacher became the crucial creator of, or obstacle to, a democratic society. That is, equality and opportunity were constructed in terms of access to the mathematical literacy requisite to understanding and evaluating arguments that use numerical and statistical facts.

Teachers of mathematics became in this sense the conduit to the cultivation of self-regulating individuals.[37]

In the interpretation I offer here, 'teacher' is a 'signifier', and the language used to talk about mathematics education is a system of signs. As was suggested by Saussure, a sign consists of a signifier (the sound image of the written/spoken shape) and a signified (a concept).[38] The inseparability of the signifier and the signified (the sound-image 'teacher' and the concept of 'teacher', and not, say with the concept 'student') creates the illusion of language as transparent—that language is merely the medium through which individuals transmit messages to one another (about an independently constituted 'world of things'). Debates about purposes and techniques of mathematics education appear to use commonly understood words to talk about people, activities, and things 'in the world'. The Saussurean moment pertinent to the present investigation is the realization that, on the contrary, it is language that offers the possibility of constructing a world of individuals and things and of differentiating between them. Focusing on language means focusing on the ways in which language creates a field of differences.[39]

Language for this investigation becomes a way of articulating experience; hence, it also participates in 'ideology', in the aggregate of the ways in which people both live and represent to themselves their relationship to the conditions of their existence. Ideology is 'inscribed' in discourses, myths, presentations, and re-presentations of the way 'things are'. To this extent the signifier 'teacher' is integrally complicit in the inscription of ideology in the language of public debate about and in mathematics education. Of course, ideology should not be reduced to language. And language certainly should not be reduced to ideology. But the 'signifying system' (language) can have an important role in naturalizing the 'way things are'; language slides into 'common sense'.

Language could thus constrain to a great degree the 'possibilities' of social organization perceived and imagined. As well, "because it is characteristic of language to be overlooked," Catherine Belsey writes, "the differences it constructs may seem to be natural, universal and unalterable when in reality they may be produced by a specific form of social organization."[40] Furthermore, if 'signifieds' are not pre-existing and given, but rather changeable and contingent, and if changes in signified concepts are related to changes in the social formation, then the notion of language as a neutral nomenclature functioning as an instrument of communication of meanings that exist independently of it is clearly untenable. Differences and distinctions that seem obvious, a matter of common sense, cannot be taken for granted because a common sense itself is to a large degree a linguistic construct. This chapter focuses on the ways in which the signifier 'teacher' integrally served the formation of common sense for discussion of mathematics education in the 1980s, and the relations between it and other signifiers (e.g., 'student', 'mathematics', etc.). The constructed myth of the 'teacher' was central to the *creation* of crises and their causes, rather than being simply a *reaction* to these crises.[41]

However, a signifier can mean its opposite as well as its ideological meaning. Roland Barthes[42] was one of the first people to point this out by attending to the ways in which ideology is naturalized in the discourses, myths, and images of twentieth-century society. Ideology, masquerading as coherence and plenitude, is in reality inconsistent, limited, and contradictory; the realist text, as a crystallization of ideology, participates in this incompleteness even while it diverts attention from that fact in its apparent ability to resolve conflicting perspectives.[43] When the teacher is identified as the nexus in the reproduction of public problems, the teacher also becomes the symbol of potential change as well as the (political) site of efforts to alter educational practice. Hence the particular rhetorical strength of a superteacher as a symbol of the ideal champion of national progress.

Indeed, stories about superteachers have had their important role in the history of mathematics education in America. When Warren Colburn published in *First Lessons in Arithmetic, on the Plan of Pestalozzi, With Some Improvements* in 1825, for example, the text was preceded by a narrative about "Mr. Wiseman." The schoolmaster presumably embodied the sound pedagogical techniques of Colburn's *Lessons* to follow; he was able to teach even "The Boy Without a Genius." In the story, Mr. Wiseman demonstrated the power of a teacher's belief in the ability of any student to achieve regardless of their appearance or previous labels. In his first meeting with the boy, he declared,

> I shall set you about nothing but what you are able to do;
> but observe, you *must* do it. We have no *I can't* here.

We are told the boy "went away . . . with more confidence in his powers than he had felt before."[44] In a letter to the boy's father, the schoolmaster clarified his philosophy:

> If by *genius* you meant such a decided bent of mind to any one pursuit as will lead to excel with little or no labour or instruction, I must say that I have not met with such a quality in more than three or four boys in my life, and your son is certainly not among the number. But if you mean only the *ability* to do some of those things which the greater part of mankind can do when properly taught, I can affirm, that I find in him no peculiar deficiency.[45]

One hundred sixty-four years later, in 1989, after riding a media wave about his achievements as a teacher of mathematics (including a successful film, a book, a presidential award, and finally his own television show on public television), Jaime Escalante explained his confidence in the ability of any student to learn in much the same way:

> I don't think kids cannot learn. That's my own philosophy. Anybody, any kid can learn if he or she has the desire to do it. . . . The teacher plays an important role in education. . . . The teacher gives us the desire to learn, the desire to be Somebody.[46]

Like Mr. Wiseman before him, who instilled confidence in his pupil that he would not be asked to accomplish anything beyond his capabilities, Escalante's classroom sports a banner declaring, "Calculus Need Not Be Made Easy. It is Easy Already." The excellent teacher's philosophy in general was well-articulated by Harold Finkelstein in particular when he said, "these children can do what every other student can do."[47] The ability to make that philosophy appear to be reality, especially in "disadvantaged" communities, made an excellent teacher a hero.

## Teacher as Hero

As I have noted above, Jaime Escalante was the consummate superteacher of the 1980s. Indeed, he met all criteria for the definition of 'hero'.[48] First, as a mythological and legendary figure, Escalante appeared as an allusion in a variety of media, in which he was endowed with great strength (both in determination and physically on the handball court) and ability (to motivate seemingly difficult students). He was depicted as an illustrious warrior, literally in terms of battling the gang-ridden urban jungle of East Los Angeles, and figuratively, in fighting for the rights of Mexican-American students to prove to themselves and all of society that they are capable of high-quality performance, if given the opportunity. He was admired for his achievements and qualities: his talent of using his own Latino background to lure his students into mathematics; his persistent and consistent hard work (arriving at 7 A.M., leaving at 7 P.M.); and for the number of Latino students taking the AP calculus examination at Garfield High (at one time more than 25 percent of all Latino AP test takers came from Garfield). Indeed, Escalante was said to display great courage: in giving up his well-paying job in the electronics industry to become a teacher; and in sticking to it, working "against all odds" to become a tremendously successful teacher. Escalante met the criteria of the secondary definition of hero as well. Jaime Escalante was the name of the principal male character in both a literary work (*Escalante: The Best Teacher in America*, by Jay Matthews) and a dramatic work (*Stand and Deliver*, a feature film starring Edward James Olmos, written by Ramon Menendez and Tom Musca, directed by Menendez and produced by Musca). In fulfilling these criteria, Jaime Escalante can be considered the central figure of mathematics education in the 1980s.

In conforming to the definition of hero, Escalante was not alone. In fact, an extensive study of all films of the 1980s with teachers as main characters concluded that the teacher as hero was the dominant and virtually universal development of the teacher character throughout the popular medium.[49] Yet he was unusual in that he was a mathematics teacher.[50] This perceived oddity of a teacher of "of all things mathematics"[51] actually made Escalante an even greater teacher hero since he was battling the enormous odds against him by teaching mathematics; that is, the construction of mathematics as a subject matter relatively more challenging to teach increased Escalante's status as a superteacher. Yet, as I will show below, the legend of Escalante ironically positioned mathematics as a model of all subject knowledge in general, so that Escalante became an example for all American teachers. Hence, it can be understood why William J. Bennett, the controversial yet highly visible U.S. Secretary of Education under Ronald Reagan, was quoted as declaring,

> Jaime Escalante . . . one of America's true heroes. His extraordinary achievement at Garfield High offers a hundred bold lessons and one shining example for American education.[52]

Such sentiments were common, as illustrated by a *Newsweek* review of *Stand and Deliver*:

> At a time when wrangling politicos, moral cretins, and drug-dealing dictators hog the headlines, Jaime Escalante is an authentic American hero.[53]

The sensationalism surrounding the myth of Jaime Escalante, when balanced by its basis in 'truth', was thus taken as a necessary vehicle for generating important public discussion of education, as exemplified by this quote from *Commonweal*:

> With its heroic but realistic treatment of a teacher, the film also stands as an important cultural hallmark of a nation at risk (but will 1989 bring us, as so many candidates promise, "an education president"?).[54]

Indeed, the image of Escalante as a hero with a message for all teachers in all schools in America still has resounding implications for public discourse, as is evident in a 1991 syndicated column by Mona Charen:

> [What] Jaime Escalante—arguably the nation's premier teacher (and if you haven't yet seen the movie based on his story, "Stand and Deliver," rent it)—has achieved in East Los Angeles. He taught his barrio kids calculus by touching their souls as well as their minds. But above all he refused to expect little from them. That is a critical lesson for every American school.[55]

Moreover, I want to argue that Escalante, as portrayed and re-presented in various media, exemplified Britzman's three cultural myths. In doing so, the Escalante legend illustrated what it was about a particular individual that made them a 'good teacher'; in turn, the cultivation of specific qualities about individuals became the 'solution' to fundamental educational crises. But, as Britzman's work suggests, the reduction of social problems (and their solutions) to the appropriate personalities of isolated individuals effectively obscures social and institutional constraints on educational practice, while simultaneously enabling certain educational practice to become 'commonsense'. In this way, the legend of Escalante is an example of how attention directed to teacher heroes resolves complex social, political, and economic conflicts by rendering them extraneous.

However, I want to suggest that the constructed dualism between 'the individual' and 'society' is an ideological phenomenon of language, and that the particular way in which the mathematics education discourse of the 1980s negotiated this dualism had significant implications for the construction of social and political concepts as well. That is, I want to argue that the portrayal of singular individuals as excellent superteachers was one manifestation of a simultaneous characterization of concepts such as ethnicity and class. In the case of the Escalante legend, the notion that the story was 'about' a great teacher obscured the fact that the legend constructed a particular 'story' about what it meant to be a Mexican American in an American school, the relationship between class and Hispanic culture, and what it meant to 'learn', 'know' and 'use' mathematics. It is in this way that the use of the Escalante myth in public policy discussion inhibited the articulation of educational 'problems' as associated with social and institutional issues.

## Escalante: The Best Teacher in America

How did the re-presentations of Escalante actively reconstruct Britzman's cultural myths of teachers and teaching? By crafting the notions that everything depends on the teacher, that the teacher is the expert, and that a teacher is self-made. And by communicating these conceptual frameworks in ways that rely on highly individualistic descriptions and images, thus valorizing the individual and making 'inconsequential' institutional and social contexts of teaching.

In the legend of Escalante, we learn that our hero is the quintessential American immigrant and self-made man. He left Bolivia to escape political chaos and impending economic hardship; he chose to live in California because a relative was already there. Upon arrival in the United States, he spoke no English, but he found a job as a busboy in a local restaurant. He enrolled in night courses at Pasadena City College, taking English, mathematics, and electronics. After receiving his degree, he went to work as a technician with Burroughs Corporation. It was a well-paying job, but he wanted to return to his first love, his profession in Bolivia: teaching. In 1973, he earned a degree in mathematics from California State University, and later was awarded his teaching credentials. In 1974, at a considerable cut in pay, Escalante left Burroughs to become a mathematics teacher at Garfield High.[56] Once a teacher, our hero fought the school bureaucracy as well as student apathy.[57] Later, he was attributed with the unique qualities that enable an individual to become a great man: to take chances and dare his students to succeed. Great teachers, as exemplified by Escalante, are often 'impatient'; they are 'abrasive'. They "rock the boat, and because they do, they are not always wanted."[58] Simply stated, Escalante is not the kind of person to let anything or anyone stand in his way.

One way in which the film version of the Escalante story supported and helped sustain the personality-cult orientation of the myth, and hence the emphasis on the teacher as self-made, was via the particular approach to acting used by Edward James Olmos. Olmos believed that the key ingredient for film is character development, and he studied Escalante relentlessly, in person and on tape; he put on forty pounds and had his hair thinned.[59] Indeed, Olmos saw the film as a victory for his approach to acting: giving integrity to ethnic experience by grounding it in individual character and event.[60] Apparently, the on-set debate between Olmos and director Ramon Menendez was quite turbulent; but by the end of filming, Menendez was convinced by Olmos that individual character development is key: "From now on," he said, "I would always start out from character instead of plot."[61]

Matthews' biography also sustained this emphasis on the individual. Of course, the structure of biography itself tends to be oriented towards a particular isolable or identifiable character. But Matthews wrote in his introduction that his explicit purpose was to suggest that great teachers are great because of something about their personality. He had not encountered another educator in this country, he wrote, who had produced such spectacular results in such a difficult setting; nor had he met any other teacher who

offered so many encouraging answers to some of the most important social and educational questions of our era.[62] His purpose in
writing his book was to provoke a response from readers: He hoped
they would confront their own views of "what makes a good
teacher" and subject his story of Escalante, and the educators they
encountered in their own lives, to their own, personal test. Matthews' approach was to go back to Escalante's childhood, to his
"roots"; his presumption, within a popular version of psychoana-
lytic discourse, was that the personal qualities of an individual are
revealed in the narrative story of his or her life.[63]

> I have gone back to his childhood, to the roots of his
> intensity and commitment, so that readers can ponder
> what makes exceptional teachers and decide for them-
> selves if there is any hope of duplicating the process.[64]

In my interpretation, however, the idea of Matthews' book, to strip
away the myth and legend,[65] revealing the 'true', genuine, man,
creates a new 'fiction'—a character called Escalante, which re-pre-
sents an individual whole and complete, without the complex contradictions of social life.

The way in which the Escalante myth portrays its main character as 'the expert' is somewhat indirect, partly due to the fact that
mathematics is understood as difficult to understand and impossible to make entertaining. Hence, stories of Jaime Escalante reveal
little detail about his actual teaching of his subject matter. (The
details are off-screen.) For example, one reviewer of *Stand and
Deliver* complained he got a strong feeling for Escalante's personality, but not much about his teaching methods.[66]

But the relegation of the actual day-to-day grind of teaching
and learning to 'behind the scenes' worked directly to sustain the
presumption that the teacher of course did have a superb command
of mathematics. Nevertheless, there were some examples of how
"Escalante combines the best of pedagogy [that he is an expert 'at
teaching'] with the best of content;" Lee Shulman, for example, a
"Stanford education expert," was able to identify one scene in *Stand
and Deliver* that illustrated how superteacher Escalante

> not only knows what he's talking about, he knows how
> to talk about it. He knows his audience, how to fire their
> imaginations and enthusiasm. That is great teaching.[67]

In an article in *Educational Leadership*, Escalante was asked, as if the question need not be verbalized, if he had a thorough knowledge of mathematics.[68] Escalante quickly gave nodding approval to the assumption that such knowledge is essential; but he carefully emphasized that, for the excellent teacher, this is not enough. He had a strong command of skills, he said, such as in communicating with his students and in motivating them to learn. Most important, he stressed, was the ability to give them *ganas*—"the desire to do something—to make them believe they can learn."[69] Indeed, such a focus on how the superteacher can surpass an easy reference to the difficulties of teaching less advantaged students in hostile environments in order to achieve a "pedagogy of substance" became the foundation of professional educational theory. The National Conference on Higher Education, for example, embraced "Stand and Deliver" as its theme in April 1989. In his presentation at that conference, Lee Shulman not only held Jaime Escalante's teaching as a model of such a pedagogy of substance, but also recommended that all in attendance read Matthews' biography for the in-depth understanding of "good teaching" not available in the film version.[70]

The separation of content from method in Escalante's educational practice helped create the perception that he had a message for all teachers regardless of their subject matter. The crucial element in his teaching, we learned, was that he won over his students by example. The students could not help but respect a teacher who was at the school from 7 a.m. to 7 p.m.: "Even students not much interested in math work hard for him when they see him working so hard for them."[71] Escalante personally provided 24-hour support for his students, accepting telephone calls at home, interceding with parents, arranging field trips, and organizing expeditions to McDonald's. Escalante enhanced students' feelings of participation and self-esteem via clean-up paint squads for his classroom, car-wash fundraisers, and by finding funding to pay advanced student-tutors. He further achieved these goals by using a team approach, treating AP calculus test training like a varsity team: Students wore team jackets emblazoned GARFIELD HIGH—APCALCULUS, warmed up with loud cheers to invigorating music, etc. Matthews highlights the significance of these extramathematical teaching practices by comparing his hero with another Garfield teacher, Ben Jimenez, who has a startlingly different personality (no showmanship, quiet and reserved); he, too, worked hard for those students who also worked diligently themselves.

This style of teaching required students to become so overwhelmed by the efforts of a particular teacher that they were willing to put in extra effort simply out of their desire to please him.

> "Everyone wants to please him," explains Delia Mora, 17. . . . "He puts out such an effort that you want to put out just as much and even more."

> Josie Richkarday, 18: "You make a lot of sacrifices. I gave up track, baseball, and cheerleading because Mr. Escalante is a once-in-a-lifetime teacher."[72]

Here the mathematics teacher forms a cult of himself.[73] The devotion of his students to his particular personality is the main motivation. Hence the achievements of his students are attributable directly to him—his intrinsic 'self'—and to few 'external' factors.

Central to the educational strategy of the Escalante story, however, is the extremely high expectations the superteacher holds for his students. Equally crucial was the insistence on not allowing any student *not* to meet these expectations. Matthews discusses numerous episodes in which students were not allowed to drop out of Escalante's demanding class. Instead, they are required to attend extra study sessions before and after school. Indeed, Escalante required signed contracts from students and their parents, giving permission for his pupils to come to school for these extra study sessions, as well as weekend classes. In addition, his students studied mathematics in special summer courses. The key message of the story was that students will meet such expectations if they are required to do so.

> Inside most teenagers, including those at Garfield, lurks a visceral respect for honest labor. The feeling transcends class and ethnic background.[74]

> Most students will rise to the expectations held before them. . . . The secret of great teaching . . . hinges on raising expectations and launching them on the Quest.[75]

The Mona Charen quote above illustrates the tenacity of this moral in public discourse.

Do Mona Charen and others expect all teachers to work 12-hour days, and add weekend and summer sessions on top of that, in order to impress their students into devotion and require their students to live up to their high expectations? Clearly, with a heavy focus on the particular qualities of an individual superteacher, few alternative work structures will be suggested. The only possibility is to attribute success to the extraordinary efforts of the individual teacher. The Escalante myth further enabled such a discursive formation by bestowing numerous accolades upon its hero, thus glorifying the perception that everything depended on the individual teacher.

His gift of reaching his students was directly linked to his own Latino background. His skill at capturing their attention was also one peculiar to him as an individual: his "mocking hipster's wit," taunting his pupils with mean cracks like "tough guys don't do math; tough guys fry chicken for a living."[76] "Eventually, the burros [became] thoroughbreds, driven by their teacher, who reaches beyond the classroom into their lives."[77]

It was Escalante the superteacher who formed the first AP class. It was Escalante's extra-valiant effort, staying at school from 7 to 7, that impressed his students. It was Escalante who encouraged his pupils to come in and work with him before and after school, and to eat lunch at their desks in order to talk calculus.[78] It was Escalante who demanded discipline and self-sacrifice.

Then, when his students were accused of cheating by the testing service, it was Escalante, in the reports and in the film, who made the decision to 'stand and deliver' by having his students retake the test and prove that no cheating occurred. (This was, I would suspect, a decision to be made by the students. Indeed, the testing service—for their own reasons—consistently portrayed the decision as an individual decision for each student.)

But it was Escalante who 'gave' the students *ganas*.[79] Later, he would be nicknamed 'The Champ', because he was a maker of champions (no mention of school and community support, including extensive financial support to pay student-tutors).[80] Finally, whole school/community efforts were traced to this one individual. For example, it was said that the repercussions of a dynamic teacher like Escalante extended beyond his classroom:

> AP courses in numerous subjects sprung up at Garfield. Peer pressure is encouraging attendance and homework. The entire aspiration level of the school has been lifted.

> "We have decreased the amount of vandalism, graffiti, drug and gang involvement because we're creating role models," says Garfield principal Henry Gradillas. "We're turning out kids who will be able to extend a positive influence when they graduate. Thanks to Jaime Escalante, we're turning out champs!"[81]

In fact, Escalante "generated so much *ganas* that the once-scorned Garfield [became] a mecca for barrio kids."[82] This special individual, who "manage[d] to take a class full of presumed math morons and turn them into whiz kids,"[83] "proved that the flood of new Americans from Mexico and other Latin countries need not be the liability so many have feared."[84] Simply stated, Escalante was "the man who helped start Garfield High's revolution."[85]

It is no wonder, then, that *Fortune* magazine's advice to the corporate vice president was to "Just tuck away the textbooks, open up the labs, add an inspired teacher—and stand back." Teachers like Jaime Escalante needed the freedom to spark their social revolutions.

> There are thousands of exceptional teachers struggling with students as disadvantaged and with resources as meager as those at Garfield. Like all good teachers, they sense potential in young minds but wonder if unimaginative administrators, deficit-conscious school boards, and distracted parents will give them the necessary support.[86]

The myth of the teacher as the educational expert upon which all depends helped focus criticism and satisfaction on isolated individuals while turning students and the wider public into passive receivers of expert service.[87] In this way, individual teachers were expected to see through and solve problems assigned to schooling, while lay people were justified in being perplexed. The teachers simply exchange inclusion in the wider society for membership in a special community of the technically proficient. And the "skills" of teaching, as suggested by Jaime Escalante, become definable and codifiable as part of a professional, scientific knowledge base.

Escalante himself argued that an individual teacher must find within himself the particular techniques that he can use to force students to live up to the teacher's expectations.[88] Ironically, the public response to a superteacher is to seek to identify and codify specific techniques as foundational to the teacher's success.[89] The ideological result is that it is the teachers and the teachers alone who become the vehicle of policy change. It is thus the teachers who become the focus for political conflict over the goals and objectives of schooling, and the teachers who are blamed for perceived educational crises. As Robert Welker wrote:

> At its most ideologically stringent level, the image of the teacher as expert supports the idea that the real lever of social progress lies within the domain of scientific advance. If we can only attain expertise or put the experts in charge, the metaphor seems to suggest, then the means to educational excellence will be achieved.[90]

As Welker noted, teacher education research has traditionally sought to identify those distinct instructional practices which mark the labor of an able teacher. Even today, the hope echoes Jay Matthews, that such practices and particular characteristics of personality might be fostered in novices and be institutionalized in programs as part of a more scientific and standardized conception of teacher education. Yet, as Welker argued,

> This very view can impose upon teachers a more rigid view of instructional technique and tie them more dependently to teacher educators, who now rule because they claim to have established a more precise scientific knowledge of what works in the classroom. More critically, expertise can tie teachers ideologically to a view of practice which continually seeks in a mechanical way to reduce what is best to what works and which thus neglects wider questions of value as the true foundation of professional training.[91]

Unraveling the Myth

Expertise further enhances the emphasis on the individual teacher independent of social and political aspects of educational practice, reifying the individual-society dualism as an essential component of commonsense. But careful attention to the re-presentation of Jaime Escalante reveals the particular ways in which his story establishes ethnicity and class as categories of social comprehension and conflict.

These categories of conceptual "commonsense" are crucial to the development of the Escalante legend, because descriptions of him as an individual are made in terms of them. That is, the language of ethnicity and class make the creation of the individual possible. Particular individual characteristics that make him special as a superteacher, that establish his uniqueness, do so in opposition to a normative dimension constructed by this language. The illusion of language as transparent—as merely the medium through which people transmit messages to one another—establishes a ground of commonsense agreement; yet descriptions of Escalante as an individual contain within them contradictions that help direct us to conflicts within the ongoing public discourse on education.

The construction of Escalante's and his students' ethnicity is a good illustration. Matthews' biography, for example, was subtitled "the best teacher in *America*," and much was made of his American identity: he was a "genuine American genius" (Bill Honig, California State Superintendent of Public Instruction); "one of America's true heroes" (William Bennett, former U.S. Secretary of Education); and a "national treasure" (Edward James Olmos, star of *Stand and Deliver*, and known for his role in the popular television series, *Miami Vice*).[92] The book itself was dressed up in patriotic red, white, and blue. Yet Escalante was the best teacher *in* America—not the best *American* teacher—as if to suggest that his origins in Bolivia still tainted his citizenship.

Indeed, his description as an outsider fighting educational bureaucracy seems to have been directly attributable to his foreign origins. His interest in the AP examination stemmed from the Bolivian practice of outside examiners. And his high expectations for his students was Bolivian in origin as well. American teachers were too soft on their students; but Bolivian schools still demanded discipline and hard work. Years later, Escalante was still very much the Bolivian: "It took [Matthews] some time to adjust to his accent. He seasoned his English with bits of Spanish and two Bolivian Indian dialects."[93] When Escalante was invited to the White House to meet Ronald Reagan, it was partly due to his status as a superteacher, and his "up-by-the-bootstraps" talk;[94] but it was also because of his Latino heritage that the president needed to be seen meeting with him.

What better location would there be for this Latino transplant than East Los Angeles? More than 95 percent of the Garfield student body was Latino. Some of their families had recently immigrated to the United States from Mexico, often illegally. Even long-term residents usually spoke Spanish at home.

What, then, brought so much interest in the story of Jaime Escalante?

> The local Spanish-language press reported Garfield's progress nearly every year, but the national press largely ignored it. East Los Angeles was an isolated enclave; without the hint of scandal that had fueled the 1982 story [in which students were accused of cheating], few reporters were very interested.[95]

It began with the counteraccusation that the Educational Testing Service had singled out the Garfield students because they lived in East Los Angeles, known for its high percentage of Latino residents, and because 90 percent of the students had Hispanic surnames.[96] This then led people like Jay Matthews (the Los Angeles bureau chief of *The Washington Post*, who won the National Education Reporting Award in 1983 for his coverage of the Escalante story), and Ramon Menendez and Tom Musca to ask how a teacher had rounded up so many students with Hispanic surnames to take the AP test in the first place, whether they cheated or not. The 'Hispanic' part of the story was the foundation for curiosity in Jaime Escalante, Bolivian-American teacher teaching mostly Mexican-American students.

The film *Stand and Deliver* had its origins in 1983, when Menendez read about Escalante in the *Los Angeles Times*;[97] he and Musca brought the idea of a film about Escalante and his students to the public television series *American Playhouse*, which gave them seed money to write a screenplay.[98] Hollywood had meanwhile discovered a new form of box-office success in *La Bamba* (a film about

Latino Rock star Richie Valens) and the interest of big-name stars in, for example, *The Milagro Beanfield War* (an Hispanic romance directed and produced by veteran actor Robert Redford); it was the Hispanic theme in *Stand and Deliver* that led Warner Brothers to take a chance with its distribution. Olmos, a well-known television actor in a successful series, was cast as Escalante; not surprisingly, Lou Diamond Phillips, the star of *La Bamba*, and Andy Garcia, a young Hispanic actor fresh from the successful *The Untouchables*, were cast in prominent roles as Escalante's student and the Testing Service representative. The plot of the film was summarized as "Latino kids accept the challenge to defeat the stereotype";[99] and it was this theme which was played up in advertisements accompanying early distribution.

The Hispanic culture of the Garfield community presented both the problems with which Escalante fought, and much of the potential solutions. For example, Latino parents were depicted as discouraging academic aspirations despite wanting the best for their children:

> Your first priority should be your religion, your family, and your friends . . . What good is a nice B in some class if you're in the hospital? Lay off the studies. Go have some fun.[100]

Typically, older children were forced to drop out of school and work to help support a large family. Indeed, one of the scenes of the film often cited as moving involves Escalante visiting a girl's family restaurant to tell her father that he must let her continue with her studies, and then to go on to college. Yet, families

> go out of their way to help each other. That sense of family loyalty gives the community its emotional core.[101]

And Escalante used this aspect of Hispanic culture by demonstrating the 24-hour concern of a father, and by establishing his calculus class as a self-supporting "team."

Escalante was Latino, a *Bolivian* American. But, because he was successful, he was labelled 'American'. Nevertheless, he was successful largely due to his non-American foreignness, which in turn enabled him to bring in 'new' old ideas about discipline and hard work. He became the 'solution' to the Latino problem:

The problem is particularly acute in Latino communities and had led many commentators and politicians to suggest that the United States can no longer accept so many newcomers from Latin America. According to the National Commission on Secondary Education for Hispanics, 40 percent of all Latino youths who drop out of school do so before the tenth grade. 45 percent of Mexican-American and Puerto Rican children never finish high school. 76 percent of all Latinos score in the bottom half of standardized achievement tests. Just in California, more than 13 percent of all high school graduates, but only 5 percent of Latino graduates, were eligible for admission to the University of California in 1983.[102]

Yet, Escalante's 'solution' directly influenced only the small percentage of Garfield students who took his advanced mathematics course. He searched the junior high schools for potential students. We do not hear about the majority of students. What we do know is that Garfield's new principal, Henry Gradillas, supported efforts to improve test scores and increase the number of Advanced Placement courses. Escalante's America was a meritocracy which allows a token number of Latinos into the professional middle class. The nontokens lived 'behind-the-scenes'. Escalante "wanted to prove that Mexican-American children with fathers who were fourth grade dropouts could match the best seniors at Beverly Hills High."[103] What he did prove was that he could pick out a few students to train relentlessly, and these few would then do as well on AP tests.

Indeed, how did Garfield compare with Beverly Hills? What message did the Escalante myth trace about categories of class in the United States? At least 80 percent of Garfield's Latino students qualified for the federal free-lunch or reduced-price lunch program, which meant their annual income fell below $15,000 for a family of four. (Most students' families were larger than this "norm.") At least 25 percent of the students came from families that received Aid to Families with Dependent Children, and that figure, we are told, would have been much larger if so many of the poor were not illegal aliens afraid to seek government help.[104]

The students who passed an AP exam in calculus would then earn college credit—saving time and money at most of the nation's universities. After Escalante sold the concept of a college education to his students, such ways around the costs of this education became important.[105] "But," we are told, "nearly all the people in East Los Angeles, like Americans anywhere, prefer to rely on their own resources."[106]

The Escalante legend pits wealthy school districts, like Beverly Hills, against working class immigrant districts like Garfield's East Los Angeles, to demonstrate that the wealthier districts have 'higher' expectations for their students. Yet this class distinction was constructed as ethnic in the myth, as in the story about Escalante's attempt to quit working at Garfield and teach at a fancier school. After discussing his enthusiasm for what could be accomplished in the fancy school, thanks to its facilities and community support, he was told the school did not need his kind of teaching. He was needed, he was told, back in the barrio. Nevertheless, the moral of the Escalante myth was supposed to have meaning over in Beverly Hills anyway; surely the wealthy, like Americans anywhere, prefer to rely on their own resources.

"[What happened at] Garfield offers lessons for schools even in affluent neighborhoods."[107] But what happened at Garfield could only have happened at Garfield. It would not have been heroic had Escalante taught at Beverly Hills High. Only in the barrio did he succeed 'against all odds'.

> Drugs, rape, murder. From reports on the news and accounts by survivors, Americans know inner-city school life can be a recurrent horror movie no child or teacher awakes from. But reality is worse still. To the students squirming in their homerooms, the life spread before them may offer either the drab subservience of a fast-food job or the glamorous apocalypse of teen-gang death. In their too knowing eyes, anyone can see the restless despair of an underclass programmed to fail.
>
> Time for a barrio hero. Jaime Escalante . . . will do just fine. He came to East Los Angeles to teach computer science. Sorry, no computers here: Only kids from wealthier districts need apply for the crucial jobs of the 21st century. So Jaime decided to teach advanced math to students who could count to 20 only by removing their shoes. He used every trick in the book, and a few from the streets. . . . Indeed, they had done it: passed a national calculus exam with scores that would delight any Beverly Hills pop.[108]

## Mathematics Teacher

It was also only because Jaime Escalante taught mathematics that he was noted as succeeding 'against all odds'. After all, large numbers of Garfield students had been taking AP tests in another subject for years, and had been doing well: in Spanish. Calculus was the symbol of achievement, in mathematics in particular, and for the school in general. The number of students studying calculus, and the number of students taking the AP test in calculus, were indicators of the school's overall success. This was probably because the traditional mathematics curriculum followed a sequence of courses; to arrive at calculus meant one had traveled through all of its prerequisites. And mathematics itself was perceived as a difficult and challenging subject. So that accomplishment in mathematics, by any criteria, meant success in school. ("No matter how talented Escalante might be, how could such a school produce 18 students willing and able to risk a program as difficult as Advanced Placement calculus?"[109]) That is, what was accomplished by Escalante had already been happening—large numbers of students taking AP tests; it had to be calculus AP tests to mean something. In general, however, the handling of Escalante's subject matter was typically kept 'behind-the-scenes', suggesting that a commonsense understanding of what it "was" was possible to achieve and naturally evident.

More students studying calculus came to mean greater focus, challenge, and vitality in their education:

> A study released in early 1987 by the National Research Council said that in most countries all advanced mathematics students take secondary school calculus, while in the United States only about one-fifth do. It said American mathematics education "lacks focus, challenge and vitality."[110]

And the more 'disadvantaged' students studying such a 'difficult' subject increased the relative greatness of Escalante as a teacher. By doubling the number of students interested in advanced calculus every year, Jaime Escalante and Garfield High doubled the number of young people who believed that they were going to be Somebody someday.[11]

In this way, an education without mathematics, or even without the stellar movement through the mathematics curriculum up to and including calculus, was defined to mean an education lacking focus, challenge, and vitality, and hence an education leading to nowhere. Thus mathematics became a critical component of a meaningful education. One reason for this was the perception that mathematics was "an essential tool of modern science;"[112] mathematics in this sense became a body of important skills to be mastered should one have an interest in a scientific career. ("This school has so many students in chemistry, biology, and physics—it's because they believe they can do it. One of the things the kids always repeat in front of me is 'You said, 'I believe in what you're doing.'"[113])

But, more important, Escalante's mathematics training was a vehicle for his students' "transformation from hooligans and daydreamers into a worshipful cadre that hangs on his every word like the extras in an E. F. Hutton commercial."[114] Hence his methods of teaching, separable from his actual subject matter, became transferrable to any teaching with the same, 'obviously' valuable goals. Escalante provided his students with a kind of 'boot camp', full of warm-up exercises to loud music, rigid drills, and inspections of their knowledge while they stood at attention.[115] Standing in line, they one by one spewed answers rapidly without needing to reflect.[116] Through long hours of hard work and extra drill and practice sessions, they learned to appreciate the value of discipline and determination.

> Like so many American movies of late, *Stand and Deliver* winds up being about grit and determination and victory.[17]

Similarly, Escalante's story naturalized standardized testing as a fundamental component of American education. Needing some way of evaluating his own progress as a teacher, Escalante recalled the outside examiner system from Bolivia. The AP test was the closest practice he could find in the United States: a standardized norm reference on which his students could be compared with any other students in the country. The mathematics itself became testable mathematics: a tool kit of methods for solving pre-given problems. The Escalante myth bypassed discussion of what it might have meant for the students to provide answers to preformed questions, and to do so without reflection. (Is this a question I would want to help answer? Does it have any moral implications? How do people come up with questions, and am I capable of posing interesting and important ones myself?[118]) Oddly enough, we never heard of students doubting the need to work so hard to answer questions that had already been solved. (Why not just look at the answer key?)

As David Denby pointed out, the Escalante myth suggested that

> Escalante's success may be due to his reducing education to a kind of game—passing a tough test. The kids win a race—and that, somehow or other, is going to save their lives. No larger idea of education is offered or even hinted at. (I couldn't help wondering if the students were reading anything at the same time as they were mastering calculus. For all we can see, they could be illiterate.)[119]

The Escalante myth directly addressed a key educational debate: how to combine excellence and equality of opportunity. "As [Escalante's] passionate pursuit of excellence from the barrio makes clear, these are not choices, but equally valuable goals," wrote Tom O'Brien.[120] But nevertheless, wrote O'Brien, the legend of Escalante might have fed an unwary public some illusions about educational improvement and the achievement of excellence. Surely, better test scores have some connection to amelioration in some skill areas; yet the Escalante emphasis (at least in the myth) on using an entire high school career to prepare for that final AP test at the end, is one example of what came to be called "test mania."

> Schools are increasingly pressuring instructors to "teach to the test," framing the curriculum around likely test topics and strategies instead of more valuable skills. The emphasis on testing is hurting teachers, who fear they must raise test scores or lose their jobs . . . But . . . the real victims are students whose prowess on standardized exams might come at the expense of critical thinking and creativity.[121]

While purporting to be the story of a singular individual, then, the story of Jaime Escalante indirectly provided straightforward answers to a number of complex curriculum issues. Using a collection of eight sets of curriculum questions originally suggested by Michael Young,[122] but recently reemphasized by Landon Beyer and Michael Apple,[123] it is possible to understand the general perception of education mythically represented as commonsense. Beyer and Apple label these question categories epistemological, political, economic, ideological, aesthetic, ethical, and historical.

The first questions have to do with deliberations over what should count as knowledge, and as knowing. "Should we take a behavioral position and one that divides knowledge and knowing into cognitive, affective, and psycho-motor areas, or do we need a less reductive and more integrated picture of knowledge and the mind, one that stresses knowledge as process?"[124] Though the 'real' Escalante might say otherwise, the message we get from the story (that pares away the myth and leaves the real man) is one that defines knowledge as a received body of facts and algorithms; providing solutions to given problems within classified problem types, these facts and algorithms conform to subtopics within the curriculum. Knowing is understood as being able to do well on a standardized written test, as being able to provide immediate solutions to decontextualized problems within a short, specified time limit.

Political curriculum questions address who should appropriately control the selection and distribution of knowledge, and through what institutions. The traditional mathematics sequence followed by Escalante, with calculus as the final destination, accepts knowledge as predetermined by the historical development in mathematics up to the eighteenth century, when calculus was codified. The perception of mathematics is of a collection of facts and algorithms slowly marching forward in the service of humanity. Of course, textbook writers and publishers have selected specific topics; but for the most part they have been standardized. For the calculus course, the nature of the AP test requires a rather conservative approach to the subject to maintain consistency from year to year in establishing a normative reference for test scores. The idea of calculus as the main goal of school mathematics was called into question during this decade, as discrete mathematical models became increasingly important in the sciences. Nevertheless, school mathematics continued to be based on eighteenth-century models of science and technology.

Mathematical knowledge was perceived as accessible to all who provided the interest and effort to obtain it. Teachers may need to force their students into expressing interest, or persuade them that their efforts are worthwhile; they also may need to help them make their efforts most productive.

The learning paradigm used by Escalante assumed that students vary in their aptitude, ability to understand instruction, motivation, and perseverance. But these factors were only relevant in so far as they affected educational performance. They were not, for example, considered in terms of their contribution to nonperformance educational goals, such as moral growth, growth of aesthetic appreciation, and growth of inclination toward political participation. Most significantly, however, the mastery-learning paradigm assumed that all students are able to achieve mastery *given enough time*. As Michael Streibel noted,

> This pedagogical assumption treats learning as a rationally managed process because sufficient time and resources will guarantee predictable performance. Considerations such as the dialectics of learning, accommodation to individual uniqueness, and the possibility of emergent goals have been factored out of the process. Yet these considerations are essential for learning—even at the level of simple skills.[125]

Streibel also identified the commonsense background of mastery-learning for classroom and school practices and instructional arrangements. For classroom and school practices, the paradigm manipulates the *time* allowed for learning (Escalante increases time studying in his classroom, before and after school) and the quality of instructional stimuli to help students achieve mastery (Escalante persistently chides students into attending to the lesson, shocks them by loud butchering of apples, and incorporates multiple forms of showmanship). Therefore, the paradigm entails the rational planning of classroom time, schedules, organization, and conditions of instruction, as well as the rational design of instructional materials. (Such design and planning are called 'rational' to the extent that they are guided by the pragmatics of instructional and organizational theories, and possibly by the pragmatics of classroom teaching.) Predictability and manageability of process and product become prime considerations, not whether some unique classroom event becomes an occasion for further learning. Hence, as Streibel points out, the 'conception' of instructional events is separate from and directs the 'execution' of such events. In this scheme of things, we would expect to evaluate teacher performance (and ultimately administrator and even system performance) in terms of student performance, because correct student behavior is the ultimate product.[126] Indeed, Escalante's original interest in the AP test was its efficacy as an indicator of his own achievement as a teacher. Thus student performance is a euphemism for teacher performance, consistent with the notion that the teacher is the nexus of educational discourse.

Instructional arrangements are dictated by the prior acceptance of the mastery-learning paradigm as well.[127] Initial teaching methods are used to inform the learner of the objectives and prerequisite knowledge. Training procedures are used to help the learner acquire the appropriate knowledge and skills. Continual assessment procedures are used to ensure the presence or absence of subskills (Escalante used daily quizzes). Immediate remediation procedures are used if the subskills are not present. Finally, certification of mastery is added when some predetermined criterion performance is reached (passing the AP test). That is, the paradigm conceptualizes the instructional process in quality-control terms. Each step is expressed as a procedure and all instruction is arranged to maximize output. Knowledge, categorized as a hierarchy of prerequisite knowledge, annihilates the possibility of any focus on higher-level skills before lower-level skills; higher-level skills (higher in the hierarchy) are in a sense the sum of all component subskills. Mastery-learning thus specifies what kinds of things are to be achieved—measurable performance, and how these things are to be achieved—through the manipulation of time and instructional stimuli. Alternative educational possibilities must conform to these expectations.

As I have already noted, the Escalante myth constructed particular ways of talking about ethnicity and class. These categories of understanding have important implications for curricular deliberations over how the control of knowledge is or should be linked to existing unequal distribution of power, goods, and services in society. People in East Los Angeles, as in many large urban centers, were overwhelmingly Mexican American; most had little access to power, goods, or services, because they were poor or lower middle class. According to the story, they needed to seize knowledge, and prove that they could do whatever anyone else (i.e., any middle-class Anglo-American) could do; they should have made a place for themselves within the access-rich professional and educated world (e.g., by going to college).[128] That is, no special arrangements were needed to adjust access to knowledge and its distribution, beyond relying on a pool of superteachers who, through their own personal mission, enabled the window of access to be widened.

Ideological questions regard what knowledge is of most value, and whose knowledge this is. For the Escalante story, such questions were not particularly relevant. Knowledge was not seen as linked to ideology. Hence, notions about particular kinds of mathematics being connected to Western European and commercial interests, for example, were not possible to consider. Instead, Escalante pointed out to his students that their ancestors, the Mayans, had developed abstract mathematical concepts, such as zero, long before the Europeans. In this way, he encouraged ownership of calculus-related mathematics in its entirety without critical consideration of its specifically European uses. Mathematics in the Escalante story was a universal and neutral medium of reflection and communication.[129] He also simplified issues of ethnicity, mixed-coupling, a complicated history of regulated citizenship, and imperialism, reducing all Latinos to Mayan heritage.

The Escalante story sustained as well commonsense comprehension of the technical facets of curriculum design. This was inherent in its glorification of an individual teacher isolated from context; in actively participating in the construction of the three basic myths of teachers, it perpetuated nonreflective acceptance of current practice. Schools, in this story, provided the opportunity for access to knowledge by providing spaces in which students in groups can meet with teachers. Content was transmitted in sequential courses. A student was told facts and techniques in small increments, and given the opportunity to practice applying them daily. He or she was tested for minimal mastery and was required to practice daily to achieve this stature. Discipline and perseverance would bring mastery. The teacher spent time with each student who was willing to make the effort until such mastery was achieved.

Aesthetic curriculum considerations concern how one should link knowledge to the biography and personal meanings of the student. For Escalante, this was an especially important component. He hoped to help his students develop the willingness to display *ganas*: guts—no fear, and the tendency to take risks; and desire—the will to succeed, the need to prove oneself by being able to survive any reasonable test of mastery. His daily quizzes were like practice for the ultimate obstacle course at the end of basic training.

Escalante had much to offer in terms of the art of cultivating *ganas*. His practice sessions occurred in a supportive team-oriented environment in which progressively reasonable risk taking could occur. He helped his students accept the presentation of *ganas* in a school setting, and he encouraged them to help each other as a team. The pertinent metaphor for a teacher was the coach of a football team, or a drill sergeant in the army.[130]

Associated with such a view of the teacher was a particular notion of each student as an individual, arising out of the basic fundamental belief that individuals differ from each other, but subsequently generating generic outcomes for generic individuals rather than personal goals for unique individuals.[131] Each student is believed to have a unique set of characteristics or aptitudes that ultimately influence the rate at which competent performance in a particular skill can be achieved. It is presumed that a well-defined and well-structured sequence of instructional events will facilitate progress toward preplanned outcomes. It is, moreover, presumed that the time and quality of instruction (i.e., of the teaching) will influence the successful achievement of mastery. A related notion is that an evaluation mechanism can be found for constantly monitoring the student's progress toward preplanned outcomes. But this construction of the individual student simultaneously has crucial implications for the commonsense understanding of what a teacher is: the mastery-learning paradigm shifts the role of the teacher from a pedagogical one toward an instructional, decision-making one. Hence we find Escalante carefully searching for potential students in junior high schools and placing them in the proper level within a sequence of courses, selecting a new classroom space—the old music room—and adapting it for controlled allocation of space, time, and materials, and collecting daily data on student performance.

Ethical curriculum questions ask about how we should treat others justly in education; they ask about how various ideas of moral conduct and community serve as the underpinnings of the ways students and teachers are treated. The Escalante story made the important argument that it was the teacher's responsibility to provide students with very high expectations and to make it impossible for the students to avoid them.[132] At the same time, the teacher was required to help the students meet these expectations by providing a caring atmosphere[133] and by teaching them how to help each other.

Teachers, on the other hand, needed to be given complete control over how, where, and when they teach their students. The metaphor cultivated was that of a master craftsman with student apprentices. The students give up all other ties and obligations, and in return, the teacher/master provides training and financial support. Here is where we find the myth's answers to historical curriculum questions, those that seek to understand what traditions in the field of education already exist to help develop responses to all other curriculum deliberations.

Because students are not sold into apprenticeship in the United States, the teacher must convince them to voluntarily submit to his or her authority. It is for this reason that Escalante seemed to display many characteristics of the Weberian[134] prophet: He needed to win over his students with his charisma before demanding discipleship of them.[135]

## Why Does Everything Depend on the Teacher?

We educationists spend a lot of time talking about the teacher and how to prepare new teachers. Some of us want to help our students fit into the established culture of teaching in public schools. Others of us allow the notion that our students can have a role in the slow process of institutional change. But all of us tend to think of education in terms of the teacher and what the teacher does. Nevertheless, we have not been able to find the key ingredient for the teacher's personality and leave much of his or her training up to field experience in the hopes that somehow or other, personal interactive skills will be developed (or, that the student-teacher will find within themself their natural gift for working with children). "Teacher education programs have sought to meet the demand for more technical competence and more expertise by centering their programs around practical matters," suggests Robert Welker.[136] Hence, we unwittingly find ourselves sustaining Britzman's three myths of the teacher: that everything depends on the teacher, that the teacher is the expert, and that the teacher is self-made.

Welker notes that recent research by John Goodlad[137] identified an avoidance of attitude and value in teacher education programs. Technical conceptions have been advanced, it seems, by a

disregard for some of the major moral and social questions connected with teaching and by programs in which there appears to be
no coherent understanding of purpose. Yet, as I have argued
through an analysis of the Jaime Escalante story, superteacher leg-
ends of the 1980s transmitted a relatively clear purpose (discipline,
hard work, and *ganas*) while constructing a purportedly commonsense agreement on values associated with community building
and individual achievement. That is, superteacher myths played a
major role, not in "serving ideology" by masking questions of value
and ethics; but rather, as Britzman suggested,[138] they acted more as
an 'ideological trap', locking the teacher in isolation and naturalizing the institutional pressure for social control through the glorification of discipline and an obsessive determination to achieve.

In fact, several important educators made compelling arguments for attention to ethics and value during the 1980s; yet they
did so by maintaining the focus on the individual teacher as the
locus of theorization. Alan Tom, for example, criticized the view
that teaching could be merely the most efficient means to reach
specific ends. Instead, he urged viewing educational practice as a
"moral craft"; but what he meant by this was that teaching involves
a subtle moral relationship between teacher and student. He hoped
educators would switch from what he perceived as too much attention to curriculum to a renewed concern for the moral relationship,
hence the day-by-day experience of the classroom teacher.[139] Henry
Giroux provides another good illustration of alternative perspectives sustaining the larger commonsense focus on the individual
teacher. He artfully culled neo-Marxist and continental poststructuralist philosophy in order to develop a holistic social conception
of the role of schooling in society. But his translation of such theory
into educational practice involved the cultivation of the teacher as
a "transformative intellectual."[140] That is, the individual teacher
was responsible for developing a pedagogy that attended to global
political cultural and social contexts of teaching and learning. Such
examples make a strong case for the power of ideology to sustain
social structure by including within itself apparently contradictory
perspectives, which actually support an encompassing commonsense comprehension of 'reality'.

In exploring the relationship between individual superteachers and the construction of possible discourse about mathematics
education, I have noted a number of supposedly commonsense,
hence transparent, assumptions about educational practice.[141]

First, teaching was presented as an individual act, despite the necessarily social relationship involved—at least among the teacher and the group of students, possibly including the school administration, parents, state and local government, and the surrounding community. Second, knowledge became reified, which obscured social and political problems of knowing. And finally, the internalization of the school structure into what appeared to be an individually determined practice of pedagogy implicitly claimed to resolve the complex interactions among institutional and social constraints on teaching, the social self, and curriculum deliberations. While these interactions may have been experienced by a single teacher as an individual problematic situation, they were socially generated. I conclude along with Britzman that "presuppositions of individualism, buttressed by the tacit acceptance of social control in a compulsory setting, result in the individualization of contradictions that are collective in origin."

## 2

# Ezekiel Saw the Wheel:
# Problem Solving on and off TV

## The Opposition of Method and Content

In chapter 1, I examined how the discourse of mathematics education in the 1980s reduced most discussion to the consideration of individual teacher attributes. The focus on particular personality characteristics of 'successful teachers', I argued, precluded consideration of social and political issues relevant to school mathematics. This chapter explores another aspect of the occlusion. Might it be possible to interpret the generation of mathematics superteachers as necessary to their chosen subject matter? That is, would it be reasonable to consider the individualization of mathematics education within the isolated teacher as, in retrospect, the result of a fundamental need structured by the discipline of mathematics it*self*? Indeed, it is possible to identify such an argument as present in the public discourse of mathematics education in the 1980s, which has continued into the 1990s.

The assumption that epistemology drives educational encounters was injected into public discussion of mathematics education under several separate but mutually confirming rubrics. First, "a dramatic rise of the culturalist wing of the Far Right,"[1] evident for example in the best-seller status of several books by conservative university professors,[2] helped turn attention to the role of schooling as a guardian of Western civilization, promoting a canonical notion of Western knowledge. Additionally, President Reagan's secretary of education, William Bennett, redefined the purpose of education and the nature of teachers' work, setting the stage for a number of ideological assaults against such threats to classical Western tradition as 'modernity', 'democracy', 'difference', and, above all, 'relativism'.

Second, popular, professional, and school representations of mathematics mutually reaffirmed a commonsense understanding of knowledge and problem solving as static and substantially algorithmic in nature. This notion of a clearly identifiable epistemology made it possible to imagine that pedagogy could be based on an accepted knowledge base. For example, *Reader's Digest* published an article on math "for grownups." In order to help their readers avoid the public embarrassment of not being able to handle commonplace problems, the authors suggested a variety of simple procedures for figuring percentages, fractions, and decimals. They quoted the current president of the National Council of Teachers of Mathematics, Shirley Frye, who dismissed the notion of math people and nonmath people; "anyone can achieve confidence in math if properly instructed," she said. The vision of proper instruction in mathematics in such articles was the explication of easy-to-memorize and easy-to-mimic manipulative algorithms for everyday arithmetical calculations. "With a little practice" in these algorithms, "you too can be fluent in mathematics," said Frye, according to the authors.[3] This nexus of mutual affirmation is ideologically important because, as I will discuss, the world of school and the world of popular culture were constructed in opposition. Hence, both legitimate and popular knowledge were confined to self-supporting power/knowledge practices, which reduced problems to puzzles, and mathematical activity as the solution of these puzzles. Similarly, human and print-based 'teachers' were at least partially synonymous, as in the case of "proper instruction" advocated by Shirley Frye for the teacher-members of her association, yet also satisfactorily represented in the *Reader's Digest* article.

The particular plague of relativism was seen to be running rampant throughout academic thought, in the social protest movements of students, in the increasing cultural and ethnic diversity of the United States, and in the expanding sphere of popular culture (which was viewed by Bennett as a tasteless and dangerous threat to the notions of civility and order). Bennett's critics, on the other hand, claimed he was hoping for an outdated nineteenth-century brand of elitism by appealing to a narrowly defined 'Western tradition' conveyed through a pedagogy unencumbered by the messy concerns of 'equity', 'social justice', or the need to educate a critical citizenry.[4]

The conservative discourse on education found a catalytic ally in the concurrent concern for linking educational reform to the imperatives of big business. Schools, in this perspective, were understood as training grounds for different sectors of the work force: They provided knowledge and skills necessary for expanding both domestic production and foreign investment. Such a view was often understood as more technicist and instrumental than ideological. Nevertheless, it buttressed the commonsense notion professed by the conservative culturalists that pedagogical decisions are subsequent to the determination of curriculum content. Roger Simon and Henry Giroux critically summarized this position in 1989:

> [Pedagogy] is what follows the selection of ideologically correct content, its legitimacy rooted in whether or not it represents the proper teaching style. In the dominant discourse, pedagogy is simply measurable, accountable methodology used to transmit course content. It is not a mutually determining element in the construction of knowledge and learning, but an afterthought reduced to the status of the technical and instrumental.[5]

A similar conception of pedagogy was also the foundation of traditional work in the field of mathematics education. Historically, curriculum theorizing had been organizationally based in subject matter disciplines, so that those who developed programs in mathematical education typically identified themselves as wielding primarily mathematics knowledge expertise, and secondarily an interest in the teaching and learning of the subject matter knowledge, or in assisting mathematicians in the teaching of their subject by supplying educational recommendations. Professional work in mathematics education was thus an attempt to merge in some way the distinct conceptual arenas of mathematics and education. But, as is often the case with such mergers, the strategy of integration of two spheres of thought forced the perpetuation of a conceptual distinction that manifested itself as a theoretical opposition within the professional discourse.

### Precedent: Professional Knowledge Overrides Teacher Personality

Historically, the profession of mathematics education emphasized primarily subject matter expertise and secondarily pedagogical theory, both over individual teacher attributes. The early twentieth century is generally regarded as the key historical moment in the development of mathematics education as a professional practice and is indicative of the field's theoretical character. For example, *A History of Mathematics Education in the United States and Canada*, published by The National Council of Teachers of Mathematics (NCTM), identifies David Eugene Smith and J. W. A. Young as the representatives of a new development in pedagogy and teacher training.[6] Smith was a professor of mathematics at Teachers College, Columbia University, from 1901 until his retirement in 1922. He played important roles in the American Mathematical Society (AMS), the Mathematical Association of America (MAA), and NCTM. He served on many important committees, including the National Committee on Mathematical Requirements. He was one of the American Commissioners on the International Commission on the Teaching of Mathematics, and the director of numerous studies in the teaching and history of mathematics. His book, *The Teaching of Elementary Mathematics*, which appeared in 1900, was the first book to resemble a modern methods text. In his equally influential *The Teaching of Junior High School Mathematics*, he clearly delineated the notion that good teaching of mathematics originates in a distinction between the subject matter and the teaching of that content; he further established attributes of an individual as secondary to a grounding in these two knowledge areas.

> A Latin writer long ago remarked, "Poets are born, not made." In a way the same is true of teachers and, indeed, of those who succeed in any other walk of life. But however valuable inherent qualities of native ability may be, mere knowledge does not suffice; mere "knack" will not serve the purpose; the successful teacher must not merely be born, he must acquire knowledge of his subject and must profit by the counsel of experts in his chosen field. It is therefore important that we should consider with care the question of method.[7]

J. W. A. Young began his career in mathematics with a dissertation on group theory; later, as the author of *The Teaching of Mathematics in the Elementary and Secondary School* (1906, 1920), he was listed as "Associate Professor of the Pedagogy of Mathematics at the University of Chicago."[8] Young was thus indicative, suggests the NCTM's *History*, of a number of people who were primarily mathematicians but who also maintained an interest in school programs.

The NCTM's *History* notes moreover issues significant to the foundation of mathematics education as a scholarly endeavor, issues that further established the clear conceptual separation of content and method.[9] For example, the dilemma 'what are the goals of mathematical instruction?' requires a link between 'mathematical' and 'instruction'. Similarly, a conceptual merger was required between content and method within the question, 'how can the mathematics curriculum and teaching methods be adapted to the needs, backgrounds, interests, and abilities of students?' New issues arising in this early developmental period of mathematics education maintained these distinctions, while reflecting the need to establish specialization and technical expertise unique to the subject matter itself:

> What is the proper role of inductive and intuitive approaches to mathematical teaching and learning as compared with a rule-giving and theorem-memorizing approach?
>
> Should mathematics instruction be compartmentalized or integrated in some manner within itself or with instruction in science?[10]

Although the content aspect of the content/method opposition was played down in the Escalante myth of the 1980s, it was not entirely absent. Indeed, interpretations of Escalante's superteacher attributes often glorified his ability to eloquently negotiate the tensions inherent in this opposition.

> Is it a triumph of pedagogy or content, process or substance? Both, according to Les [sic] Shulman, a Stanford education expert. As Shulman describes it, the lesson is revealed in a powerful colloquy between Escalante and his students when he tries to communicate the concept of negative numbers. What do you have when you take two buckets of sand from the beach? Escalante asks the class. Plus two. What's the hole? Minus two. So far so good. Escalante then asks, what happens when you put the sand back in the hole? One of the tough kids in the class answers, "Zero." You're right, Escalante says. "And do you know that your ancestors, the Mayan, knew about zero before the Greeks did?"

> In one flash of insight, Escalante combines the best of pedagogy with the best of content; he not only knows what he's talking about, he knows how to talk about it. He knows his audience, how to fire their imaginations and enthusiasm. That is great teaching.[11]

Thus, it is possible to read the presentation of Escalante's unique personal status as an argument for a particular method of teaching requisite to the successful communication of a particular form of mathematics. Individual skills notwithstanding, his abilities became a flexible adaptation to the needs of his subject, rather than evidence of good teaching applicable to any subject in the curriculum.

The above historical characterization of mathematics education as an evolving profession does of course disregard to some extent continued significant attention to the student and psychological theories of learning that became prominent in American educational discourse. The pioneering and influential work of E. L. Thorndike at the turn of the century, for example, established learning theory as a crucial element of pedagogical theory. Moreover, progressive educators of the twenties and thirties developed important concerns for the relevance of the curriculum to students' lives, and societal needs for an educated citizenry as fundamental to mathematics education reflection.[12] The psychological became in fact a dominant theme for mathematics educators for the rest of the century, evident in the sixties and seventies, for example, in the significant attention paid to the work of Jean Piaget, Jerome Bruner, and Zoltan Dienes.[13] In the eighties, an adaptation of Piaget's work was actively applied to the geometry curriculum.[14] By the 1980s, artificial intelligence models of learning, using computer processing models of information management, were also firmly established within the profession. These models are evident, for example, in the work of Robert Davis, a professor at the University of Illinois; author of the book, *Learning Mathematics: The Cognitive Science Approach to Mathematics Education*; and founder of a new professional periodical, the *Journal of Children's' Mathematical Behavior*.[15] The decade of the 1980s also witnessed an interest in social contexts of mathematics education, influenced mainly by the publications of educators in the United Kingdom and Scandinavia.[16] As mathematics educators began to consider their own field as a developing area of intellectual inquiry, and as they increasingly analyzed their own work historically, William Higginson proposed a tetrahedral model of mathematics education, contending that mathematics education was an intellectual hybrid of four disciplines: mathematics, psychology, sociology, and philosophy.[17]

The point of my discussion is not to ignore these important elements of professional discourse and the awareness of the complexity of the profession's history by its own practitioners, but to highlight the historical origin of theoretical and professional practice within the domain of mathematics as a discipline, and to stress the critical placement of mathematics as a signifier within the professional discourse.[18] Although educators have posited other important areas for consideration other than the discipline itself, they have done so in opposition to the central role of subject area knowledge, either rhetorically, within a strategy for distinguishing mathematics educators from what they perceived as their more highly regarded colleagues in mathematics, or practically, as they expanded the scope of their professional practice.

The issues involved in understanding the role of professional mathematics educators become more complex in the recognition of another opposition, between mathematics as a static body of knowledge and as a dynamic process of thinking or applying a certain body of knowledge. The opposition originally entered the discourse in 1902 with E. H. Moore's outgoing presidential address at the American Mathematical Society. Moore was concerned about the disjunction within the field of mathematics between its pure and applied branches. Fearing an evolution of two independent groups that would not benefit from a constant interaction of abstract ideas and the newly mushrooming applications of these ideas, he recognized a related pedagogical difficulty: Many people viewed 'basic' mathematics as formal, symbolic muck. Moore surprised his audience by seeking a solution at the professional level, not in a hollow call for all mathematicians to pay heed to their fraternal relations and rally together, but in a charge to work together, actively devising a curriculum for school mathematics that would unify the pure and applied. He advocated a new, four-year curriculum involving laboratory group work pioneered by the British educator John Perry. Perry's curriculum was designed to make the "students feel like they are studying the subject itself, and not the words."[19] Twenty-five years later, the National Council reprinted Moore's address in a book of articles mostly by professional mathematics educators. By then, the integration of the pure and applied had come to be known as problem solving, and this was essentially subsumed within a traditional sequence of mathematics courses. Raleigh Schorling of the University of Michigan, for example, cited John Dewey's conception of education—not as preparation for life, but life itself—as another road to applications of mathematics.[20] Yet the applications had been transformed from physics and the other sciences, becoming economics, business, and problems of everyday life.

Nevertheless, problem solving consistently maintained its fundamental focal status and continued to do so well into the eighties. Alan Schoenfeld, for example, argued that mathematics should be taught not because of its superficial utility but because of its immersion in a problematic context. He noted that many problems (e.g., optimizations in calculus) could be done more efficiently or appropriately by rough empirical methods. But he concluded it was worthwhile to have students solve these problems because solving them required practice in valuable problem-solving activities.[21] Patrick Thompson provides another example of the attraction to problem solving. He began with the philosophical argument that anything one would call mathematical knowledge would be a structure of thinking, and that the structure would be a structure of process. Assuming that mathematical structures arise from abstracting invariant features of one's thinking in problematic situations, he concluded that any curriculum aimed at promoting mathematical thinking would have to be problem based. For Thompson, the task of the curriculum designer was to select problematic situations that would provide occasions for students to think in ways that lead to mathematical, hence problem-based, knowledge.

Recent public discourse tends to accept the subject matter as a given and static collection of knowledge to be transmitted within schools, transferring pedagogical dilemmas to the site of the individual teacher and his or her transmission of that knowledge. But professional discourse maintains a fundamental focus on a concern for subject matter selection, ordering, and presentation, maintaining curriculum development as its primary agenda.[22] Influential in this discourse has been the work of Robert Gagne. For him, mathematics education is defined in terms of learning a set of skills and applying them to solve problems. He understands a mathematics class largely through its potential for the transmission of basic information; the educational environment is supposed to provide a good format for efficient acquisition of information as well as successful drill and practice in applications that could enhance retention and transfer of knowledge.[23]

Policy influenced by professional research reports have carried the centrality of the discipline into public discourse. Meanwhile, the discursive distance between public and expert language has indeed been noticed by professional mathematics education organizations, who have made a concerted effort to bridge the gap via an employment of professional lobbyists in Washington and in direct suggestions to their members in newsletters and reports. It is, therefore, not surprising that these organizations began to encourage their members to become acquainted with popular culture images of mathematics teachers in the 1980s and to use them to their advantage in reinterpreting their "message," as well as to familiarize themselves with congressional debates about educational funding and national educational policy.

A theoretical point can be made regarding the discursive construction of mathematics education within the public and professional arenas as well. Whether or not the discipline of mathematics is understood as the driving force of educational character or as the foil by which theory could undermine disciplinary primacy, the combined effect of the conceptual distinction of the subject matter from other possibly relevant realms of consideration is perpetually to recreate through practice the notion of knowledge and social dimensions of education associated with issues of power as separate entities. As David Parkin wrote, the specifically Western propensity to regard knowledge and power as distinct is a governing and virtually universal epistemological assumption. The ideological function of this conceptual framework is especially harmonious with an emerging professional entity such as mathematics education. Indeed, "it enables us to aim to expand or improve knowledge without necessarily worrying about how much power we thereby put into whose hands."[24]

I suggest that we can enhance much comprehension of mathematics education as a practice by following the theoretical spadework of writers such as Michel Foucault, who have conceptually collapsed the power/knowledge distinction within a new discursive notion of material and symbolic practice.[25] One implication of this approach is to examine critically how the commonsense construction of knowledge as a distinct entity obscures important power/knowledge links.

Similarly, I agree with a number of researchers who, influenced by poststructuralist anthropology, recognize mathematics as produced in social practices[26] rather than as collections of knowledge independent of practices.[27] Such a position argues against a single pathway model of cognitive development and for the possibility of specific skills being learned, produced, and accomplished within the practices themselves. Moreover, this position argues against a model of out-of-school practices being mere sites of application of a central set of skills acquired at school, or that mathematics, mirroring the underlying structure of the physical world, is to be found 'everywhere', providing the basis for an experiential child-centered pedagogy. Rather, such an approach suggests that specific practices are regulated in particular ways and that any understanding of learning or pedagogy would need to take account of this.[28]

Poststructuralist accounts of practices avoid various psychological models as their base, choosing instead to understand practices as 'discursive'.[29] Discursive practices are conceived of as historically constituted rather than being the product of universal and transhistorical structures. As Valerie Walkerdine notes, Foucault's analysis of educational and other practices as "technologies of the social" suggests that the practices themselves become sites through which power/knowledge relations are produced and are part of apparati of government and regulation of the population. Any analysis of mathematics education must, within this perspective, trace the history of particular forms of discursive practices so that we can examine how present 'truths' are constructed as well as the effectivity of those commonsense truths.

## Teachers as Epistemological Metaphors

The portrayal of Jaime Escalante, and its use, had much in common with previous 'stories' about teachers designed to convince people of a particular epistemological basis for mathematics. Escalante should thus be compared with several influential teacher characters from before the 1980s, including George Polya's postwar teacher of heuristics. Polya had a brilliant career as a mathematician extending more than seven decades. He was called "a brilliant teacher, a teacher's teacher, and an expositor."[30] He believed in a craft of discovery, and that the ability to discover and the ability to invent can be enhanced by skillful teaching. By putting 'himself' in the student's place and by "trying to understand what is going on inside the student's mind," Polya's teacher asks questions designed to cultivate "independent problem-solving" tendencies, giving the student "a taste for, and some means of, independent thinking."[31] The teacher is described in terms of method—techniques of questioning, selection of "problems," and issues of teacher and student responsibilities. But the method provides a powerful argument for problem solving as the central activity of mathematics and for the categorization of various heuristics, creating a science of problem solving as the basis for this particular notion of mathematics. Although Polya was himself a university-level educator, he argued that his vision was applicable to all "genuine" mathematics, and gave workshops for teachers of any grade level.

In fact, the 1980s witnessed a professional embracement of Polya's mathematical epistemology. Responding to what it perceived as a narrow-minded public movement for a return to the "basics" in education, the NCTM issued *An Agenda for Action* in 1980, declaring problem solving the premium basic skill of mathematics.[32] Combining many of the recommendations of previous NCTM position papers, this document stated eight primary objectives of mathematics education, effectively defining goals in terms of curriculum content;[33] heading the list was the demand "that problem solving be the focus of school mathematics in the 1980s." Curriculum specialists responded with innumerable packages for teaching heuristics at all educational levels. It is not surprising, therefore, that the NCTM *Standards* campaigned for problem solving as the overarching context for the learning of all mathematics in the 1990s.

The image of Escalante should also be compared with two conflicting notions of a teacher arising from D. E. Knuth's 'anti-text', or dialogue in novel form, *Surreal Numbers*.[34] Popular reading mostly among college and university mathematicians and mathematics educators, Knuth's mathematical novelette was the inspiration for a number of new college-level problem-solving courses in the late seventies and early eighties, influencing an emerging concern for the preparation of students for independent creative work.

> Namely, I wanted to provide some material which would help to overcome one of the most serious shortcomings in our present educational system, the lack of training

for research work; there is comparatively little opportunity for students to experience how new mathematics is
invented, until they reach graduate school.[35]

*Surreal Numbers* tells the story of two young adults who by engaging
in an entertaining dialogue effectively become their own self-teach-
ers. Such an image of a 'teacher' is consonant with Knuth's implicit
philosophy of mathematics: "My aim was to show how mathematics can be 'taken out of the classroom and into life,' and to urge the
reader to try his or her hand at exploring abstract mathematical
ideas." Thus Knuth effectively integrated his portrayal of self-teach-
ers with an argument for understanding mathematics as an active
mental process, of "developing a theory."

Nevertheless, while Knuth "decided that creativity can't be
taught using a textbook, but that an 'anti-text' such as this novel
might be useful," he also offered his book as supplementary reading
material for an introduction to abstract mathematics, or as the
principal text in an undergraduate seminar. Thus Knuth constructed a conflicting image of a nonself mathematics teacher who
assigns mathematical novels for reading and leads spontaneous
class discussions; he also "risk[ed] destroying the purity of this
'novel' approach, [by] compil[ing] a few suggestions for supplementary problems." The "novel" approach thus became incorporated within a traditional epistemology/pedagogy practice in
which the teacher assigns problems for the students to "solve."[36]

Knuth's argument for the student as self-teacher gained rhetorical impact when linked with a larger field of discourse; promot-
ers of educational technology pedaled innovative uses of computers as tools for students to teach themselves. In response to a
general notion of computers as tutors that provided drill and practice in algorithmic and memory-based mathematics learning, educators such as Seymour Papert developed computer-based media for
nondirected mathematical exploration. Papert's book, *Mindstorms*,
which told the success story of his programming language, *LOGO*,
introduced to the language of mathematics education the notion of
students learning through 'teaching' a computer to perform geo-
metrical tricks.[37] *LOGO*, it was implied, provided a world of thinking in which the student could develop for him or her self problem-
solving and geometric skills and the language for communicating
about these skills. Similarly, a new educational software company,
Sunburst, developed elementary and secondary software packages

which, when implemented, created spaces for mathematical explorations by students.[38] *Geometer's Sketchpad* from Key Curriculum Press is an example of more recent software in the same vein.

One more fictional educator providing an interesting epistemological context was Imré Lakatos' "Teacher" in *Proofs and Refutations*.[39] Here the dialogue is explicitly intended to be an epistemological argument about mathematics, and it thus places the teacher and student roles in an intriguing narrative light. "Teacher" combines the best of the Socratic method with Polya's specific heuristic-oriented questioning strategies in order to help his (or her) students reproduce an historically accurate development of mathematical theory. The goal is to demonstrate mathematics as a social practice, "elaborat[ing] the point that informal, quasi-empirical, mathematics does not grow through a monotonous increase of the number of indubitably established theorems but through the incessant improvement of guesses by speculation and criticism—by the logic of proofs and refutations." Here Lakatos established the modern terrain for the fundamental epistemological battle over the philosophy of mathematics, introducing "quasi-empiricism" to counter what he labelled dogmatism, formalism, or Euclideanism. The political implications of Lakatos' dialogue suggest further that the unfolding everyday verbal exchange and drama within each real-life classroom is both an enacted argument for a particular epistemology of mathematics and an affirmation that this epistemology drives the enactment itself. That is, his work suggested that classroom interaction actively constructs an epistemology, and that human action perpetually reconstructs a commonsense philosophy of mathematics.

## Philosophies of Mathematics Hide the Social

Hence, as 'problem solving' became the overarching theme of mathematics education, these textual images of teachers of mathematics became key symbolic components of ideological conflicts regarding the nature of mathematics and mathematical knowledge within the professional mathematics education community. It is ironic, then, to look back on the professional literature, much of which articulated the hope of identifying 'the' unique nature of mathematics. That is, much research in mathematics education agreed with a famous quote of the 1970s from Rene Thom, reprinted from chapter 0:

> All mathematical pedagogy, even if scarcely coherent, rests on a philosophy of mathematics.[40]

Ruth Parker's superb book, *Mathematical Power*, published in 1993, continues to construct this conception of mathematics education even as it offers profound insights into the possibilities of school mathematics.[41] Parker establishes a dynamic argument for a "culture of mathematics" for "All Children" by noting the ways in which the culture of school mathematics is the antithesis of the culture of mathematics as a discipline.

> Examining the differences between the culture of school mathematics and the culture of mathematics in the real world leads to the inescapable conclusion that school mathematics is unlikely to result in mathematically powerful students. . . . The goal of mathematics reform efforts is to develop students who are challenged by messy, ill-defined situations or complex problems. . . .[42]

The reform movement indicated seems to bypass the "epistemological sources and consequences" Stephen Lerman worried about, or the dilemmas regarding "what is mathematics really all about" which frustrated Reuben Hersh. While earlier authors felt that "controversies about . . . teaching cannot be resolved without confronting problems about the nature of mathematics," the National Council's *Standards* for the 1990s and those who buttress exciting and innovative classroom ideas with the Council's *Standards* have accepted a problem-solving context as resolving any and all epistemological, political, or aesthetic criteria for judging what it is to 'do' mathematics.[43] The notion, as indicated in chapter 0, is that the 'correct' or 'most accurate' epistemology, by prescribing the nature of mathematical knowledge, supplies a stable source of criteria for the development and evaluation of educational programs and associated techniques. What this approach tends to do, however, is to temporarily bury deeply entrenched disagreements over the nature of the discipline's knowledge content, only to have them resurface within a cyclic pattern of 'reform movements' as shifting factions regain political power on the national level.

By abandoning the philosophical question in favor of a socio-cultural analysis, we can understand the relationship between theory and practice as less linear and as more intricately intertwined in the production of both. In this way, we can interpret various epistemologies of mathematics as parts or aspects of the practices of mathematics, that is, parts of a woven fabric of truths, facts, fantasies, hopes, relationships of power, and social action. This approach widens the terrain of mathematics education to include an appreciation of how such complexes of practice come to be, and how and through what relationships of power and identity fluctuation they are created by those involved in their maintenance and production.

An entrance into this form of analysis can be located in the mutually confirming public and professional discourse. That is, by focusing their attention on how pedagogy must adapt itself to the nature of a particular discipline, professional mathematics educators share a common ideological thread with the conservative culturalists and the technicist imperatives of business interests. Likewise, the adherence by public discourse to mathematics as a central, unique component of an education allows the continued acceptance and evolution of mathematics education as an important subspeciality of pedagogy.

One other commonsense link among these various sources of educational possibility is their agreement on schools as the locus of teaching and learning within society. They seem to legitimate the conception of the school as a singular educator, while obscuring other societal and cultural educative institutions and organizations. Lawrence Cremin had declared this in the particular case of mathematics in 1976:

> In some subject areas, of course, the school originates much of what it teaches. Mathematics is an example. In mathematics, the student learns much of what he [sic] needs to know for the first time in the classroom.[44]

Comments such as the above became important because they were issued by scholars of great stature and because they occurred within the context of an attempt to expand reflection on schooling in society. Cremin, for example, sought to establish a wide-ranging "ecological" approach to educational practice and policy. Although published in the late seventies, Cremin's apparently empowering approach echoed into the early eighties, constructing mathematics as a peculiarly special discipline even as it attempted to argue that in other realms,

> languages and literature, for example, or social studies or hygiene, or the arts, or the domain of values and morals, the child has his (sic) first learning and possibly his [sic] most persuasive learning earlier and elsewhere. In these areas, it may be that the best the school can do is *engage* the instruction of the other educators and seek to strengthen or complement or correct or neutralize or countereducate or, most importantly, perhaps, try to develop in students an awareness of the other educators and an ability to deal with them on their own.[45]

For Cremin and those who followed him, however, mathematics had little to do with such a pedagogical approach. Thus we find Elizabeth Fennema writing in 1990 that "mathematics is learned, for the most part, in classrooms."

> While the environment outside of the school undoubtedly contributes to what is learned, most mathematical knowledge is built upon classroom experiences. Classroom interactions and class-related homework assignments provide students with the activities to learn mathematics.[46]

Educational discourse maintained this commonsense understanding of mathematics well into the 1980s, despite numerous studies of folk and informal mathematics learning external to or in direct conflict with school mathematics,[47] or investigations into non-Amero-Euro-centric mathematics in developing countries.[48] In retrospect, the commonsense view can be understood as a fundamental denial of nonschool arenas as pedagogical sites.

This was partly due to the construction of a knowledge hierarchy privileging the "formal" over the "practical," as in Lauren B. Resnick's 1987 presidential address to the American Education Research Association (AERA):

> Recent research on the nature of everyday, practical, real-world intelligence and learning is beginning to provide a basis for understanding what distinguishes practical

from formal intelligence. Drawing on this work, I want to explore . . . four broad contrasts which suggest that school is a special place and time for people—discontinuous in some important ways with daily life and work.[49]

Resnick pointed to a consensus on individual cognition in school versus shared cognition outside; pure mentation in school versus tool manipulation outside; symbol manipulation in school versus contextualized reasoning outside; and generalized learning in school versus situation-specific competencies outside.

## Pedagogy and Popular Culture

An emphasis on the dynamics of knowledge transmission and imposition also legitimated forms of pedagogy that neglected the voices, experience, and histories through which students gave meaning to the world. I argue in this book for consideration of schools as sites of social struggle, and for pedagogy to be recognized as a form of cultural politics. Thus, I take educational practice to be a social and cultural form that at once prescribes and expands human possibilities so as to mediate people's formations of their own subjectivities. I further understand such practice as enabling people to exercise power in the interest of transforming ideological and material conditions into other social practices; these practices in turn promote social empowerment and demonstrate possibilities.

It becomes important in this chapter, therefore, that I interrogate how the symbolic and material transactions of the everyday can provide the basis for rethinking how people give meaning and ethical substance to their experiences and voices. Thus I want to highlight the parallel denigration of both pedagogy and nonschool popular culture in the discourse of mathematics education under consideration. I choose the comparison with popular culture because I believe, as do Giroux and Simon, that "popular culture represents not only a contradictory terrain of struggle, but also a significant pedagogical site that raises important questions about the elements that organize the basis of student [and teacher] subjectivity and experience."[50]

However, as Giroux and Simon noted, classroom pedagogy and popular culture do not naturally appear related. While popular culture is associated with pleasure and entertainment, schooling is understood mostly in instrumental terms; popular culture is typically conceived of as part of everyday life, while schooling concerns itself with the legitimation and transmission of 'cultural capital' (the language, codes, and values of the dominant culture). Dewey notwithstanding, pedagogy removes students from everyday life and places them in a limbo of preparation for the future. I make these sweeping generalizations despite the wealth of studies we have highlighting differing uses of schooling and the physical grounds of schools among students and adults. That is, I believe that even students whose main utilization of school is as a site of social encounters, drug dealing, gang interaction, etc., still are very aware of a societal agenda that attributes schooling with the above goals. This places popular culture functionally in a 'noneducative' role for both students and adults. Yet, popular culture is appropriated by students and helps authorize their voices and experiences; pedagogy instead authorizes the voices of the adult world, the world of teachers and administrators.

Nevertheless, pedagogy and popular culture share the commonality of denigration within commonsense educational discourse, now as in the 1980s. While pedagogy becomes whatever is left after curriculum content is determined, the dominant discourse defines popular culture as the leftovers when "high culture" is removed from the totality of cultural practices. Popular culture is commonly recognized as the trivial and insignificant of everyday life, a form of popular taste deemed unworthy of either academic legitimation or of high social affirmation.

Yet the popular was (and is) also feared by educators as potentially disruptive, as a threat, and as a profane desire. Allan Bloom's 1988 bestseller, *The Closing of the American Mind*, for example, declared that popular culture, especially rock music, had "resulted in the atrophy of both nerve and intelligence in American youth."[51] Commonsense discourse rejected pedagogy as a cultural production; but it also denied the popular as pedagogical. I argue that popular culture is an important force in shaping how students, teachers, and others view themselves and their relations to various forms of teaching and learning. "In fact," wrote Giroux and Simon,

it is precisely in the relationship between pedagogy and popular culture that the important understanding arises of making the pedagogical more political and the political more pedagogical. Popular culture and pedagogy represent important terrains of cultural struggle which offer both subversive discourse and important theoretical elements through which it becomes possible to rethink schooling as a viable and important form of cultural politics.[52]

This chapter interrogates the interaction of pedagogy and popular culture within the field of mathematics education. Using the phenomenally successful *Wheel of Fortune* television game show, I examine the discursive construction of the popular as at once external to pedagogy and implicitly educational. I note the concurrent construction of a commonsense conception of intelligence and problem solving; ironically this occurred within the informal cultivation of complex problem-solving strategies.

## Game Shows Hit the Jackpot

Television in the 1980s witnessed the comeback of the game show.

In a world where letter turners become superstars, it is perhaps not surprising that *Wheel of Fortune*, an almost comically unassuming game show, is the highest-rated syndicated series in television history. Or that the venerable game-show genre has suddenly hit the jackpot once again. Following the No. 1-rated *Wheel of Fortune*, two more games, *Jeopardy!* and *The New Newlywed Game*, currently rank in the top five on A. C. Nielsen's list of the most-watched syndicated shows (those sold directly to local stations by independent syndicators rather than distributed through the networks). In addition to the 10 games aired weekdays by the three networks, at least 15 game shows are currently running in syndication, and no fewer than 19 new ones have been proposed for next fall.[53]

Game shows have had their ups and downs, their scandals and excesses, but they've never lost their hold on the American audience. This salient fact of television history was not lost on Mike Levinton early in 1983, when he was looking over the new shows that syndicators were pitching to stations for that fall. As head of programming for Blair Television, largest of the national rep firms that sell advertising time for local stations, Levinton advises clients on choosing shows for their all-important "prime-time access" slot—the half hour preceding network programming. In 1983, Levinton noticed that audiences for several popular game shows— *Family Feud, Tic Tac Dough* and *Joker's Wild*—had peaked or were beginning to slip, particularly among women 25 to 54, a key demographic target for advertisers. At the same time, new forms of syndicated programming such as *Entertainment Tonight* were starting to draw off the game show's traditional audience.

Many interpreted these developments as signs that the game show's days in access time were numbered. But Levinton's faith in the form could not be so easily shaken. He liked game shows so much that he once appeared as a contestant on *Jeopardy!*, doing quite respectably until the final round. Levinton thought the access period merely needed a fresh game show, one with "all the classic elements—simplicity, a clear focus and a high degree of audience involvement," as he puts it.

Levinton found what he was looking for in a game show that Merv Griffin Enterprises had been producing for NBC's daytime schedule since 1973, and that King World Productions was syndicating for the first time that fall. The show was called *Wheel of Fortune* and Levinton recommended it to many of his stations. Blair was the only major rep firm to do so, and roughly a third of the 59 stations that bought *Wheel of Fortune* in its first season were Blair clients. Without them the show might never have gotten off the ground.[54]

By June 1986, Michael Pollan, executive editor of *Harper's Magazine* and contributing editor to the journal *Channels of Communications*, would be able to write:

Station executives who heeded Levinton's advice have reason to gloat. *Wheel of Fortune* will surely become the most successful show in the history of syndication, and the game show is again king. Now in 193 markets (reaching 99 percent of all homes with televisions), *Wheel of*

*Fortune* consistently achieves a national rating of 20 or better. It is as popular as one of the top 15 shows in prime time, which is unheard of for a syndicated program. Aired five times a week in syndication, usually in the access period (as well as weekday mornings on NBC), *Wheel of Fortune* lights up more screens each week than any other program on television, and it should earn its producers and syndicators well over $100 million this year alone. But *Wheel* is much more than a money machine. Its business success is built on the abiding appeal of a well-crafted game show to the American audience. *Wheel* is one of those rare programs that, in becoming a national obsession, opens up a small window on the national consciousness.[55]

It was hard for many to understand the success of Wheel. As Lewis Grossberger wrote in *Rolling Stone*,

The first time I saw *Wheel of Fortune*, I thought it was a vapid piece of fluff that could appeal only to brain-dead TV zombies. Five minutes of this tedious dreck was all it took to waft me sleepward.[56]

Nevertheless, Grossberger, like many others, took a second look and decided that it was, "in fact, a fascinating, deeply significant national phenomenon, the comprehension of which was essential to any proper understanding of our era." He noted the *The Washington Post's* TV critic had said the program was viewed by 42 million people a day; *The New York Times* said *Wheel* was so popular that it had become a dominant factor in TV scheduling, sometimes "wreaking havoc with local and network news." The show's "hostess," Vanna White, had been featured in *People*.

Even the show's host, Pat Sajak, was baffled by the cult status of the program. "I swear on the grave of every game show host who ever lived that I have no idea," quoted Grossberger.

*Wheel* combines a roulette wheel, a game of chance, with Hangman, the children's game in which players guess letters to form hidden words. Three contestants take turns spinning a giant Wheel sectioned off with different money amounts, then guessing letters to a puzzle—usually a person, place, or common phrase. The wheel is set horizontally in front of the three contestants, so they can lean forward and spin it. The puzzle is mounted on a big vertical display board on a platform hauled on and off the set, usually with Vanna aboard. A display of blank tiles tells how many words and letters there are in a mystery phrase; as the contestants guess at the letters, Vanna runs purposefully about uncovering those correctly called out, and allowing the puzzle solution gradually to emerge. Winners amass credited "money," which they then use to "go shopping" for prizes ranging from cars and vacations to golf clubs and toasters. At the end of the show, the day's or night's champion tackles a bonus round for a grand prize.

## Games and Schools

*Wheel of Fortune* affirms John Fiske's description of game shows as reproducing the game and ritual functions of the educational system. As Levi-Strauss noted, games start people off as equal, with equal opportunities, moving them from similarity into difference; they finish differentiated into winners and losers. Rituals take differentiated groups and provide equalizing communal meanings and or identities, moving them from difference into similarity. In general, our educational system ritualizes all students as equal. Those with natural ability pass successively discriminating tests and emerge as a highly qualified few fit (by nature) for high-income jobs and positions with high social power and influence.[57]

A game show follows the same model. Contestants are chatted with informally in the opening ritual sequence, which sheds their individuality in order to construct them as undifferentiated participants, equal in opportunity to win prizes by performing well in the game. Differences of natural ability are discovered through the play of the game; the reward is upward mobility into the bonus round, a realm of social power that brings with it a natural right to material and economic benefit. The daily winner is accorded a ritual of equality with the bearer of social power—the host—who takes him or her by the hand into a reserved part of the studio, "where the prizes are displayed in fetishistic splendor, and made the objects of a ritualistic celebration." In this way, game shows replicate cultural conceptions of chance and choice and their roles in the construction of an individual's ability to achieve culturally formulated notions of success. Fiske concludes that game shows are an enactment of capitalist ideology; ideology plus the ritual-game-ritual performances ground social or class variations in individual natural differences and thus naturalize the class system and its particular mediation of chance and choice.[58] The skill of a participant, his or her ability to effect the interaction of chance or choice, functions ideologically to obscure social inequality and differential opportunity in favor of individual attributes.[59]

Game shows also construct a commonsense hierarchy of knowledge; different shows focus on varying forms of knowledge, and similar shows tend to be broadcast at the same times of day in order to capture a specific audience. The type of knowledge most closely associated with power is the 'factual', 'academic' type. Such knowledge is found in reference books, dictionaries and encyclopedias. Game shows utilizing factual academic knowledge are usually shown in the prime-time access slot, and more men comprise the audience. Next in the hierarchy is also factual knowledge, but a kind that is less academic and more everyday. Knowledge of this type is not gained through school or reading, but through common social experience and interaction; it is thus available to a wider range of people and so is more democratic and less elitist. An entirely different category produces very different kinds of game shows. This is a knowledge of the human or social, of people in general; it has no absolutely right or wrong answers and thus cannot be guarded by an elite, depending instead on the ability to 'see into' people either as general or specific individuals. The more individualistic version, in which a game show requires knowledge of one particular person (e.g., *The New Newlywed Game, Love Connection*) is the most intuitive and least scientific. Programs utilizing lower-level knowledge tend to be broadcast at times targeted for homemakers, unemployed women, and shift workers. Shows that rely on nonacademic and devalued knowledge, such as *The New Price is Right*, highlight skills associated with women (e.g., shopping and household management), skills that are often devalued or at least made invisible and confined to the private, domestic sphere.[60]

*Wheel of Fortune* ostensibly requires a general knowledge of words and popular sayings and thus would be categorized in this scheme at the lower level of factual knowledge. Shows like *Jeopardy!* and *$64,000 Question*, in which the atmosphere is as tense as an examination room, would be placed 'above' *Wheel* in this hierarchy. These more academic shows employ a host who must skillfully combine the authority and stability of the school examination with the excitement and pleasure of the carnival; he[61] becomes both a stern but fair schoolmaster for the contestants, and the genial master of ceremonies for the audience. As the public guardian of knowledge, he controls access to it and uses his possession of it as a means to coordinate the competitors and the progress of the game, as the high priest in a ritual.[62]

*Wheel of Fortune* presents itself as more distant from the schoolroom. Its knowledge is more proletarian. And its host Pat Sajak does not replicate the schoolmaster. Nor does he create the sort of frenzy associated with lower power/knowledge shows: His "low-key, faintly ironic style" is "a welcome break from most game-show gush."[63] In this way, *Wheel* suggests a more accessible and democratic audience, and projects a popular nonelitist atmosphere, but still maintains a link with the seriousness and influence of legitimate knowledge.

According to Levinton, the single most important factor in a game show's success is the degree of participation it offers the home viewer.[64] *Wheel's* game is immediately accessible to viewers, thanks to its similarity to Hangman. At the same time, viewers do not just watch the show or identify with the contestants; the program seems to create a degree of vicariousness through which viewers became contestants.[65]

Not only is *Wheel* easy to understand, but it combines two feel-good games promising easy success. The wheel itself, played mostly through luck, is better than a classic roulette wheel—only two sections hold bad outcomes (Bankrupt or Lose-A-Turn); any other spin is a success. The word puzzle is simple but compelling: It becomes easier as one plays, because more and more letters are filled in.[66] In general, a game show utilizes mini-narratives structured around a hermeneutic code that poses and then solves enigmas. Significantly, the enigmas are not enacted fiction, but are presented as live events. Fiske argues that such a narrative structure constructs an active audience that tends to vicariously participate.[67]

Most viewers feel they can figure out the puzzle answer a little before the contestants on the show.[68] With a whole family watching, someone at home is bound to come up with the answer.[69] Guessing the solution a moment or two before the contestants is an intellectual feat that makes a viewer feel pretty good about themself.[70] Unless they begin to suspect, as some do, that the contestants are chosen specifically to achieve this effect.[71] Indeed, becoming a *Wheel* contestant is extremely competitive,[72] so it is possible that the selectors have this in mind.

Nevertheless, producers of game shows go to tremendous lengths to disguise behind-the-scenes planning as well as the prerecorded fact of the program's broadcast. The liveness and nowness, suggests Fiske, is crucial to its appeal: The realness of the enactment positions the viewer as the equal of the characters in the narrative (the contestants and hosts), so that the narrative seems as yet unwritten. Because the resolution of the puzzle is as much a mystery for the viewer as the characters, the suspense appears real rather than fabricated and controlled as in a novel film, or television series. Hence, the engagement of the viewer is greater than in these other media.[73]

Of course, advertisers want an active audience, because that type of audience will most effectively incorporate the image of their product into its imagination. Game shows are an extension of television advertisements, glorifying products as prizes to be sought and won. Yet the ideological function of a game show like *Wheel of Fortune* is not that straightforward. As Fiske notes, the generation of an active audience, by making the viewer and the characters equal in regard to the resolution, also creates a text with less authority to impose itself. Many more viewers gain pleasure from commercials with a pun or puzzle than convert that pleasure into an actual purchase. Similarly,

> the origin of a text neither guarantees nor determines its mode of reception, however powerful a party it may be in the process of negotiation. Viewers who participate in the pleasures of quiz shows are not necessarily incorporated into the consumerist ideology.[74]

Nevertheless, the constructed articulation of *Wheel* as lower in the knowledge hierarchy than other, more school-like shows, by enabling greater engagement of its audience of "ordinary people,"[75] also allows a richer potential for the program's educative function to be successful.

### Probability and Profit

The roulette wheel is one example of this educative potential. It provokes a repeated representation of mathematical probability. The *Wheel of Fortune* in fact has inspired a number of projects on probability for middle-school science fairs.[76] On the show, however, as the contestants continue to spin, they can develop aiming skills for obtaining the higher dollar amounts while risking the costly bankrupt or cruel lose-a-turn; they appear to be altering fate. The lesson is that repeated effort and practice can alter the odds.[77] Yet the amounts have been carefully selected by the program designers to make sure that winning totals do not lose them money, even as they create a big winner for every game.

Such risks for the designers are somewhat limited for game shows because the production costs are incredibly low when compared with alternative forms of programming. Partly because merchandise manufacturers are more than happy to donate prizes for the plugs that attend their display, and partly because of "freebie exchanges" (e.g., Vanna White's wardrobe was credited as furnished by Climax in the credits in exchange for the loan of the clothes[78]), these expenses are bypassed. When such production considerations are combined with the fact that the same set is used over and over again inside a studio, eliminating elaborate filming costs, it becomes easy to see the attraction of the game show industry.[79] Nevertheless, a profitable balance between prizes and production costs must be maintained. For *Wheel* this is made simpler by awarding credited money that is in turn "spent" on the donated prizes. For *Wheel's* producers, therefore, the balance is among the "credit" and the shopping choices; they never need a large cash flow.

A believable but fabricated probability is a key component of every game show. Luck, according to Fiske, plays a vital role in the hegemonic structure of societies that are both competitive and democratic.[80] The dominant ideology insists that everyone has a chance to rise up through the class, economic, and power systems. Those who do not rise (by definition, the majority) have failed through their own "natural" deficiencies. But luck mitigates the harshness of this judgement: it is an ideologically acceptable explanation of success or failure.[81] On the *Wheel of Fortune*, however, there is always a winner; and the odds are one in three that a particular contestant will pass through the portals of change each night.[82]

> Three contestants drawn from every conceivable walk of life "take their shot" in this exaggerated land of fabulous wealth, overnight success and, of course, equal opportu-

nity. "Whose life will it change tonight?" intones the announcer in the promotional spot.[83]

A more subtle lesson in probability is vicariously experienced in the choice of which letter to guess. Engaged viewers weigh the options: Which of 26 letters would most likely appear in the mystery phrase? They use their knowledge of letter use in the English language, their ability to recognize words in the provided pattern (the command of general factual knowledge), and the possibility of repeated letters within a phrase (which simultaneously could help decode the mystery while also winning more money for later shopping). Immediate feedback regarding this choice is presented as the contestant calls out his or her own selection. Even as the contestant's letter is evaluated by an external judge—its 'rightness' or 'wrongness' indicated either by Vanna turning tiles or a sympathetic disappointed sigh from both her and Pat, the viewers themselves determine whether or not their own choice would have been better. In this way the viewer becomes a self-teacher, embodying both Socratic schoolmaster and student. At the same time, probability is embedded within practice rather than external to or applied to experience.

### Problems and Problem Solving

As educators pondered strategies for the NCTM's Agenda—that problem solving become the number one "basic skill" for the 1980s, *Wheel of Fortune* was dubbed "back-to-the-basics television."[84] New middle-school textbooks helped students develop problem-solving skills by simplifying the wording of their word problems.[85] Similarly, successful game shows wanted the puzzle resolution objectives of the game to be instantly accessible.[86] On *Wheel of Fortune*, the puzzle and the procedure for its solution are well-known elements of a children's spelling game. Significant features of this problem-solving model include the unique and objectively determinable solution and repeated practice with problems of identical type. As in traditional school mathematics, the viewer/student's purpose is to replicate a previously designed solution algorithm in order to identify an already known (to the poser) solution. In a textbook, a student needs to look at the answer key to verify the unique result; on *Wheel of Fortune*, part of the thrill is the slowly revealed clues culminating in a celebration of the answer key.

However, while school mathematics problems generally result in a numerical, factual, and academic resolution, *Wheel*'s enigma is a popularly spoken phrase, a cliche known to everyone, "with the possible exception of poorly briefed space aliens."[87]

> In a perfect illustration of television's ecological self-suf-ficiency, Griffin comes up with many of the puzzles him-self by watching TV and jotting down linguistic flotsam as it drifts by.

And unlike school mathematics problems, the solution of *Wheel*'s mystery phrase also requires a perspective on social interaction, because the three contestants, as well as the viewers at home, are all competing to be the first solver, even as they help each other to fill in the puzzle. Despite the program's de-emphasis of direct compe-tition, contestants need to evaluate the risks of using letters that might later help someone else solve the puzzle first.

Yet school and popular culture mutually confirm the com-monsense notion of problem solving as replicating an algorithmic procedure for determining the answer to a puzzle. It is assumed that the puzzle must have an answer. Missing are any conceptions of problem posing, problem redefinition, moral evaluation of prob-lems, etc.; problems are cues for the application of algorithms, and problem solving is constructed as enigma resolution external to the social context of the problem's articulation.[88]

The commonsense construction of problems and their solu-tion positions the student as a passive receiver of puzzle problems imposed from without. Unnaturally confrontational, this image of a problem as a puzzle is similar to the classical model, in which one must reckon with a threatening barrier to progress. It also creates the expectation that the student/viewer will solve the puzzle with-out inquiring about why it might be posed in the first place. The problem is given: hence it is to be solved. Possible questions intro-duced by marginal voices in the professional discourse include: What does the solution illuminate regarding a body of knowledge being investigated? Regarding one's understanding of that body of knowledge? Is the problem selected to give the student experience in applying a technique? Is the problem suggested for expanding or recapitulating a body of knowledge? Is the problem intended to help clarify a misconception? The commonsense discursive position of the problem posed from a preordained range of potential "barriers to progress" thus reduces the status of the student/viewer. It also denies the possibility that she create her own problems, or construct her own criteria for successful interaction with a problem.[89]

Here *Wheel* offers a contrasting image of puzzle solution to that provided by a contemporaneous and popular three-dimensional toy or cube puzzle, *Rubik's Magic Cube*. Designed by a Hungarian professor of architecture and design,[90] the cube is composed of 23 component cubes of varying colors; the aim, or solution, is to rearrange the cubes so that each face of the larger composite cube is a single color. For *Rubik's Magic Cube*, the solution is already known, while the process of obtaining it is unknown. One has to persist in trying combinations of cube movements and rotations, hoping to guess the right ones. On *Wheel of Fortune* the puzzle is presented so that the issue to be resolved is already defined. There is minimal need for interpretation. *Rubik's Magic Cube* is a popular culture representation of the 'ill-defined' problem, interesting because it also does not require much interpretation despite its confusion of solution strategies.

Because the reduced interpretation on *Wheel* fosters an extremely limited view of problems as puzzles, it discourages the creative generation of conjectures, or the cultivation of an ability to handle situations that do not appear so defined at first glance; it also enhances the misconception that an answer to a puzzle or problem is unique but mysterious. Many 'less able' students become so because, as far as they can tell, there are many possible 'answers', and their objective is to guess the one which the teacher declares correct. (Hence the trend for students to blindly combine all numbers mentioned in a word problem—that is, for example, not discriminating between relevant and irrelevant information.[91]) The students perceive the problem as ill-defined because they do not have a clear notion of the proper algorithm, and they have been taught to expect that one can be found. For some, *Rubik's Magic Cube* demonstrates the contingency of such a unique algorithm despite its single 'solution state'.

Moreover, the commonsense surface interpretation of *Wheel of Fortune* as a contest among individuals to decode the puzzle first effectively obscures the opportunity the program offers for an experience in the simultaneous practices of hypothesis generation and hypothesis testing. That is, a particular letter choice is always at once a guess that generates a pattern or solution hypothesis and also a potential confirmation of a particular hypothesis. While this type of higher-level problem-solving skill can easily be ignored in both school and popular culture mathematics, it is clearly evident in the play of *Wheel*. For example, a letter guessed in the effort to decode one word of a puzzle (testing an hypothesis) might possibly help the player both at home and in the studio rule out options for other words (generating hypotheses).

Both legitimate and popular knowledge are confined to self-supporting power/knowledge practices, which reduce problems to puzzles. Academics, for example, often focus research on task variables in problem solving.[92] They scrutinize problem-solving processes to identify generalized, prescribed, and essential tasks for the successful completion of a problem. In doing so, they construct learning tasks independent of the student, thus requiring minimal self-investment by the student. They also establish problem solving within a context of 'immediacy'; that is, there is no expectation that one might work on a problem over a period of years, or a lifetime. Without recourse to a cheater's guide to *Rubik's Magic Cube*, one might very well devote a lifetime to solving the puzzle, or quit with the impression that a solution is impossible. But on *Wheel of Fortune* (as in school problems) puzzles are intended to be solved in a minimal amount of time, and the solutions are easily accessible within the realm of popular culture.

Popular and school problem solving also actively confirm a focus on the 'answer' in opposition to the process of interaction with a problem. On *Wheel of Fortune*, the completed puzzle is the particular subgoal, earning a contestant the right to go shopping. *Rubik's Magic Cube* has a clear goal to obtain, while the nature of solving the puzzle makes it difficult for someone to remember, record, and reflect on strategies used. In the discourse of school mathematics, this emphasis on answers is maintained through the practice of testing, in which only the correctness of responses is scored, ignoring the processes used by the problem solver.[93] Another pedagogical reinforcement is constructed through the notion of 'goal-oriented' planning. Theoretically, the idea of a specific goal or subgoals is considered essential to successful interaction with a problem.[94]

The above approach to problems is directly challenged by educators concerned with the lack of theorizing about school and nonschool experiences in the lives of students. In a new adaptation of Cremin's ecological theorizing about schooling, the late 1980s witnessed an interest in forms of postmodern education, in which the curriculum would best support learning only when school knowledge begins with the tacit knowledge derived from the cultural resources that students already possess.[95] Postmodernists accurately recognized that this should not mean substituting popular culture for traditional high-culture topics; little critical literacy would be established by replacing one version of academic factual knowledge with an alternative, popular version of the same knowledge. Instead, they argued for educators to rethink the nature of legitimate knowledge itself.

Aronowitz and Giroux asked about the "significance, apart from sorting, of the predominant operational approach to mathematics."

> Learning the procedures helps students to solve prefigured problems, and the exercise surely measures, to some degree, students' mental discipline and their ability to abstract from particulars. But math pedagogy as currently practiced does not necessarily develop an ability to use and discover mathematical concepts among nonspecialists. On the contrary, it encourages the student to learn the logical processes that follow from accepting the axioms of the discipline and its postulates. As opposed to the intellectual claims made on behalf of math education by those who insist on expanding the role of these subjects in primary and secondary schools, math is generally taught as an applied discipline, not as an intellectual pursuit.[96]

Other educators sought to expand the general conception of mathematics, hoping to incorporate forms of folk and non-Western versions within the school curriculum. This arena of knowledge production also effectively challenged accepted conclusions about the nature of mathematics and the learning and teaching of mathematics. Adopting anthropological research methods, these scholars identified the necessity of exploring the cultural conflicts between school and nonschool mathematical practices. This 'ethnomathematics' perspective denied the superiority of standard Amero-Euro-mathematics. But theorists using this perspective recognized that popular knowledge would never be included within intellectual knowledge simply because it could not be grounded in an explicit philosophy and methodology that would be evaluated from a (Western) foundational perspective.[97] They argued instead that contemporary popular culture could become an object of legitimate intellectual inquiry. Much like ethnomusicology, which was invented to collect and classify folk songs and other traditional musical expressions, the legitimation of popular culture would be accomplished via an integration of mathematics education into one of the accepted disciplines, such as anthropology or sociology. Also noted was the contrasting success of mathematics learning within culturally specific everyday practices when compared to traditional school pedagogy. Such a move away from the high-culture canon was remarkable; but even better, from a postmodern perspective, would be to interrogate the priority of canonicity itself: to deconstruct the canon in specific ways.

## Imitators and Echoes

At this point I want to introduce the concept of 'articulation' as a theoretical tool for cultural analysis. First developed by Stuart Hall, John Fiske describes articulation through two meanings, both of which are relevant.[98] First, to articulate is to speak, and speaking is a two-way process requiring a response; therefore, game shows may articulate a particular ideology, but viewers can articulate a variety of responses particular to their own interests. Second, articulate means linking with a flexible, movable point of contact, as in a hinge; instead of examining the text, its production, and its reception, this meaning of articulate forces us to interrogate the ways in which the text (or the game of which it is an example) is linked to other cultural domains. "The multiple articulation of [game] shows is a function both of their textual openness (their "unwrittenness," their use of excess and metaphor) and of the way they can be read in terms of their relationship with a number of cultural domains, particularly those of school, of the family, of shopping, of leisure, and of social relationships."[99] *Wheel of Fortune* articulates with school, school mathematics, and notions of numeracy in crucial ways.

Studies have suggested that viewers from higher socioeconomic groups, who are likely to be the better educated, prefer and use factual academic knowledge programs to test their own 'academic' knowledge. Viewers from lower socioeconomic groups, however, who are likely to have had a shorter formal education, tend to use game shows to prove to themselves that they are as clever as the contestants; they demonstrate for themselves that their formally assessed academic performance is not an accurate measure of their ability. Others use game shows as a basis for self-rating; by noticing improvement or by surprising themselves with their ability, they produce the sort of self-esteem that they never received from school.[100] Because the *Wheel of Fortune* skills of pattern recognition and probability are embedded within an everyday practice, and because these skills are not necessarily indicated within school as 'mathematical', these potential uses of the program actively reconstruct a separation of school and popular culture mathematics in respect to self-esteem and its relation to assessed mathematical ability or performance.

For young viewers, the representation of adult participants suggests that the competitive testing of school is not confined to children, but continues into adult life—and into a different realm of pleasure. A kind of vicarious empowerment is established when children see adults subjected to the disempowerment they regularly experience in school. The game show lets them compete equally with the adult contestants; it also allows them a peek at adults making mistakes and immediately suffering the consequences. These are ways in which children can find meanings that validate their interests and give them a source of self-esteem not usually found in their own school experiences.[101]

Often, children role-play game shows. This gives them a chance, as do many role-playing experiences, to assume adult roles. When role-playing game shows, however, by knowing the answer to a posed problem, they reverse the adult-child power relationship and become the teacher. At other times, teachers incorporate the pleasure of game shows into the classroom, making the metaphorical link more explicit.[102]

In the 1980s, Children's Television Workshop began to make repeated use of game show parodies on both *Sesame Street* and *Square One Television*. These parodies typically mock directly, or destabilize the excesses of the games show's ambience. For example, in the *Square One Television* parody of *Wheel of Fortune*, the hostess role is played by a very tall and clearly very intelligent African-American woman, destabilizing standard conceptions of beauty, intelligence, and femininity. In contrast to the original programs, *Square One* intentionally attempts to 'teach' mathematics and to emphasize the excitement of problem-solving tasks through game show and other television genres. The 'teaching' aspect is largely downplayed, however. *Square One* is " . . . not intended to teach specific math skills,"

> and must be presented in a beguiling way to lure young viewers away from competing fare. "We understand that we're not going to teach a child how to do an algebra problem," says CTW president Joan Ganz Cooney. "We're trying to change the attitude toward problem solving and to show how very useful it is to know mathematics in your daily life."[103]

*Square One* makes active use of the rearticulation of the game show at the end of their sequence, just as the original. That is, the losers chat about their experience on the show, validating the fun they had; this is a form of rearticulation in which the program is dearticulated from the school metaphor and rearticulated to the domain of entertainment and leisure.[104] Losing becomes a positive experience for the participants, constructing a discursive distance from school, in which failure has little chance of rearticulation. *Square One* uses television parodies for this very distancing effect, in a way 'tricking' its young audience into thinking that learning mathematics is really a fun source of entertainment. However, it is also possible for young *Square One* viewers to carry this orientation over to the *Wheel of Fortune*, where they would maintain their attention to the mathematics.

### Numbers and Money

Reversing the direction of articulation, school mathematics also links with viewing *Wheel of Fortune* when viewers carry their classroom experiences into the popular culture realm of consumerism and conspicuous consumption. That is, the articulation of large numbers with money and shopping interpretations needs further clarification. In school, texts and teachers make extensive use of shopping examples to teach arithmetical skills. Arithmetic becomes the recording of real-object exchange transactions. On the *Wheel of Fortune*, the numbers are signifiers gaining meaning through their use: The winner exchanges large 'credit' numbers for commodities in a rapid whirlwind spending spree; amounts accumulated during play indicate potential shopping power.

Elementary mathematics education predominantly accepts the theoretical 'truth' that children's understanding of money comes first through their manipulation of coins or other objects representing very small amounts of money, and that the notion of exchange value is a highly abstract concept and therefore outside the conceptual power of such children; they are limited to learning through concrete manipulation.[105] Nevertheless, shopping games are often utilized to introduce topics such as 'subtraction from 10'. The children handle concrete examples of small numbers and then record them on paper as illustrations of the particular topic. The reason for using small numbers is that the theory suggests children cannot manipulate and fathom numbers beyond those with which they have had concrete experiences. Part of the exercise requires the eventual translation between the shopping language code (e.g., "how much change?") and the arithmetical algorithmic language ("10 take away five leaves five").

As Walkerdine points out, however, everything about the task testifies to the disjunction for the children between this task in mathematics and the knowledge of money they have obtained outside of school. In her analysis of at-home family dialogues, she notes an emphasis on the high cost of goods. Children are encouraged not to be wasteful of commodities because of the high costs and labor involved in earning money to pay for them; and exchanges often bear witness to a struggle for power between children and adults, in which the children want the parents to buy goods for them to consume, while the parents retort with the high cost of such items and their lack of money to buy them with. In contrast to the school mathematics money games, home arguments about exchange value and the money economy are highly abstract and complex; the elements of the arguments are presented to children in such a way that they have actual material consequences in their everyday lives.

The pedagogy assumes that children learn about money only from the handling of small coins which leads to the real understanding of arithmetic processes, whereas the understanding of money on the part of children is one in which large sums of money are involved; these sums have important value attached to them and are inserted in crucial domestic economic practices.[106]

The disjunction of life and school money mathematics becomes evident in the ways in which children position themselves within the school practice by introducing fantasy; they use the disjunction between actual shopping practice and the absurd low prices to shift their position within the practice. In fantasy, they become what is not possible in real life, namely rich people who can buy expensive items, have exotic holidays, return goods they are tired of, and, as Walkerdine noted in her ethnographic study of classrooms, behave badly toward those who role-play the store employees. This is not unlike the representation of numbers on *Wheel*, which has to be "spent" during the visual climax of the program, "the ultimate strike-it-rich fantasy."[107] "As the winner shops, the camera lovingly roves around the prize showcase, as though the viewers' own eyeballs have been let loose amid the VCRs, Isuzu pickups, Tahitian vacations, and ceramic Dalmatians."[108]

> Here too the show offers viewers vicarious kicks. Since we at home actually solved the puzzle first and, were it not for a mere accident of space and time, would be up there shopping right now, we find ourselves deliberating whether the cat lithograph or the backyard grill makes more sense. *Wheel* has brought the pleasures of window shopping to television.[109]

Greed is often bandied about as "the dirty little secret" of games shows; but Blair television's Mike Levinton doubted this was the key to *Wheel*'s popularity, because one of the unique features of the program is its relative decorum—"nobody screams, jumps up and down, or otherwise visibly lusts after inanimate objects."[110] Nevertheless, the prizes do offer an important clue to *Wheel*'s appeal. The traditional game show gift had been fairly practical: a bedroom set, a washer-dryer, luggage ("all the accoutrements of the suburban middle-class lifestyle"[111]). But Wheel prizes are always the "stuff of conspicuous consumption."

> The brand names come from Fifth Avenue and Rodeo Drive: Cartier, Tiffany, Van Cleef & Arpels. Contestants win gift certificates from Gucci instead of from the Spie-

gel catalog. Many of the prizes are strictly for show: $5,000 grandfather clocks and sets of gold-plated golf clubs "guaranteed to make an impression on the links." What contestants on *Wheel of Fortune* vie for are not so much valuable commodities as the outward symbols of contemporary success.[112]

And, for those who do not get to go on to the bonus round, that flair for excessive consumption is allowed to linger back home.

I wasn't leaving with the ceramic Dalmatian under my arm. But I guess that my consolation prizes were tacky enough to compensate. After all, who would really buy herself a year's supply of nonstick cooking spray?[113]

## The Transformation of Problem Solving

*Wheel* offers a very palatable social mathematics similar in form to that found in school.

The social and economic rules that govern *Wheel* approximate closely what most of us consider proper and just. As Horatio Alger knew, the American race did not go to the swiftest, but to the average fellow who was diligent and deserving. He also knew it wasn't really a race at all—according to the American dream, success does not depend on beating the other guy so much as making your own way. And in fact, *Wheel* is surprisingly non-competitive. There are no clocks or buzzers, and no head-to-head competition. Everyone politely roots for whoever is "up," and each contestant gets to take his or her turn unmolested by host, clock or opponent. Nothing, however, is handed to you, as the *Wheel of Fortune* vocabulary makes it clear: You don't win, but "earn the right to buy a prize . . . at the actual retail prices." *Wheel* is the only game show on television to strike the proper balance between skill and luck, accomplishment and good fortune, or, in the Puritan vocabulary, between works and faith.[114]

Returning to the first definition of articulation, it should be noted that *Wheel* also offers the same options as school for those uncomfortable with positioning themselves as "buying" into the system. Michael Pollan suggested that, by June 1986, *Wheel's* audience was so large that, "in addition to the dedicated game show fan, there must be a significant number of viewers for whom the show is at least partly an exercise in camp." In the same way that many students cannot admit to pleasure in classroom activities—it just would not be acceptable in front of their peers—'Wheelies' might point to the elements of irony and nostalgia in Vanna White's extraordinary popularity, or to Pat Sajaks's self-deprecating humor ("the mild sense of absurdity he confides from time to time"); and the audience's exaggerated oohs and aahs might suggest that "the whole experience is something less than sincere."[115]

Many teachers drop hints of irony in the classroom. Walkerdine's teachers noted with amusement the coins with which they could cheaply purchase an airplane; similarly, *Wheel of Fortune* gives its vast audience license to indulge in something many would otherwise consider beneath them without admitting they find the crude success fantasies or the antefeminism of White pleasurable: They can have it both ways. In the classroom, students can find outward comfort in the 'camp' as well; detachment through denial of real interest enables pleasure in learning to occur.

As the 1980s wore on, however, professional discussion maintained its focus on the subject matter and its organization within school programs. The end of the decade witnessed an interest in the complexity of problem-solving research and teaching, incorporating concerns for the necessity of open-ended and ill-defined problems, as well as the social context of problem solving, social cognition, and group problem-solving techniques. The central curriculum design issue for schools seemed to rest on conflicting comprehension of the location of the problem in problem solving. If problems exist independent of any solver, then the design task is accomplished without regard to cognitive variations, selecting those problems that characterize mathematics within the philosophy of mathematics the designer wants to espouse. It then becomes the teacher's responsibility to 'connect' the student to the problems. But if problems are determinant factors in a student's problem-solving activities, then they are in a way located within the student. It becomes uncertain what problem a student is solving at a given time. This second approach requires a loss of control over what the curriculum designer takes as the foundation of the curriculum: He or she maintains control over the activities—the problematic situations, but not the content of the problem.

Yet such design was often argued as demanded by societal needs:

> At best, the current system of education prepares young people for preexisting jobs in an industrial economy. Few students are taught critical thinking and decision-making skills. Few students are taught how to work collaboratively to solve novel real-world problems, the essence of an information-era economic system.[116]

This intriguing entry into the complexity of problem solving as a professional focus demonstrates one facet of how professional practice constructed problem solving as a professional problem. Educational practice thus constantly recreated itself by creating problems to be solved—how to make children into successful problem solvers—and then searching for solutions to the problems. By defining mathematical activity in terms of problems, mathematics educators needed to research how people solve problems, how they might solve problems differently or better, and how to judge when problem solving was successful. This led to a professional language and the evolution of techniques for improving problem-solving performance and its assessment. But this professional practice constantly recentered professional attention on problem solving as an activity to be understood and as a body of skills to be taught. Teachers needed to categorize when problem solving was occurring or not, and whether or not their teaching was contributing to this general objective.[117]

Meanwhile, the popular culture conception of problem solving was largely one of puzzles with clear and precise solutions. This constructed a discursive distance between professional language and commonsense public discourse, but also mediated professional and policy notions of problems as ambiguously related to puzzles and puzzle-solving techniques. Because professional practice disassociated itself from popular culture, and because some aspects of popular culture actively reinforced this distance (as I demonstrated above in the case of *Wheel of Fortune*), the more general educative potential within, for example, game shows and puzzle toys was not only denied but implicitly reduced to affirming puzzle interpretations of all problems. This denial also belittled the complex higher-level problem-solving skills of hypothesis testing and generation untapped for education in both popular culture and professional discourse.

A careful reading of the NCTM's latest *Standards* should note, however, the subtle shift from the teaching of problem solving to the use of a problem-solving context for the development of all mathematical conceptual and procedural knowledge.[118] It is possible that this indicates a shift from Polya's teacher of heuristics to Knuth's student who uses evolving problem-solving strategies to learn mathematical content. Ironically, the companion volume of *Professional Standards* for teachers of mathematics subsequently transfers the assessment questions to the teacher:[119] Has the teacher provided a genuine problem-solving context? How 'much' of a problem-solving context is generated? What teacher questions foster a problem-solving context?

It is crucial to ask where and why problem solving was actively established as a category of mathematical practice and knowledge. The reading of *Wheel of Fortune* in terms of problem solving is itself a symptom of an overwhelming concern for problem solving as a signifier in educational discourse. Is it 'really' a meaningful term for organizing discussion of mathematics education, or does it split the attention of educators into misleading arenas of reflection? The circularity of problem solving defining mathematical activity, which in turn incorporates problems into a curriculum of topics taught through problems, calls into question the interests served by such an organization of educational practice. Do we take the efficacy of problem solving on faith, or by the grace of God? On the *Wheel of Fortune*, contestants consistently spin the wheel as many times as they possibly can to maximize their shopping potential: There are only two chances of failure, and they are clearly visible. Whether we should keep spinning our problem-solving wheel is something maybe only Ezekiel might know.

# 3

# Gender and the Construction
# of Social Problems

A couple of issues from the previous chapters lead into a key area of mathematics education discourse: the fact that no superteacher heros are women, and the symbolically supportive information that all game show hosts—who have been interpreted as representative of the ideal teacher—are men. The focus on women as all-too-few models of people successful in mathematics and its teaching, and the related identification of gender as correlative with the study and use of mathematics, were indeed important themes in the discussion of mathematics education during this period, both in popular and expert discourse. The particular and consistent placement of an African-American woman in confident, successful, and powerful roles on *Square One Television* thus represents an important statement by Children's Television Workshop relative to the norms of popular commercial television.

Indeed, the terrains of gender differentiation in ability, participation, and performance in mathematics together provide an interesting example of the ways in which mathematics education as a social practice constructs social problems that in turn need to be administered to. Chapter 1 explored the tendency of professional and public discourse to reduce educational issues to problems concerning individual teachers; the isolated teacher is simultaneously, then, the site of problem solutions. Similarly, chapter 2 analyzed the ways in which the definition of mathematics as fundamentally 'problem-solving' structures curriculum dilemmas and subsequent failures of mathematics education within a reified, commonsense conception of the discipline. The 'agenda' for the profession, and for the nation's schools, is a response to the problems structured by this conception. That is, the professional discourse becomes a part of the popular culture, as the popular culture is integrated within the professional discourse.

In this chapter, I examine more meticulously the features of mathematics education as a social practice that can supply a platform for the more theoretical and philosophical work to follow in chapter (-1). Before considering the power/knowledge implications of a 'practice' orientation to the profession, it will be worthwhile to examine in detail one particular example of how a social practice actively constructs social problems through its ongoing practice. It is important to study the role of gender as a signifier in the discourse of mathematics education at this point because attention to gender as a category of analysis is even more important for the development of applicable notions of power and identity politics. My subsequent theoretical work owes much to critical feminist reflection based heavily although not exclusively on the cultural and political construction of gender as a discursive category.

However, the 'problems' of gender and mathematics are important in their own right for a comprehensive interrogation of recent mathematics education discourse. As I indicate below, many central problems of mathematics education for all students have their origin in (feminist) concerns about gender differentiation. Furthermore, the ways in which mathematics education enters public discourse as news or as a crisis of national import can be elucidated simply through attention to gendered discourse, because it is through the sensationalistic attraction of the 'battle of the sexes' that many issues of mathematics education not necessarily related to gender problems become identified publicly as news. Hence I present first the professional discussion of gender and mathematics. This is followed by a consideration of the mediation of this development of power/knowledge via a translation of 'facts' into 'news' (and thus 'truth'). At the same time, however, it is important to keep in mind that academic researchers at once formulate their own conceptions of 'important' research questions and attempt to 'fit' their research questions within a larger social agenda. Thus the direction of influence is multifaceted: The media and the profession both mediate the creation of gender as a suddenly important 'problem' for schools as they each attempt to negotiate the new discursive terrain. One prominent feature of this terrain, as we will note, is a paramount concern for the competitiveness of the United States internationally, both militarily and economically. The gendered interpretation of particular problems of mathematics education within this context also significantly influences the construction of gender as a category itself.

## Gender as a Social Problem

Lorelei Brush's seminal work, *Encouraging Girls in Mathematics*,[1] is a good example of professional discussion at the beginning of the 1980s. Brush defined a significant 'problem' for mathematics educators:

> Too many students, particularly girls, are dropping mathematics in high school as soon as they can. They do not realize that their lack of mathematical preparation will restrict their job opportunities, keeping them out of many of the higher-paying jobs and seriously limiting their opportunities for growth and advancement in other jobs. We need to know why students decide to quit mathematics, in order to reverse the process and encourage them to keep studying the subject.
>
> There is a critical problem for education in the low female enrollment in advanced mathematics courses. We are not properly preparing students for the job market they will face on graduation from high school or for enrollment in college courses that are required for better-paying jobs for college graduates.[2]

In a review of relevant literature, Brush emphasized a significantly lower rate of participation in school mathematics by girls and women. This difference had been variously explained by lower mean scores on tests of mathematical ability, more negative attitudes, the comparatively rarer perception of mathematics as a useful body of knowledge and skills, and discouraging influences of the social milieu. Sex differences had been found by other researchers in each of these four reasons for avoiding mathematics. Brush posited that each reason might be related to the lack of participation in advanced (elective) mathematics by all students; but she also sought "to isolate the particularly potent causes for girls."[3]

Attention to student gender as an important field of reflection for mathematics educators was consistent with a widespread belief that individual differences among students were pertinent to the performance of successful teachers. That is, it was possible to use 'gender' as a relevant fact about individual students in assessing appropriate pedagogical techniques. Concern for differences in mathematics participation by gender was largely motivated by public awareness of gender as an important category of social inequality; this was a general result of the women's movement of the twentieth century. But research about variations by group was commonly translated into pedagogical techniques designed to maximize opportunity and fair treatment for all students as unique individuals. This more general consensus around the importance of interpreting performance in mathematics classrooms in terms of what each individual student brings to the experience (rather than, for example, the structural organization of schools or political or social factors influencing curriculum development) was an important legacy of child-centered pedagogical theories.[4]

Hence, variables identifiable as individual characteristics were often not compared with other (group) characteristics, such as class or ethnicity. For example, in a compilation of variables studied in relation to gender differences in mathematics, Gilah Leder listed learner variables interpreted as controlling cognitive development and beliefs.[5] Environmental variables related to society, home and school were also included; yet discussion of such variables consistently simplified their role by framing them in terms of how they might affect an individual student. Moreover, research directly linked environmental variables to the classroom via the construct of "internal influences"; here the goal was to make explicit relationships between affective variables (including the relevant "psychosocial") and cognitive outcomes, so that a complete and comprehensive model of (internal) influences on gender differences in mathematics could be established.[6] The result was that these variables had to be interpreted in terms of appropriate treatment for an individual student based on gender. In this way, a generalizable category of analysis (gender) worked to reaffirm professional practice as oriented to the teaching of individual students, despite their consistent placement within group learning situations in school mathematics (i.e., the classroom).[7]

Mark Driscoll's summary of relevant research for secondary mathematics teachers is a good example of how this orientation to professional practice mediated the production of professional knowledge about teaching and subsequent recommendations to practitioners.[8] The publication was funded by the National Institute of Education, developed through a project of the Institute's Research and Development Interpretation Service (RDIS), and published by the National Council of Teachers of Mathematics. Although it did not directly address gender, Driscoll's book is particularly relevant to the concurrent discussion of gender issues because it examined concerns of mathematics teachers in the junior high and high school—those places in which gender-associated research located the crucial development of differences in mathematics performance and participation. In preparing its report, RDIS collected "around 150 questions" in telephone interviews of a national sampling of junior high and high school teachers. A Mathematics Consultant Panel reviewed the questions and identified "topics which were represented by the questions and for which there exists a research base for answers." Literature searches resulted in the National Council's book, which introduced "individual differences among mathematics learners" as the second topic, following only "effective mathematics teaching." Because each chapter of the book began with a question from a teacher, and the subsequent chapter was constructed as an 'answer' through which "research information and the classroom implications of that research are clear," the book appeared to be a direct response to the reality of classroom practice. However, the coordination of teachers' questions by a panel of experts into themes connected to current research, as well as the subsequent organization of particular research findings as pertinent to specific questions, structured the ways in which research conclusions could be understood as relevant 'facts'.

While the placement of the chapter on individual differences positioned this type of teacher practice as significantly important—that a teacher should seek to identify differences among students, and use that information in making both macro and micro decisions about his or her teaching practice—its content was illustrative of the mediation process as well. It began with a pair of questions:

> What are some of the major differences in learning styles and levels of development among secondary school students? How should such differences be dealt with in the mathematics classroom?[9]

These questions already placed the ensuing discourse within the confines of a particular theory that assumed a teacher must respond to identifiable variations among students. But they also asked for the 'experts' to provide the categories of difference: that is, the differences were not to be found by individual teachers through their own experience, but via general professional knowledge distilled by researchers. The response, however, redirected the identification of differences; it was not the experts who had found them but teachers themselves:

> Despite the fact that much of the secondary school curriculum is designed on the assumption that students all think in the same way, secondary level mathematics teachers know differently. Every year, they meet many students who seem unable to think logically, or who become confused whenever symbols are used to represent mathematical concepts. Furthermore, many students approach mathematical decisions without a sense of what is reasonable.[10]

It seems, then, that teachers do in fact deduce empirical differences from everyday practice. Yet the relevant differences are those labeled by researchers, and which provide possible deficiencies locatable in the student. Expert advice thus enables 'unsuccessful' mathematics teaching to be blamed on particular characteristics of individual students through the authority of experts.

The diffusion of blame among large numbers of individuals, each constructed in a different way according to different rules of inference, demonstrates how this professional practice defines professional knowledge to be codified as 'truth' while its political implications go unnoticed. For example, Driscoll's book suggested differences in cognitive development might manifest themselves in students reaching different stages at different times; thus some students might not be cognitively ready for certain kinds of mathematics knowledge. Individuals may differ in their cognitive style—the ways in which they process information; teachers thus have to reconcile interaction styles and information delivery techniques to adapt to different individuals. Questions about how such identifications of 'problems' (for the teacher to deal with) result in various power relationships between teachers and students, however, were not evident as relevant to the ongoing development of professional discourse. Nor were inquiries about the nature of students as groups working collectively rather than as isolable individuals interacting with the teacher as distinct entities. Broader concerns about the social, cultural, or political contexts of schooling in society did not enter this discourse at any point; all relevant features of pedagogy were responses to characteristics of individual students. Teachers were not directed to the more global issues. It instead became imperative that they examine each student as a distinct learner of mathematics:

> Every secondary level mathematics student (1) is some-where on the continuum between concrete thinking and full formal thinking, (2) has a position on each of several cognitive style continuums, and (3) differs from many other students in the kind of bridge he or she has built—with language, intuition, and the formation of personal rules—between mathematics and the real world.[11]

Yet, at the same time, it was conceivably teachers who constructed the 'reality' of these categories of difference through ongoing everyday practice, even as they appeared, according to common-sense wisdom, to be reacting to "the state of things." One essential skill of 'effective mathematics teaching' was categorizing each student along these continua and then administering to the problems created by the juxtapositions of such widely varying individual attributes within a single class of students. Hence, the differences were constructed as relevant via a complex interaction of actions and interpretations within such widely varying practices as topic selection and organization, pedagogical techniques, and student evaluation: In a collection of examples of how such problematic situations arise and become the subject of professional reflection on practice, Driscoll included implications for specific subject topics as well as common instructional techniques.

However, it further became possible to recognize the teacher as the source of gender differences in participation and performance in mathematics, making it reasonable to blame the individual teacher for this societywide inequality. The teacher was trapped in a double bind, in which his or her attempts to meet the expectations of professional practice were simultaneously the sources of unprofessional behavior. Surely it would be appropriate, following the above argument, to locate gender differences within the criteria of individual variations. Yet teachers were also accused of perpetuating spurious gendered expectations with negative ramifications, simply through their attention to the important category of "gender." That is, teachers were posited as holding outdated notions of gender roles and stereotyped ideas about gender and mathematical ability.[12]

As late as 1990, Elizabeth Fennema declared that "teachers' thinking" plays an important part in teaching. Students' learning, she wrote, is directly influenced by classroom instruction; but, more importantly, classroom instruction is determined by the decisions that teachers make, which are directly influenced by their knowledge and beliefs.[13]

> Partly based on what teachers know and believe about gender differences in mathematics, decisions are made about what each female and male should do in the classroom; these, in turn, influence what that female or male learns in mathematics.[14]

I suggest further that the attention to gender as an appropriate category of knowledge created the possibility of excessive attention to gender as an issue for teachers even as it attempted to reveal a 'hidden curriculum' that discouraged girls and young women from enrolling in advanced mathematics courses. Indeed, it might have given credence to the identification of mathematics as a male domain, or to the perception that males possessed higher mathematical ability overall than females.

### Gender and Sex

The power/knowledge[15] implications of the above for the complex issues of gender redirect me to consider how it is that mathematics education constructed gender difference through its ongoing everyday practice in the 1980s and early 1990s. Here I am making a crucial distinction between 'gender', which I take as a culturally and socially constructed concept (hence contested and perpetually recreated through practice), and 'sex', which is more readily understood as a kind of essential biological distinction that can be made regarding human beings. That is, while gender is sometimes understood within traditional social scientific frameworks as one term in long-standing formulations that provide (universal) causal explanations, in the sense that the existence of phenomena or realities are explained, it is also possible to theorize about the nature of such phenomena as realities, seeking an understanding of how and why they take the form they do. In this second approach, gender becomes 'cultural constructions'; in rejecting the biological (material) determinism implicit in 'sex', 'sexual difference', etc., gender becomes a social category imposed on a sexed body.

The issues become even more interesting when we also consider the implications of categories such as 'mathematical' and how they interact with 'gender'. The phenomena under study becomes, how the discourse of mathematics education directs the teacher to be responsible for the recognition of categorical distinctions, and then redirects the teacher to be responsible for the codification of these distinctions through his or her practice; these distinctions are constructed in turn as 'reality'. This requires different tools of scholarship than ordinarily used in educational research.

For example, it becomes important to understand how a teacher might be perceived as interpreting a particular student's performance as attributable to an ability to do mathematics, as opposed to being the result of 'hard work' or rote memorization. Thus, a particular 'learning style' might be understood as evidence of placement along various continua, depending on interpretation; the placement would be linked to an assessment of the individual's ability or beliefs about herself. In comparisons with other countries, Americans were found to "give more importance to native ability, so they have less incentive to work hard in school." "Americans think of mathematics as some esoteric skill like perfect pitch that some people have and others do not."[16]

Historian Joan Wallach Scott draws an explicit, revealing connection between conceptual or categorical knowledge and the ways in which they are important to the study of practices and the power relationships within them by making a comparison with grammar:[17] looking at the grammar of discourse, we analyze the formal rules that follow from categorical designations; the grammar provides a way of classifying phenomena, a socially agreed upon system of inherent traits. Classifications suggest a relationship among the categories, which in turn make distinctions or separate groupings possible. Thus, memorization or hard work becomes linked with 'female' in some contexts, while challenging teacher authority becomes established as a 'male' sign of ability in others.[18] It is within school mathematics that particular aspects of gender are produced, rather than where particular actions are the result of an originary category of gender. That is, I locate the production of gender as a social construction within classrooms and elsewhere, rather than somewhere else and prior. Thus, for example, I disagree with

Fennema's description of "classrooms as mediators of gender differences in mathematics."[19]

How gender became an important category is interesting because the differences attributed to this individual attribute—in either of the four fields of research noted by Brush—while typically statistically significant, were rather small in magnitude when compared with the extensive overlap across gender. Often the variance within gender was greater than between genders. Thus, conclusions drawn from large-scale surveys and standardized tests bypassed some questions while being ineffective at engaging with how gender was actively produced in the classroom.[20] I bypass the issue about whether or not there were or are sex differences, preferring to ask how and why the application of tests of statistical significance had the rhetorical authority to establish these conclusions, how the conclusions were then interpreted as important as well as relevant to classroom teaching, and how they came to represent the reality of classroom life.[21] I am, moreover, wary about some of the inferences drawn from such work because the issue of statistical significance itself is the object of major debate within social science research. The term 'significance' applied to such research gives it a legitimacy that might not be appropriate in certain contexts.[22]

Of course, if one looks for something, it is possible to find it somewhere. And once the line of inquiry is established, it is hard to repudiate it, because results never evaluate the initial questions. Instead, research conclusions suggest new directions. As research on gender in mathematics education became further ensconced in the profession, it became a science within itself. Thus, as we entered the nineties, Leder and Fennema maintained the importance of monitoring outcomes in the affective as well as cognitive areas; but they recommended a new focus.

> We need to ask more specific questions, such as On what type of mathematics do gender differences exist for students with certain characteristics? For example, do high-achieving females achieve as well as high-achieving males in algebra? Is the situation the same for geometry? Are low-achieving females more confident in one kind of mathematics than another?[23]

In other words, keep looking until we find the differences.

All of this should be put in perspective, however. I believe the motivations behind most if not all gender-related research in mathematics education have never required a defense. As Fennema stated, "there should be justice for females and males in mathematics education."[24] And, while it can be argued that mathematics achievement and participation should be increased for everyone,[25] lower achievement and participation of females in mathematics-related careers is a partial explanation of the economic problems faced by many women: "Mathematics has been and continues to be a critical filter that successfully inhibits participation in many occupations and in career advancement and change." Furthermore, there are documented examples of girls and women being denied the opportunity to contribute to mathematical knowledge because of social attitudes about females as mathematicians; and there are arguments that the so-far male-dominated field of mathematics and our mathematical way of thinking would be enriched if females were encouraged to pursue mathematics.[26] Finally, because mathematics is a unique and powerful product of human culture wielding tremendous authority in everyday life, it is important that girls and women be enabled to understand this cultural production for their own appreciation of its potential for beauty, for their own participation in social life and discourse that makes rhetorical use of mathematical arguments, and for understanding how mathematics contributes to their own perception of themselves and their identity. An important issue, however, is why the stress has been on mathematics and science, rather than, for example, the potential crisis created by too few students—especially males—electing advanced courses in the humanities, home economics, and the so-called helping professions.[27]

Nevertheless, it is the case that research in many countries notes concrete implications of the 'lack' of mathematical learning and negative beliefs about themselves and mathematics among females. Typically, until age 10 either no differences are found, or the differences that are found favor females. In the middle-school years a mixed pattern develops, either of small sex differences—sometimes in favor of girls, sometimes in favor of boys—or no differences. Exceptions to this are studies of "gifted" youth in which substantial differences favoring males are consistently noted. Throughout the high school years differences favoring males are common; they are particularly apparent in problem-solving and application tasks.[28]

The most recent example is a series of studies of mathematics achievement of girls and boys in 20 countries, using data collected by the Second International Mathematics Study (SIMS), which was conducted by the International Association for the Evaluation of Educational Achievement (IEA).[29] In a majority of the countries, girls were found "not to be underprivileged in relation to their achievement in mathematics in grade 8." This finding suggests an historical change, since some previous studies had noted seventh and eighth grade as a transition period; a possible conclusion is that pedagogical changes and concern about gender differences in the middle-school years has had an effect. Echoing previous research, however, this was seen to change by grade 12. Meanwhile, girls were found to perceive mathematics less as a male domain than boys, suggesting worldwide social expectations about gender and mathematics.

The importance of these findings lies not in their specific statements but in the way in which they fit into a general approach to understanding females' achievement and beliefs about themselves and mathematics through a comparison with males' achievement and beliefs. The whole enterprise presumes the identity of male and general human achievement, beliefs, and goals. Importantly, Fennema does note that

> Studies based on this type of thinking, which use male behavior as the standard against which female behavior is measured, are not unusual and have been severely attacked by many. In what is perhaps the best known discussion of this, Gilligan points out that using the male standard as a benchmark against which to measure female behavior has resulted in a psychology that is both inaccurate and misleading. It has been shown that the resulting generalizations about the human condition are often lacking in validity where females [and I would add as a correlative, where males] are concerned.[30]

The net result is a pathologizing of female behavior in which it must be either different because of gender and hence a problem, or a problem because it is the same despite gender when it should not be. Research basically "proves" its own presuppositions.[31]

This power/knowledge strategy is eloquently described by Valerie Walkerdine as "subtracting the feminine," a dangerous trap.

Girls and women are said to be different, lacking, while boys' and men's "mastery" of mathematics, their claim to superior rationality and scientific truth, is unchallenged, as though their "attaining higher eminence" were proof enough. When examining these issues one can fall into the trap of attempting either to prove exactly what girls lack so that it can be put right, or to demonstrate that there is no lack at all. We think that such approaches trap us and the girls and women . . . like fli          ving the game by patriarchal rules.          necessary to avoid stepping into th          fresh why the questions were posed i

### itical Context

As Murray E(         's noted, the interesting thing about social problems fro         t of view of discourse is not their relative importance f          it how they are constructed and arise as 'problems'          . Edelman argues that such problems enter discour         exist as reinforcements of ideologies. In the case of          mathematics, beliefs about the importance of math          iance and the centrality of mathematics and scien   n          for economic and military advantage internationall   iave          uted to more general ideological commitments; the   e commitments have in turn constructed a commonsense notion that greater levels of participation in school mathematics and better scores on achievement tests are basic educational goals. We have lived through an era in which the National Assessment of Educational Progress reported a 4 percent decline in the mathematics scores of 17-year-olds, a 2 percent drop for 13-year-olds, and a 1 percent drop for nine-year-olds from 1973 to 1978.[34]

A 1980 report prepared by the Education Department and the National Science Foundation on orders from President Carter declared that the nation had lost the momentum of its space-age commitment to science and that most Americans were headed "toward virtual scientific and technological illiteracy." Fearing a loss of "our competitive edge," the report concluded that the United States lagged behind the Soviet Union, Japan, and West Germany in elementary and secondary school programs in science and mathematics.[35] By 1982, the "wobbly state of science and math education in the nation's schools" was branded the "top education story" and was expected to "continue to be of crisis proportions for several years."[36] Numerous reports were issued throughout the year from science and mathematics associations, technical schools and industries, the National Science Association, and federal legislative bodies.

> All noted the emergent high technology era is no time for math and science education to be falling down. America will lose out in the global education race, and even national defense will suffer if the deteriorating system isn't patched up, then rebuilt, several authorities warned.[37]

A 77 percent decline was found in the number of new mathematics teachers in the previous decade.[38] In 1981, 43 states out of 45 in a survey reported a shortage of math teachers.[39] It was not unusual to find professional leaders such as Bill Aldridge of the National Science Teachers Association using "a catastrophe" to describe the fact that 30 percent of those who did teach science and mathematics were underqualified.[40]

President Reagan followed through on the 1984 presidential election issue of education by pledging in his State of the Union Message to upgrade science and math instruction; but many educators faulted the administration for not doing enough.

> The clamor in Washington for increased productivity and strategic superiority, critics suggest, should lead to considerably more federal support. "Even if the Soviet Union didn't exist, our science education is still badly out of whack," charges James Rutherford of the American Association for the Advancement of Science. "What kind of a country puts computers in arcades but not in a physics classroom?"[41]

As the above suggest, and as Michael Apple has demonstrated, the eighties witnessed a collapse of public confidence in the ability of the state and educational institutions to make 'correct' decisions about what should be taught in schools or how to teach it.[42] 1983 became the "Year of the Report on Education,"[43] as numerous government and professional groups both created and tried to fill the vacuum of 'solutions' to the developing national crisis. This was, of course, nothing new. Every decade or so in American history has witnessed the appearance of education reform reports calling for public attention to critical problems with the nation's schools. However, the reports of the early eighties seemed to demand a more substantial response proportionate to the degree of crisis they purported to reveal. As Harry Passow asked,

> Why this burst of activity on the part of such diverse groups at this time? Why so many panels, commissions, and study groups? Some 29 different ones participated in the Wingspread Conference in November, 1982. . . . Since reform reports have been issued regularly for almost a century, why should the reforms called for be expected to be implemented at this juncture in our educational and national history?[44]

These questions are especially interesting considering the absence of novelty in the content of reform encouraged by the reports. As John Goodlad pointed out at the time,

> The "obvious" and "logical" solutions to the schools' curricular inadequacies being bandied about today are those that were most frequently bandied about yesterday and the day before that. Essentially, they involve a "get tough" approach combined with a dose of elitism. Course requirements in basic subjects are to be extended; textbooks are to become "harder," with less watering down to the lowest common denominator of student abilities.[45]

The power of these arguments in the early 1980s came, however, from their placement in a populist call for rectifying the disastrous results of government 'intervention' in the public institutions of the nation, and a call for parental involvement in educational policy decisions. Apple noted a dramatic increase in the local censorship of a wide variety of books and materials for classroom use, a substantial increase in the number of Christian fundamentalist schools throughout the country, and a resurgence in home schooling. Moreover, the conservative political right had been successful in mobilizing considerable numbers of people around seemingly anti-statist (e.g., centralized government) themes. For example, one of the major victories of the conservative political movement was "to shift the blame for unemployment, for the supposed breakdown of "traditional" values, and for tensions within the family *from* the economic, cultural, and social policies and effects of capital *to* the school and other public agencies."[46]

Apple also noted a "fracturing of the previous consensus over education," which altered some of the major long-term educational alliances. In the past, minority groups, women, teachers, administrators, government officials, and legislators had often acted together to propose social democratic policies for schools, such as expanding educational opportunities, developing special programs in bilingual or multicultural education. Peculiarly, the new multiplicity of responses in the 1980s had the ideological function of presenting the appearance of contested views on the nature and purpose of education within an extremely narrow conception of schooling as training for the technological workplace. The 1984 presidential election, for example, out of which came the notion of the 'education president', provided a spectrum of 'opinions' in the public space, all of which were steeped in the discourse of discrete competencies, technical knowledge, and empirically verifiable abilities. We heard nothing of alternative visions of pedagogy (critical and reflexive, aesthetic and imaginative, democratic and empowering) and were left with "the pervasive valorization of positivist values in the statements of these political leaders," which "reif[ied] this view of education—that is [made] it 'natural' and the only possible version of educational practice."[47] According to Apple, the new alliance of power combined industry with the 'New Right': "Its interests are less in redressing the imbalances in the life chances of women, people of color, or labor, and more in providing the educational conditions necessary both for capital accumulation and for returning us to a romanticised past of the 'ideal' home, family, and school."[48]

This was a massive shift concerning the appropriate approach to educational problems in the United States. Reformers of the seventies had enlarged the scope of educational issues to include informal learning, education in nonschool settings, and the sociological ramifications of schools in terms of generational segregation. The point had been to shift the emphasis from comprehensive schools to comprehensive education, arguing that the confines of one building were no longer enough to contain all of the valuable and necessary experiences for young people.[49] Reform reports of the

1980s returned to the simplicity of a "strong curriculum,"[50] and to the enlistment of parents in the education process.

Several educational policies and proposals illustrated the power of the new alliance Apple identified. Recommendations for voucher plans and tax credits hoped to make schools more like the idealized free-market economy.[51] State legislatures throughout the country made attempts to "raise standards" and mandate both teacher and student "competencies" and basic curricular goals and knowledge.[52] The decade witnessed increasingly effective attacks on the school curriculum for its antifamily and anti-free enterprise bias, its "secular humanism," and its lack of patriotism.[53] And, particularly, there was growing pressure to make the needs of business and industry into the primary goals of the school.[54]

As Edelman has noted, most academic writing accepts the same view of the link between social problems and attempts to solve them as public officials like to espouse: As problems appear, responsible agencies search for the best way to cope with them. The emphasis is on the rationality of the search process, even if it is bounded. But, Edelman writes,

> the striking characteristic of the link between political problems and solutions in everyday life is that the solution typically comes first, chronologically and psychologically. Those who favor a particular course of governmental action are likely to cast about for a widely feared problem to which to attach it in order to maximize its support.[55]

Following Edelman, I suggest the problem of gender differences in mathematics performance and participation was bound up in the problems to which 'solutions' such as voucher systems, raising standards, and meeting the needs of business were 'responses'. In other words, there was a clearly perceived concern over the lack of discipline in schools, the lowering of quality and standards, the poor quality of teachers, and especially declining economic, moral, and intellectual results.[56] As Apple noted, while it was not necessarily the case that these 'conditions' were actually deteriorating, the 'solutions'—rationalizing, standardizing, gaining greater economic and ideological control of teaching and curricula—assumed the worse.[57]

Public concerns about education were crystalized in official documents and reports sponsored by the federal government. One excellent example is the Report of the National Commission on Excellence in Education, *A Nation at Risk.* "In language that leaves no room for the false hope that our educational system is working,"[58] the report's authors declared:

> Our nation is at risk. Our once unchallenged preeminence in commerce, industry, science, and technological innovation is being overtaken by competitors throughout the world. This report is concerned with only one of the many causes and dimensions of the problem, but it is the one that undergirds American prosperity, security, and civility. We report to the American people that while we can take justifiable pride in what our schools and colleges have historically accomplished and contributed to the United States and the well-being of its people, the educational foundations of our society are presently being eroded by a rising tide of mediocrity that threatens our very future as a Nation and a people. What was unimaginable a generation ago has begun to occur—others are matching and surpassing our educational attainments.
>
> If an unfriendly foreign power had attempted to impose on America the mediocre educational performance that exists today, we might well have viewed it as an act of war. As it stands, we have allowed this to happen to ourselves. We have even squandered the gains in student achievement made in the wake of the Sputnik challenge. . . . we have, in effect, been committing an act of unthinking, unilateral educational disarmament.[59]

The same declaration also was found in publications particular to mathematics education. For example, *Counting on You*, a document from the Mathematical Sciences Education Board, placed its recommendations within the context of a "momentum for change in U.S. education," which necessitated "Our National Challenge."

> U.S. students should be first in the world in mathematics and science achievement by the year 2000. So states the fourth of six national education goals set in 1990 by the President and the governors of the 50 states. This special focus on mathematics and science reflects a growing awareness of their direct impact on:

The quality of the nation's work force—its ability to function well in an increasingly technological work place.

The ability of business and industry to compete effectively in the international marketplace.

The ability of each of us to carry out our roles as worker and citizen in a world increasingly shaped by mathematics, science, and technology.[60]

The authors of this report noted elements of a crisis in their concern for "national well-being." Students were described as lagging far behind pupils of other nations in achievement; and too many of these students were seen to be leaving school without having acquired the mathematical and scientific literacy necessary for the workplace.[61]

National reports on education in general, and about mathematics specifically, thus indicated a shift in the terrain of debate. Thus, it is possible to place the sudden proliferation of concern for girls' and women's participation and achievement in mathematics within the context of a discourse that evolved from the expression of a more social democratic concern to the language of efficiency, standards, and productivity. It is also possible to interrogate the connections between concerns about female achievement and participation and the ways in which it might have been more acceptable to make these into 'news' while equally relevant comparisons of achievement and participation by race, ethnicity, class, or urban demographics went unnoticed. These concerns were underplayed by both educators and the media as long-standing problems; they were thus not worthy of the label news, nor were larger issues of democracy and empowerment conceived of as foci for a consensus for action across the country. The national reports should also be understood, then, as constitutive elements of the cultural production of the indicated ideological shift.[62]

In this respect, the 'failures' of female students in mathematics, whether located in the students or their teachers, was conceivable as an act of economic or military aggression against the United States as a nation. Repeated comparisons of mathematics performance with that of other countries continued to bring home the crisis component of the nation's failures. When coupled with the identification of a new social order dominated by high technology and international economic competition, and which demanded greater mathematical literacy than previous eras, the crisis assumed paramount importance. In 1987, for example, tests found no single high school in Chicago with an average score as high as the lowest average in three cities in China and Japan; "the best individual Americans were not even close to the best Asians." Compared with foreign students, U.S. middle schoolers performed "fairly well;" but even so, their geometry rated among the bottom 25 percent of 20 countries. Calculus became an important symbol of curricular rigor in this decade, because college-bound students typically studied the subject routinely, while merely one-fifth of such American students did so;[63] this helps clarify the connection between issues of gender and the failures of mathematics education practice and the relevance of the Escalante myth to potential solutions.

In 1989, James Coleman, an "eminent sociologist," spoke in Congress:

> The United States is virtually outside the range of science achievement in . . . developing countries. . . . This is a problem which . . . could turn the United States from the most affluent . . . into a less developed country.[64]

In 1990, Andrew Kupfer wrote in *Fortune* of an even more serious crisis to come:

> As the world turns ever faster on its computer-imaged, digitally controlled, microprocessed axis, companies increasingly need a numerate and technophilic work force. What they face is this: According to a 1988 study by the Educational Testing Service, 58 percent of American 13-year-olds cannot solve simple scientific problems, like predicting which way a plant will bend when exposed to light; 62 percent spend less than one hour a week on math homework. The National Science Foundation estimates that the U.S. will suffer a shortage of 700,000 scientists by the year 2010.[65]

### Liberal Feminist Research: A Professional Context

Mathematics education can be understood as a practice that was influenced by the rhetoric of crisis and declining economic power, even as its own language and actions were constitutive elements of the ongoing development of this ideological context. The issue is not whether mathematics educators "bought into" a good or bad ideology, or whether they mislead themselves or their students. Certainly, many educators may have understood their professional language and actions in terms of serving their students. But the particular ambiguity between (liberal, feminist) goals and the ideological milieu allowed these educators to support various rhetorical positions in order to obtain ideological and financial support for their own practice. Thus, it was possible for Brush and Fennema to describe inequity or injustice in terms of economic opportunities (e.g., preparation for the job market) and to place the 'problem' of gender differences within a wider terrain of national concern (or 'crisis').[66] Nevertheless, the research focus on internal influences and variables attributable to individual students did not necessarily enable the further theoretical investigation of gender within the parallel and more encompassing social and cultural realm. Schooling itself was not understood as taking place within a complex social, cultural, and economic context. It seems that education was conceived of largely as a service supplied by the government to all children as a preparation for the job market, and a service to business, providing workers prepared for the available jobs.

By introducing the concepts of ideology and practice, I am following a form of analysis distinct from the liberal feminist theory that underlies much of the work on sex-role stereotyping in schools. I find much to agree with in Kathleen Weiler's *Women Teaching for Change*,[67] which stands out as a unique manuscript published in the United States in the 1980s. In her discussion of feminist analyses of gender and schooling, she confirms Edelman's study of how policies articulated as responses to problems are commonly inconsistent and ineffective because of conflicting material and ideological interests. Edelman notes that the construction of problems thus helps perversely to perpetuate or intensify the conditions that are defined as the problem. In the case of liberal feminist approaches to gender in schooling, theorists outlined and exposed sexual bias in curricular materials and schools practices. Their focus had been on the reform of both texts and practices and on government policies toward education; classroom ethnographies and analyses of textbooks emerged from this tradition as well. Indeed, traditional feminist work had been important in documenting biases and distortions. But, as Weiler points out, liberal feminism also had its shortcomings in its narrow focus on texts and institutional structures. "It has tended to ignore the depth of sexism in power relationships and the relationship of gender and class," she writes.

> Because this approach fails to place schools and schooling in the context of a wider social and economic analysis, it does not analyze the constraints under which the process of schooling actually takes place. Moreover, the liberal approach omits any class analysis and thus ignores not only differences between middle-class and working-class girls and women, but ignores the oppression of working-class boys as well.[68]

Weiler agrees with Madeleine Arnot, who earlier wrote, with respect to the British case, that the implication appears to be that girls should match the class differentials of educational achievement and access to occupations that boys experienced:

> Equality of opportunity in this context therefore appears to mean similar class-based inequalities of opportunity for both men and women. Or, one could say, equal oppression.[69]

As Weiler notes, discussion of gender without class or race (etc.) "blurs" one's understanding of how categories of difference are manifested in and through practice.

The implicit argument about gender in most research had been that changes in texts and pedagogical practices would lead to changes in social relationships, and that girls and boys would then be equal (within capitalist society). Sexism thus seemed to exist as a concept within the realm of ideas: If the ideas could be altered, then the social relationships would follow. Weiler is helpful here as well. She notes how such a view ignores the constraints of the material world and the various forms of power and privilege that work together in a complex and mutually reinforcing process to make up social reality as it is known. Because the commonsense or liberal feminist view also ignored the complexity of consciousness and the existence of ideology and culture, it had been of limited analytic value in investigating the complexity of the social construction of gender in schools and in their intersection with other social and cultural institutions.

## Gender as News

How can we begin to assess the role of ideology and culture in the construction of gender? One route is via the realm of mass culture. Here we can examine gender as a signifier in public discourse, and the interaction of expert and public discourse in general. Indeed, as gender entered professional discourse, research and its conclusions were actively reported in popular media. Popular journals and newspapers thus helped establish gender difference as a social problem in the public space. Reading them now helps us to comprehend the particular discursive introduction of gender difference. As in my reference to national reports and professional publications, popular journal and newspaper discussions of mathematics and gender are both a measure of how and to what extent these topics are elements of public discourse yet also part of the cultural process of creating the problem of gender in mathematics education itself. Indeed, this role of public media did not go unnoticed by mathematics educators. For example, Zalman Usiskin, director of the University of Chicago School Mathematics Project, consultant to numerous mathematics education efforts, and keynote speaker for a large number of education conferences, gave a speech in 1983 at the International Conference on Mathematics Education. "Lesson 4" for the mathematics education community was that "results of research, when picked up by the news media, can have great impact upon mathematics education."[70]

Yet there is more to the media than simply reporting on 'facts' determined by research. Newspapers, television, radio, and popular journals interpret expert research and conclusions selectively in terms of what they consider constitutes 'news'. As Edward Said has written, the media "cover" a subject by portraying it, analyzing it, and giving instant courses on it; consequently, the media make the subject "known." But this coverage of news, often translated into its relevance to some crisis demanding the nation's attention, is misleadingly full. It "give[s] consumers of news the sense that they have understood," for example, the relationship of gender and mathematics education, "without at the same time intimating to them that a great deal in this energetic coverage is based on far from objective material." All the while, the topic at hand becomes reified as an object, real and stable, which exists "out there" where it ends up being intimately related to something like our national economic interests.[71]

I do not view news as an account of events to which people react. Rather, as Edelman states, news is an instantiation of political developments as creations of the publics concerned with them.

> The spectacle constituted by news reporting continuously constructs and reconstructs social problems, crises, enemies, and leaders and so creates a succession of threats and reassurance. These constructed problems and personalities furnish the content of political journalism and the data for historical and analytic political studies. They also play a central role in winning support and opposition for political causes and policies.[72]

That final role is often obscured by the assumption that people, including scholars and journalists, are observers of 'facts' whose meanings can be accurately ascertained by those properly trained and motivated. Likewise, citizens who are informed about political developments through the media would then be presumed to be more capable of protecting and promoting their own and the public interest. On the contrary, whether events are noticed and what they mean depend upon observers' situations and the language that reflects and interprets those situations. "A social problem . . . is both an entity and a signifier with a range of meanings that vary in ways we can at least partly understand."[73] Political entities such as the social problems that are most influential upon public consciousness and action are in this way "fetishes": "creations of observers that then dominate and mystify their creators."[74]

Whether or not a condition "is" a social problem "hinges," according to Edelman, "on whether a sizeable part of the public accepts it as one." In the conventional view, the news 'about' a social problem provides information that enables people to act in some rational way. In the view generally accepted by students of discourse and of political language, however, social problems "construct the social reality to which people respond and help construct the subjectivity of actors and spectators as well; in the process, they reinforce established power structures and value hierarchies."[75]

Gender had already been associated with mathematics in the media long before the 1980s. In the 1970s, particular attention to the importance of mathematics for girls and women by feminists added a new social dimension to the previous research focus on abilities and psychological (i.e., individual) attributes of females.

Thus Lucy Sells, a California sociologist, reported in 1974 on entering freshmen at the University of California at Berkeley. Of the males, 57 percent had taken four years of high school mathematics; only 8 percent of the females had the same amount of math preparation. Sheila Tobias, who pointed to Sells' report as the crucial impetus for her own celebrated work on women and mathematics, summarized the implications of the Berkeley findings as follows:

> Without four years of high school mathematics, students at Berkeley were ineligible for the calculus sequence, unlikely to attempt chemistry or physics, and inadequately prepared for intermediate statistics and economics. Since they could not take the entry-level courses in these fields, 92 percent of the females would be excluded from ten out of twelve colleges at Berkeley and twenty-two out of forty-four majors. Instead, they would be restricted to the "feminine" fields: humanities, guidance and counseling, elementary education, foreign languages, and the fine arts. All other options were foreclosed even before these women arrived at Berkeley.[76]

Previously, a common feminist argument had been that a popular preference and esteem for technical, scientific, or mathematical work was simply one other way in which to lower the status of women. It was argued, moreover, that the continuing occupational segregation of women was due to the tracking of females into the people-oriented and helping professions, because such occupations seemed to them and their colleagues to be most appropriate to their female (mother, wife, decorative object) roles. As Sells' work indicates, the 1970s witnessed a shift among some feminists from socialization arguments, which rendered women as passive objects, to the choices and actions women make early on in life. Such choices were still seen to be informed by social expectations; but the focus on women as actors enabled the theoretical perception of effective change strategies.

Tobias, a provost at Wesleyan University in Connecticut, thought seriously about the significance of mathematics avoidance by women, and conceived of a new form of mathematics therapy for those anxious about mathematics:

The possibilities excited me even more than the problem, for if we could get to the bottom of math avoidance
and find a way to demystify mathematics, we might not
only change the pattern of occupational segregation but
challenge some long-standing notions about sex difference in overall ability. Even the most recent and comprehensive review of sex differences, published in 1974, still
presented mathematics ability as sex-linked. If we could
demonstrate, instead, that incompetence in mathematics is learned in conformity to sex-role expectations,
then we might be able to design effective compensatory
programs for women and girls. And this might affect not
only female choice and female performance but also
female mental health.[77]

Thus began the creation of "math anxiety" clinics, first at Wesleyan, and later across the country. The point was "to convince
[people] that their fear of mathematics was the result and not the
cause of their negative experiences with mathematics, and to
encourage them to give themselves one more chance."[78] By 1978,
Tobias' book, *Overcoming Math Anxiety*, had made a splash in the
media, and the term "math anxiety" became an accepted description of a particular malady needing the attention of educators.

Soon, however, Tobias began to reconsider anxiety and avoidance, encompassing her feminist concerns within a larger interest
in notions of competence, pleasure, and power in mathematics and
science.

The feminists sounded the alarm. But, as a result, people
of both sexes are beginning to reassess their mathematical potential.[79]

Thus a gender-specific term became increasingly generalizable to
men as well as women. Tobias was no longer sure that it was a feminist issue by the time her book was published. "Observing men,"
she wrote, "has shown me that some men as well as the majority of
women have been denied the pleasures and the power that competence in math and science can provide."[80]

However, the "feminist" flavor of math anxiety, and the application of anxiety and avoidance mostly to females, persisted. In the
media, the subtle generalizability to both sexes was sometimes evi-

dent, sometimes not. Jane Byrne, for example, wrote a 1980 *New York Times* article using the universal 'he' to describe a math-anxious person.[81] Yet Patricia Lund Casserly, a researcher working at the Education Testing Service, was profiled in the *Los Angeles Times* in the same year as "solving the equation of math anxiety . . . in young women and girls."[82] Instead of studying why girls were not encouraged to develop skills in mathematics, or why they "clutched" years later as adults, or why their numbers were dramatically fewer than boys in advanced high school mathematics courses, Casserly examined some schools in which "these things were not happening." None of the schools had specific programs to encourage girls in mathematics. "They just expected women to do as well as men . . . They hadn't been reading the literature." Casserly identified the key to an absence of math anxiety among high school females as a correlative absence of any forms of discouragement of them from taking advanced mathematics courses. Thus, while Casserly's research noted a lack of gender differentiation in schools that neither presumed nor constructed notions of gender differentiation, both she and the news about her work identified her findings as pertinent to a prior agenda concerned with solving a 'problem' of gender inequality in mathematics. The "study show[ed] women [were] equally qualified." Yet the reporting of the study referred to Lucy Sells' previous work as foundational for the more recent efforts of Casserly and others, and grounded 'math anxiety' within the possibly marginalized, 'feminist' goal of achieving equality between the sexes. Math anxiety was another name for an historically female 'problem'. Math anxiety among males or the implications for a man associated with this 'feminine' label were not discussed.

Casserly, who had not "formally studied" the origins of "female math avoidance," was nevertheless quoted as an authority on the subject; indeed, her distance from the research establishment seemed to render an implicit "folk authority."

> Girls were socialized to believe they didn't need math, or couldn't do well, or it was unladylike. . . . There were also great differences in the kinds of information girls were getting from counselors. Now, it's become a bad habit in the culture—anytime a woman doesn't have the math background she needs, people label it 'math anxiety' and

treat it like a pathological disease. And if there's one thing women don't need, it's another disease.[83]

Tobias had mentioned in her book the success her math anxiety clinics had had with large numbers of men as well as women. But a 1982 *Newsweek* article entitled "Curing Math Anxiety" told the story of "symptoms familiar to millions of girls and women":

The ciphers on the blackboard blur, a defensive somnolence sets in, the mind goes blank—until the only computation that makes any sense is the number of minutes till the end of class. This fear of figures is known as math anxiety, and it causes many high-school girls to abandon math and science after completing the bare minimum of courses required for graduation. For nearly a decade, feminist educators have fought the widespread assumption that women are inherently less capable of excelling at math.[84]

The article reported how a program at Mount Holyoke College in Massachusetts helped "girls"—mostly college juniors and seniors—try to undo years of bad experiences in a mere six weeks.

In general, however, the 'feminist' message of the seventies—that girls and women could, if given the chance and if encouraged to do so, do as well in mathematics as boys and men—seemed to have become the dominant 'story' in newspapers and popular journals by 1980. For example, *The Detroit News* reported in April that "girls could equal boys at math," according to a national study performed by researchers from the Education Commission of the States.[85] The same study was mentioned in the *Los Angeles Times* as discovering a rising trend of female enrollment in advanced mathematics courses, suggesting a future with more women in such male-dominated professions as science and engineering. Thirteen-year-old girls in 1978 outperformed boys in computation and spatial visualization, were equal in problem solving, and at least equal in other areas. The report argued against "traditional" views of mathematics "as basically unfeminine . . . (and) a male domain; women supposedly shy away from the deductive thought required by mathematics in favor of aesthetic beauty and deductive thought."[86]

It was thus a tremendous shock when Camilla Benbow and Julian Stanley of Johns Hopkins University reported findings in the journal *Science*, which they interpreted as evidence in favor of a biological basis for differences in mathematics ability by sex.[87] For this 1980 article, Benbow and Stanley had collected data on "mathematically precocious youth"—"intellectually gifted" seventh through tenth graders participating in several talent searches. They reasoned that the girls and boys in their study had received identical formal instruction in mathematics. Hence, they argued, consistent differences between the females' and males' standardized test scores could not be attributed to varying opportunities to study mathematics, i.e., differential course-taking, as was typical in later grades. Moreover, seventh and eighth graders were seen to hold consistent attitudes toward mathematics. Benbow and Stanley based their research on SAT tests, which were designed to measure "mathematical reasoning ability," rather than achievement. According to their data, boys scored consistently higher than girls, demonstrating superior ability; and the best scores, far above the rest, were persistently obtained by only boys. They suggested that a possible explanation might lie in a superior male ability in spatial tasks, which they linked to mathematical reasoning.

The Benbow and Stanley article was rapidly reported as news. Basically, the message was that 'boys are better than girls in mathematical reasoning'. An examination of newspaper article titles alone indicates an overwhelming declaration of this 'fact'.[88] The researchers urged educators meanwhile to accept the possibility that something more than social factors could be responsible. Many women "can't bring themselves to accept sexual difference in aptitude," Benbow was reported to have said.[89]

> "You can't brush the differences under the rug and ignore them," said Camilla Benbow. . . . "That's not going to help the girls. We've got to accept it and see what we can do to make the situation better.[90]

She contended that the differences had been apparent for some time, but that most people had tried to ignore them on the grounds that they are caused by social factors.

Benbow and Stanley specifically refuted the hypothesis that test score differences by gender had been the result of differential course-taking. They also noted that the girls in the study "like[d] math just as much as the boys" and did not believe that mathematics would be less useful in their future careers than those of the boys.[91] This suggested that attitudes toward the subject could not explain test score or participation differences. However, the portrayal of the importance of this study across newspapers and news magazines was done within the context of a straightforward nature-versus-nuture debate about the mathematics ability of girls and women. Contrary to the recent National Commission Report, most of the news articles on the Benbow and Stanley article emphasized that girls simply had not been able to perform as well as boys in mathematics. *Newsweek* asked, "Can girls do math as well as boys? All sorts of recent tests have shown that they cannot," they answered. *Time* noted that boys and girls did equally well until about the seventh grade; but this equality vanished, according to general knowledge, in early high school, when the emphasis shifted from simple computation to mathematical reasoning; at this time "the boys tend to pull ahead and stay there—through college and in later life." "Boys are generally better in math reasoning ability than girls," stated *The Detroit News*, which reported that "the differences cannot be explained by social factors such as attitudes toward mathematics or course variations." According to the *Los Angeles Times*, the *Science* article was "a major volley in the continuing academic battle over the extent to which boys and girls differ naturally and the extent to which they become different at the hands of society."

The new research was reported as "challenging the view" that differences were due wholly or in great part to the "sex-based training girls get at home and school, which leads them to think math is a 'boy's subject' and not very feminine."[92] Elizabeth Fennema, known for her articulation of the course-taking variations hypothesis, was quoted by *The New York Times* as the single example of those voicing disagreement, and this disagreement was expressed as grounded in the issue of genetic differences versus socialization. She was mentioned as well in *Time*, as coauthor with Julia Sherman of an article that concluded that "sexual stereotyping of mathematics as a male domain operates through a myriad of subtle influences from peer to parent and within the girl herself." "That theory," wrote *Time*, "meets its strongest challenge yet" in the study reported by Benbow and Stanley. According to *Newsweek*, "the study's conclusions [drew] fierce objections from those who believe[d] that the environment, not genes, is the culprit." This was despite the fact that the researchers themselves had apparently admitted (in the same article) that they could not rule out "other environmental explanations." Nevertheless, detractors were consistently labeled as those whose work had been based in the unquestionable 'truth' of the socialization factors. Mary Gray, a mathematician at American University, was quoted in the *Time* article to the effect that too little was known about mathematical reasoning to conclude that genetics plays a major part. Surely a female mathematician had much at stake in the claim that her ability was likely to be lesser than her colleagues. Others, too, had developed careers around the assumption of 'social factors'. Sheila Tobias, "the feminist author of 'Overcoming Math Anxiety,'"[93] belittled the use of tests as a measure of ability. Stephen Ivers, research director for the College Entrance Examination Board, had spoken of the rewards given to girls and boys for good performance. Judy Genshaft and Michael Hirt had published a study earlier in the year about encouraging girls to do better in mathematics. And the more than 130 colleges that had begun 'math anxiety' programs were mentioned.

> Yet the dispute continues, because the two sides see the problems differently. Benbow and Stanley contend that scientists should first determine the source of sex differences in math ability. If the differences are environmental, they may be able to be eliminated; if they are genetic, we must learn to accept them. Their critics, on the other hand, insist that it is impossible to learn the true source of the disparity as long as males and females are not treated equally.[94]

The battle lines were drawn: All discussion of gender issues in mathematics education would be slotted into the appropriate side in the 'culture' versus 'genes' debate. Caryl Rivers, a professor of journalism at Boston University, concisely articulated this debate in a May 1981 *New York Times* article.[95] She called the Benbow and Stanley conclusion a good example of the "Great Leap to Genes" that had been making a strong comeback. Some scientists had been speaking of genes as responsible for certain sex or race differences, wrote Rivers, when in fact they had little evidence for their conclusions. She listed a series of objections to the swift dismissal of culture found in the Benbow and Stanley "wave of the hand." More importantly, however, she questioned how the results of their study had been received and interpreted.

> There is a growing tendency, too, to misunderstand what test scores mean. If men as a group test higher than women as a group, this doesn't mean that all men are better than all women. A great many women perform superbly in math. But politics may be more important than test scores. Girls consistently score higher on verbal abilities than boys. Has this prevented men from becoming diplomats, writers, editors? One researcher at Hopkins said, "As a woman, I don't want to think there is something about us that does not allow us to do math like men do!" Have you ever heard a man lamenting that because of his genes he can't write a sonnet, or good ad copy?

"In fact," wrote Rivers, "the genetic argument may be a handy rationale for maintaining the status quo of the sexes and races." She feared such arguments could lead to a loss of interest in, for example, ghetto schools or special programs for girls: If they had bad math genes, why waste the money on these programs? Her concern about how biological explanations focused heavily on what women could *not* do reintroduced a 'feminist' interpretation to the perceived 'sex differences'. Would women literature professors get tenure? Would women be recruited by the foreign service? Would women editors be promoted faster than men? "It seems that having 'good' math genes doesn't help much if you don't have political power to go with them." That is, a social reading of the ways in which the differences achieve meaning within a political context was still the significant issue for Rivers. Yet such articles, while powerfully altering the nature of the debate, maintained the underlying assumption that differences existed and needed to be explained. 'Feminists' described the differences as consequences of social practices; the 'bio-scientists' searched for a physical, 'real' origin of the differences. It seemed irresolvable. Yet Casserly's study, which had found no differences in schools that did not expect or believe in them, was noted merely as a clue to the solution of the problem of differences even where there were none before or after social factors were 'introduced'.

Another quasi-feminist (and hence possibly dismissable as 'radical') explanation for 'differences' was suggested by the mathematician Mildred Goldberger in a January 1982 *Los Angeles Times* "Scientific View" essay. Goldberger posited an essentialist analysis of why mathematics as a subject does not appeal to women and girls.

> Women are concerned with the human condition, not the condition of mankind [sic] as a whole, but the particular circumstances of individual human beings. In mathematics, generalization is the name of the game. It is valuable exactly because the problems it solves have nothing to do with particular cases and the answers it gets are so all-encompassing. Women just don't find those questions and answers the important ones.[96]

Leaving aside her 'all-encompassing' and easily refuted, abstract 'generalization' about mathematics, Goldberger's views present a good example of how the popular discourse absorbed information about apparent differences in mathematics 'ability' within a larger construction of gender and gendered perspectives. Indeed, her article codified mathematics as inherently opposed to the solution of human problems. That is, mathematics was for Goldberger synonymous with a distrustful abstraction and generalization that could never develop usable answers to the important questions about individuals.

This tendency to use mathematics 'ability' in the cultural clarification of gender distinctions was also evident on the front page of *The Detroit News* in April 1982. The large headline read "BOY VERSUS GIRL." In two parallel articles, "Test finds men are better built for toting loads," and "Math ability numbers don't always add up," a strong case was made "against" girls in favor of boys. On the left, readers were informed that men make better footsoldiers than women, can carry heavier loads, and perform far better when burdened with these loads. On the right, readers were reminded of the recent debate about sex differences in mathematics. The conclusion was represented by the drawing between the two articles, which depicted a man winning a race against a woman: Each carried a backpack up a ladder.

In 1982, however, a new study seemed to resuggest that no differences could be detected. Sharon Senk and Zalman Usiskin at the University of Chicago studied 10th-graders' performance in geometry, a subject including the two skills most often associated with gender differences: abstract reasoning and spatial ability. They found no discernable sex differences and argued that Benbow and Stanley had measured performance, not ability. Stanley countered that "People are so eager not to believe that there is a difference in mathematical reasoning ability between boys and girls that all kinds of people are taking potshots." Moreover, said Stanley, the Chicago study was the one that was "irrelevant" because it tested knowledge rather than "raw ability."[97]

Fennema was again quoted as an expert. "Neither study has collected a bit of data on genetic evidence," she said; she discouraged debate over mathematical genetics, because it appeared insoluble and because it burdened one sex with an implied difficiency for which there could be no remedy. She noted as well that even Stanley and Benbow agreed that both boys and girls would achieve if given capable teaching and comparable attention. Yet the "debate" was maintained despite her plea.

Benbow and Stanley continued to issue progress reports on their research, which consistently presented the same results. Far more boys than girls scored in the highest ranges on the SAT math test, even though they were matched by intellectual ability, age, grade, and voluntary participation in the Johns Hopkins national talent searches. Most were 12-year-olds in the seventh grade. In 1983, the data covered more than 65,000 youngsters. Four times as many boys as girls were found among those scoring 600 or more. The disparity was even greater among students who scored 700 or more: only one in 10,000 12-year-olds scored that high; the study found 260 boys but only 20 girls. Smaller news articles continued to be printed in newspapers whenever some study issued findings on 'sex differences'; with each report, the contours of the debate were etched more finely. A sex disparity needed to be explained. One explanation—that there was some sort of genetic reason—was argued by Benbow and Stanley. Detractors either argued a feminist line of social factors, or pointed out potential weaknesses in the generalization of the Johns Hopkins findings. For example, the results, which were summations of data about intellectually gifted youth, might not be appropriately generalizable to average or all students: Benbow and Stanley countered that most discourse was concerned with the best females anyway.[98] The appearance was one of a 'standoff'.

Then in 1984 Benbow and Stanley reported biological explanations of their findings in the theories of Norman Geschwind, a Harvard Medical School neurologist. This news not only provided momentum for the argument that sex differences were based in genetic rather than social or cultural practices, but it also bolstered the notion that the perennial debate of nature versus nurture in human skills might finally be decided after all. In the process, public discourse cemented a distinction between 'pure reasoning'—associated with a particular cultural, yet often reified, construction of mathematical practice, and verbal skills—usually associated with interpersonal interaction and communication. The significance of these discursive distinctions is identifiable in the fact that the latest 'conclusive' findings in the debate were front-page news.[99]

Benbow and Stanley had made a connection between their own findings regarding sex differences in mathematical reasoning ability and the correlation that Geschwind had found among left-handedness, allergies, asthma and an abundance of the hormone testosterone (a male hormone) during fetal development. According to Geschwind's theory, testosterone causes the right hemisphere of the brain to become dominant, resulting in a left-handed person; he also suggests the hormone is genetically linked to immune-system disorders. Benbow and Stanley found this interesting because they believed mathematical reasoning to be controlled by the right hemisphere of the brain, which is concerned with spatial abilities. Since few girl fetuses are exposed to much testosterone in the womb, Geschwind's theory could provide an explanation for boys' dominance over girls in mathematics. Indeed, they found 20 percent of their survey subjects to be left-handed, compared to about eight percent for the general population; and almost 60 percent of their gifted test-takers had allergies or asthma, compared with 10 percent of the population as a whole. Moreover, they noted that the incidence of left-handedness and immune disorders had declined in the general population along with SAT test scores. And they further found that students whose scores were close to what chance would have given them if they had simply guessed the answers had the same incidence of left-handedness, allergies and asthma as the population as a whole.[100]

As Betty Ann Kevles wrote in the *Los Angeles Times*, "There are few intellectual pleasures so sweet as discovering supposedly scientific "proof" for something we believed all along."[101] Yet the ways in which the hormone information was reported indicates more now about the cultural classifications of knowledge and gender than it did then about the power of neurobiology to provide determining facts. First of all, it is interesting to consider why the direction of implication for the scientific results was plausible and meaningful. That is, Geschwind had noted that higher levels of the hormone in the womb result in higher incidence of left-handedness, allergies, and asthma. Meanwhile, Benbow and Stanley found that the SAT test could be used to identify a subpopulation of test-takers who would have higher levels of left-handedness, allergies, and asthma. The conclusion they suggested was that the hormone might be related. But the logic is not so automatically feasible here. It is similar to arguing that, because a person will eventually die, and because a skunk will eventually die, there is a direct connection between the person and the skunk. Thus it is important to note, as did Lynn Fox (the senior researcher on one of the Hopkins studies), that social explanations for the Hopkins differences were not sought. Fox believed that the differences could probably be explained by contrasting early learning experiences and feelings of confidence; she suggested that the SAT test measured skills developed in the interaction between school and outside experience, instead of innate ability.[102]

A second way in which the reporting of the nature/nurture debate indicates cultural classifications and their construction is in the representation of disagreements over what exactly constitutes mathematical ability. While Benbow and Stanley used the SAT test to measure mathematical reasoning ability, Senk and Usiskin, for example, insisted that most of the questions were highly dependent on outside, nonacademic experience. "They concluded that the only culture-free mathematical problems—those not dependent on the different upbringing of boys and girls in our society—are geometry proofs."[103] Note the implication that the essence of mathematics is distinguishable from culture and must be a kind of pure thought or reasoning. The discourse closed off any options for an epistemology grounded in practice, realism, material experience, ideology, or any other form of conception 'tainted' by an association with sociocultural interpretations. Of course, as I have mentioned, there has always been a tendency to narrowly define mathematics in such an idealist way. But the particular ideological function of the nature/nurture debate in this context interwove within the debate a gendered epistemology that seemed inseparable from the commonsense definition of mathematics it presumed.

This can be seen in the persistent references to the parallel data on the SAT verbal scores of the same talent search subjects that Benbow and Stanley studied. They were "uninteresting" because they were comparable across gender;[104] indeed, this fact was crucial in the argument that the gender subsamples were essentially similar despite the remarkable tendency for the highest scores to be achieved by boys. Yet the verbal scores had never been significant when girls had outscored boys. That is, nobody ever tried to suggest that an overabundance of testosterone in the womb might cause linguistic performance difficulties in later life. Nor did anyone search for answers to the particular problem of declining female verbal scores in the seventies.

Tobias often suggested that, to retain "different" kinds of students in mathematics, at least at the college level, mathematics tests should be graded as follows: one-third credit for the right answer, one-third (elastic) credit for finding more than one way to get to that answer, and one-third credit for a paragraph-long essay about what makes the particular problem interesting.

> Although mathematicians admit that "going from an answer to a question" is the real stuff of mathematical thinking, rarely did I find a mathematics instructor favorably inclined to adopt my grading system. It didn't take them long to realize that a student could get the right answer, do it the "right way" and get no more than 40 percent credit, i.e., flunk! But students outside mathematics, students who dislike or are fearful of mathematics, invariably found the idea attractive. Many believed that they would be able to write a good essay even if they got the answer wrong. This means they have considerable confidence in their ability to locate what is "interesting" about a problem, and this very often keeps them from proceeding swiftly to an answer; they are simply too easily distracted by these "ancillary" thoughts . . . It is, I think, appropriate to point out how disappointing (even boring and alienating) it is for students of a certain temperament and mind set to deal with homework assignments and examinations that do not cause them to think "new thoughts."[105]

Such gaps in the research agenda are surprising in light of the virtual explosion of theoretical work during this period in the area of mathematics as a language. For example, an entire issue of *Visible Language* was devoted to such an approach to mathematics education in 1982.[106] What is significant here is the fact that language-oriented forms of pedagogy and evaluation were not suggested as appropriate, given the discrepancy between the sexes when current methods were used, and given the pervasive decline in verbal scores in general. While writing or reading across the curriculum gained prestige in this period, its strategies were absent from the debate over gender differences and from most mainstream mathematics education efforts.[107]

We can see how this might have made a difference for the construction of gender by noting the results of British research attending to language and discourse in mathematics education. The Girls in Mathematics Unit at the London Institute of Education examined the early learning experiences Fox had considered in her comments identified above. They found that the children themselves were already actively involved in the construction of gendered identities by the time they were in the preschool and kindergarten classes under observation. They also noted that the teachers in these classrooms interpreted student actions as gendered when they might not have been by the researcher, suggesting that early socialization within identical curricula was indeed plausible and in fact existed at least in some classrooms. Furthermore, the girls tended in these observations to switch the ongoing discourse in order to exercise power over boys; in this context, it was often possible to identify the girls as especially advanced in rhetorical reasoning skills.[108]

In another study undertaken by the same group, early elementary age, and especially working-class girls displayed abstract reasoning and logical skills not usually considered possible for children of this age, but which are extremely valuable later in advanced mathematics beyond arithmetic. Nevertheless, some experts noted, for example, that women are at a disadvantage with arithmetic word problems because "they require active interplay of word and image."[109] Still others noted the ways in which the ability to perceive ambiguity in meaning within the phrasing of a word problem could be a source of difficulty for those with higher verbal skills.[110] Oddly enough, word problems, which require complicated verbal 'ability', were often considered the highest level of mathematical

ability, and the level at which the sex differences begin to surface.[111] But feminists who had read Carol Gilligan noted that the
decontextualization evident in the canonical word problem literature worked against the use of discursive meaning in favor of a typically male form of linear logical reasoning.

The 'problem' seems to be that girls quickly learn that such
skills with discourse are not appropriate for school mathematics,
but that carefully following directions and keeping their work neat
are highly valued in early mathematics. Later, these very skills are
taken as indicators of a lack of innate ability, whereas the boys' willingness to challenge the teacher and create verbal arguments
begins to be identified as a sign of ability and cleverness. In the end,
the very project of becoming a girl winds up being caught up in a
switch of meanings about teacher authority, epistemology, and the
politics of knowledge.[112]

Moreover, the tests themselves, and the SATs in particular,
seemed to be selectively applied to the 'problem'. For example,
while the girls consistently outperformed the boys on decimals,
and the boys outperformed the girls on fractions,[113] nobody suggested that boys should be discouraged from careers in accounting.
Eleanor Smeal, president of the National Organization for Women,
charged that SAT tests were intentionally designed to be more difficult for women, because: "Something had to be done to make it
look objective rather than discriminatory in excluding women
from scholarships and other educational opportunities despite the
fact that women and girls had better grades."[114] Meanwhile,
increasing numbers of women were "studying and excelling in
medicine and engineering."

This returns us, then, to Tobias' early insight that the actions
of the girls themselves, in the creation of their own identity as girls,
and in making use of cultural practices toward this end, had as
much to do with the 'fact' of unequal numbers of girls and women
electing advanced courses in mathematics as the cultural circumstances in which they took place. Indeed, as has been noted, a
counter-discourse evolved in this period, in which people began
focusing on the reasons why all students were hesitant to study science and mathematics, and how this hesitancy contributed to a
generally low level of numeracy and scientific literacy across the
nation. The identification of mathematics as a 'hard' pure subject
with intangible rewards for hard work was one reason cited. The
notion of a subject as 'hard work', as it intersected with the dis-

course of social factors leading to sex differences, also fed into gendered conceptions of mathematics and the role of mathematics in the construction of identity. For example, according to one participant in a math anxiety clinic in 1987, "Girls are expected to be dainty and not work hard. And because math is hard work, a lot of them consider it unfeminine."[115] And in 1992, Mattel's talking *Barbie* doll claimed, "Math is hard." Interestingly, Mattel's tie-in marketing campaign with McDonald's *Happy Meals* offered a choice of *Hot Wheels* toy cars or miniature *Barbies*. Buyers of these meals were asked whether they wanted a "boy's" meal or a "girl's" meal and were given the car for a boy or a *Barbie* for a girl. These meals came in bags with *Hot Wheels* and Barbie theme-related activities on different panels. *Happy Meal* bags help parents justify purchasing the meal, because they have 'educational' puzzle activities on them; this particular month, the *Barbie* side of the bag had social interaction activities while the *Hot Wheels* side featured puzzles.

A greater interest in what students perceived to be the financial and personal benefits stemming from a business career also contributed to a gendered perception of mathematics in the formation of identity. This ironically codified mathematics as a pure, culture-free discipline, detracting from individual business interests even as it was identified with the interests of busines, the economy, and the larger social scale.[116] Finally, because mathematics was organized as a cumulative discipline, any absence from the subject meant permanent derailment. Hence, despite the recognition by Tobias and others that many women and men with 'math anxiety' (or who chose to 'drop math' at some earlier point in their lives) were later able to teach themselves the required mathematics they now needed, the commonsense perception was that school mathematics early in life was the only chance someone would get to learn mathematics. Furthermore, the most ideal form of mathematical education was presumed to be of a general nature; specific skills tied to employment were to be applications of the general mathematical skills honed in school, rather than learned and mastered in job training, apprenticeship, or as one adapted to the requirements of one's employment.

I suggest that the focus of is misdirected. While most people examine the middle-school years, in which sex differences suddenly become apparent, and during which young women make life-forming decisions about their further mathematical education, we might benefit from studies of the two ends of the educational lifespan. As the work of the Girls and Mathematics Unit in Britain highlights, greater attention to the very early preschool and early elementary years of mathematics are crucial. Similarly, the later work of Sheila Tobias has noted an important "second tier" of people who might be encouraged to pursue mathematics and science as adults if these fields were altered to be more alluring. It is at these sectors of curriculum development and alternative pedagogy that the most beneficial reflection can be made.

Regarding the notion that mathematics can and should be made more appealing, Pat Rogers has examined college mathematics departments with significant success in attracting women to their courses.117 At Potsdam College in New York State, for example, at least 20 percent of all bachelor's degrees were awarded in mathematics in four straight years, compared with fewer than 1 percent in North America. For the period 1980–85, there was an increase in the number of mathematics degrees by 152 percent, compared with 45 percent overall in the United States. In 1983, more than 60 percent of Potsdam's mathematics degrees were awarded to women, as compared with 43 percent nationally; and in five of seven years studied, the top graduating student in the college as a whole was a female mathematics major.

When Rogers attempted to identify some reasons for Potsdam's success, especially considering that the department had no female professors and had established no special programs for women, she needed to borrow, like Walkerdine and the Girls and Mathematics Unit, the language of power and discourse. She saw the key to success in the ways in which power was used to help students find their own voices and become independent of the need for a teacher. As Rogers noted, the authority of teachers generally resides in the fact that they control the transmission of skills and knowledge both in form and content. They also typically control the means and methods of evaluation.

> In the case of mathematics teaching this power is further enhanced by students' mistaken beliefs and myths about mathematics. Most important among these is the notion that teachers possess a great deal of knowledge which can be obtained only from them and which they will impart only if the student obeys the rules.118

The traditional presentation of mathematics, through textbooks and polished lectures or presentations, where the mathematics is made to appear finished, absolute, and a predigested product, might have much to do with mathematics avoidance. "A pedagogy that emphasizes product," writes Rogers,

> deprives students of experiencing the process by which ideas in mathematics come to be and perpetuates a dualistic view of mathematics in which right answers are known by authorities and are the property of experts. Such a pedagogy strips mathematics of the context in which it was created and is probably largely responsible for creating student' misconceptions.[119]

Meanwhile, power in the presentation mode resides with the speaker, and few students are able to cultivate their own voice. However, there are marked gender differences within our culture in relationship to authorities: While males are encouraged to challenge authority and receive support for maintaining their own voice, females are commonly encouraged to subordinate their own voice to that of authorities and are far less likely to maintain a sense of their own autonomy. Thus, the 'operating procedures' of much of mathematics education could be called 'masculine'. This has little to do with the epistemology of mathematics or the necessity of schooling; rather, it has much to do with traditional forms of mathematics pedagogy. Because "power in mathematics resides in those who have knowledge of process," writes Rogers, pedagogies that encourage and lovingly support the creation of student voices are able to help their students become independent of their teachers, as opposed to needing them for approval or for confirmation. The Potsdam faculty were noted for

> true acceptance of the students they have rather than the students they might wish they had (I heard no complaints of the "If only we had better students!" variety); . . . having their students model as "expert" [in front of the class] and trusting them to learn from experience; . . . teaching students how to read mathematical literature; . . . encouraging collaborative learning and peer tutoring; and . . . respecting the students'

ultimate right to personal responsibility for their own learning.[120]

Ironically, however, Rogers returned to the traditional narrative of an individual 'superteacher' in her description of the relevant qualities of the Potsdam faculty. An especially 'successful' member of the department, called "Dr. Alan," is described as an empowering teacher, but also as a "model father." Much like Jaime Escalante, this superteacher holds very high expectations for his students, demands that they live up to these expectations, and makes it possible for them to do so. The conflation of empowerment with male models of power (e.g., 'father') and the implications for mathematics, power, and identity will be addressed in the following chapter. Here it is important to note that women teachers were the focus of a number of newspaper articles and television documentaries in the early 1990s. But regardless of their uniqueness or talents, these female teachers were not represented as superteachers; they served as generalizable examples of new trends in mathematics education designed to counteract declining test scores and the perceived widespread innumeracy.[121] The discursive practice does not seem to allow female models of successful mathematics teaching to be 'super'. (Nevertheless, I refer to these female teachers as 'superteachers' myself in chapter (-1), and encourage others to consider whether or not that is a 'good' discursive strategy.)

Other approaches to the project of making mathematics 'more appealing' indicate how the initial identification of relevant features influences the language of change. In 1993, Janice Leroux and Cheeying Ho begin with the "greater focus of interest for parents due to the growing technological orientation of society."[122] They further borrow the rhetorical argument that mathematics is a "'critical filter' which determines entry into a host of careers requiring mathematical skills." Hence, they develop strategies for encouraging more females into the gifted mathematics program in the city of their research study, despite their own proclamation of "consistent findings of equal enrollment in the mathematics classes as well as equal achievement reported by both the students and the teachers."[123] The results of this research include the identification of female 'deficits' in comparison with a male standard (e.g., more nervousness and anxiety when taking tests, greater social stigma attached to the gifted program suggesting need for higher risk taking, poorer access to resources requisite to the program such as transportation to particular locations), and an adjustment of the content of mathematics in order to accomodate the 'needs' of female students (more discussion and feelings, a transformation of instructional methods so they become more meaningful to "females' ways of thinking").[124] In comparison, there is recent interest in single-sex mathematics and science classes.[125] These classes give girls the chance to excel when they do not need to compete with boys; they also potentially increase the enrollment for these subjects by making the appeal of the courses to the female market more of an issue. The net result is to maintain the male-based norm and deficit model.

## Coda

Thus, it is indeed possible to find within the constructed problem of gender differences in performance the new problem of attracting and retaining students. The new project can easily start at the early years and conclude with the later stages of schooling or ongoing educational experiences throughout the life cycle. However, as Tobias also recently observed, we should be careful about the responsibility we hold for this project. In the midst of the impending shortfall in mathematical and scientific literacy, there might be merely an imagined need rather than an eventual real need for people highly articulate in mathematical discourse. "Like the American Medical Association," she wrote, "the profession feels it is better served by keeping standards high and members few."

> Mindful of the devastating effects of the oversupply of physicists in the 1970s, a situation which drove many good Ph.D.s permanently out of the field, many physicists tell me mournfully, "there has never been a time when there were too few physicists." What they may be thinking is this: Until and unless there is a palpable increase in demand for working scientists, the shortfall remains a prediction and not yet a reality.[126]

After a decade of fears about the rising technological supremacy of Japan and (West) Germany, how sure can we be now about the demand for mathematically literate people on the job market? Tobias warns there is a clear need for more science (and hence . . .

mathematics), but not necessarily a need for huge increases of unemployable mathematically literate workers. More importantly, we might want to examine the demand, instead of the supply, of workers.

# (-1)

# Consumer Culture:
# Power and the Identity Politics
# of Mathematics Education

So don't try to dis it.
Just heed the word
as I serve
geometry on the board.

Now let's get to the core of the problem;
Queen Math Teacher is the solver. . . .

To the altitude
multiplying part to part
makes it come out smooth.
The groove
of the leg is almost the same;
whole to part
and it gets mad sane (sane).


The curriculum is the curriculum, but it's the way you
deliver the curriculum that counts.[1]


A remarkable transformation occurred in the discursive practice of
mathematics education in the 1980s. It is hard to trace the origin
of this change; but its impact can be assayed in 'official' professional practice as codified by position documents of the National
Council of Teachers of Mathematics, in the mainstream promotion
of 'power' as a central driving concept. The Council's "Commission
on Standards for School Mathematics" published in March 1989 its
*Curriculum and Evaluation Standards for School Mathematics*, and in
March 1991, its *Professional Standards for Teaching Mathematics*. The
*Evaluation Standards*, for example, "address[ed] the ways in which
students integrate . . . connections [among concepts, procedures,
and intellectual methods] intellectually so that they develop mathematical power."[2]

The use of the word 'power' is stunning. As I indicate in chapter 0, power is a complicated concept with varying interpretations. It also had been found up to this point only in writing primarily by left and radical academics. Its translation to professional policy in the late 1980s was therefore surprising. And its presence furthermore allows the examination of the link suggested by Saussure between the sign and the signifier. For the meaning of 'power' as intended by the National Council is not necessarily the same as that promoted by those academics who had used the sign previously.

Because I suggested in chapter 0 that 'power' would be an important conceptual tool in the reconstruction of mathematics education, it is important to analyze this discursive turn. However, as I demonstrate in this chapter, the Council's notion of power does not quench my own theoretical thirst for a power-centered practice of mathematics education. By developing power in terms of teachable skills and attitudes, the Council continues to construct professional practice inattentive to the implications of its own role as a 'technology of power'. It furthermore reproduces those dualisms of individual/society and school-knowledge/popular culture that I perceive as problematic. Nevertheless, as I will explicate, the discursive entry of 'power' into public discourse through professional policy statements might provide a unique opportunity for a more efficacious reconstruction of practice. In other words, 'power' serves as the point of articulation joining current professional discourse with my own argument for a popular culture approach to mathematics education.

Taken out of context, the Council's meaning of "the development of mathematical power for all students" displays what Maxine Greene[3] suggested as the ambiguity essential to all good slogans. As rallying symbols, they may be adapted by a variety of groups that conflict on fundamental goals for, and conceptions of, school in society:

> Mathematical power includes the ability to explore, conjecture, and reason logically; to solve nonroutine problems; to communicate about and through mathematics; and to connect ideas within mathematics and between mathematics and other intellectual activity. Mathematical power also involves the development of personal self-confidence and a disposition to seek, evaluate, and use quantitative and spatial information in solving problems

and in making decisions. Students' flexibility, perseverance, interest, curiosity, and inventiveness also affect the
realization of mathematical power.[4]

Now what might this mean for 'power'? If power is a scarce commodity, as is money or cultural capital, then mathematical knowledge needs to be distributed among social and economic classes,
age groups, races, genders, and so on.[5] The primary question might
be just how to distribute this power to 'all students' equitably; but
such an approach would likely cloud the relationship between how
much power one 'has' and the ability to label something as mathematical knowledge. Occasionally this way of thinking also contributes to a sort of reduction of mathematics to numbers and arithmetic because these areas are most readily apparent as associated
with power. As Rudy Rucker writes,

> In daily life the concept of number is tied up with vari-
> ous kinds of power. Putting together a business deal, a
> machine, or a scientific experiment involves knowing
> the relative numbers. "Having someone's number"
> means having control over them, and it is just this kind
> of number-based control that makes civil libertarians
> fear the growth of governmental data gathering.[6]

If consent holds power together, however, then power can never be
the property of an individual.[7] In this case, power only exists as
long as a group stays together. This might be what the Council
means when it writes of classrooms as "mathematical communities" rather than simple collections of individuals.[8] The Council
might agree with J. Glenn Gray that a group constructs a sense of
community which provides to each member an access to power
and a feeling of importance and self-worth.

Maxine Greene's attempt to fuse Foucault and Hanna Arendt
in a notion of power as 'actions that structure the field of possible
actions' provides a contrasting political vision of classrooms as public
spaces inextricably linked at once to the existential project and social
change. Here power is more closely tied to a discourse of possibility.

Rucker contrasts the 'power' of numbers with the 'freedom' of
space. Instead of the "static patterns" of numbers, Rucker applauds
how space suggests the "possibilites of motion." He characterizes
standard mathematical numbers as growing out of the notion of

counting various types of collections; this can suggest owning or controlling. Space, writes Rucker, is an expression of smooth change. "Our knowledge of space comes not from reading, but rather from moving around"—from our own interaction and simultaneously transformations of it.[9]

Jesse Jackson's 1984 presidential campaign introduced power into public discourse, as noted in chapter 0. Here education became directly connected to a politicized reading of inequality across subgroups. Similar discursive constructions were evident in, for example, editorial pages of African-American newspapers. Dr. Conrad W. Worrill, Chairperson of the National Black United Front, wrote in the *Chicago Defender*: "It should be obvious to all observers and participants in the education of African American children that skill proficiency in math and science is important to our survival."[10] Worrill argued that mathematics and science are crucial to preparation for the high-tech jobs of the twenty-first century, while "the foundation of Western curriculum was and still is, based on the notion of white supremacy," so that African-American students must also be clear on their identity. Harold E. Charles, like Worrill, insisted on the potential in the African-American community for high achievement in mathematics, because of the historical precedent that literacy and numeracy originated in Africa.[11] Both men stressed a concern about illiteracy among African Americans, since the National Research Council had warned that "innumeracy threatens democracy because people who understand math will join a technologically powerful elite."

We can read the meaning of power in professional mathematics education, however, in the National Council of Teachers of Mathematics' re-examination of education goals.

> All industrial countries have experienced a shift from an industrial to an information society, a shift that has transformed both the aspects of mathematics that need to be transmitted to students and the concepts and procedures they must master if they are to be self-fulfilled, productive citizens in the next century.

But, more importantly,

> The educational system of the industrial age does not meet the economic needs of today.[12]

Here we find the Council's standards based on four "new social goals for education: (1) mathematically literate workers, (2) lifelong learning, (3) opportunity for all, and (4) an informed electorate."[13] In other words, the fundamental image of 'power' for the Council is an engine: feed the workers so that they may run the economy; provide lifelong maintenance, so that the engine is a long-term investment; make use of all components, so that none may be wasted. The metaphor breaks down only for the last goal, and only if we presume to add the adverb 'critically'.

> 1. *Mathematically literate workers.* The economic status quo in which factory employees work the same jobs to produce the same goods in the same manner for decades is a throwback to our industrial-age past. Today, economic survival and growth are dependent on new factories established to produce complex products and services with very short market cycles. It is a literal reality that before the first products are sold, new replacements are being designed for an ever-changing market. Concurrently, the research division is at work developing new ideas to feed to the design groups to meet the continuous clamor for new products that are, in turn, channeled into the production arena. Traditional notions of basic mathematical competence have been outstripped by ever-higher expectations of the skills and knowledge of workers; new methods of production demand a technologically competent work force. The U.S. Congressional Office of Technology Assessment (1988) claims that employees must be prepared to understand the complexities and technologies of communication, to ask questions, to assimilate unfamiliar information, and to work cooperatively in teams. Businesses no longer seek workers with strong backs, clever hands, and "shopkeeper" arithmetic skills. In fact, it is claimed that the "most significant growth in new jobs between now and the year 2000 will be in fields requiring the most education."[14]

> 2. *Lifelong Learning.* Employment counselors, cognizant of the rapid changes in technology and employment patterns, are claiming that, on average, workers will change jobs at least four to five times during the next twenty-

five years and that each job will require retraining in communication skills. Thus, a flexible workforce capable of lifelong learning is required; this implies that school mathematics must emphasize a dynamic form of literacy. Problem-solving—which includes the ways in which problems are represented, the meanings of the language of mathematics, and the ways in which one conjectures and reasons—must be central to schooling so that students can explore, create, accommodate to changed conditions, and actively create new knowledge over the course of their lives.

3. *Opportunity for all*. The social injustices of past schooling practices can no longer be tolerated. Current statistics indicate that those who study advanced mathematics are most often white males. Women and most minorities study less mathematics and are seriously underrepresented in careers using science and technology. Creating a just society in which women and various ethnic groups enjoy equal opportunities and equitable treatment is no longer an issue. Mathematics has become a critical filter for employment and full participation in our society. We cannot afford to have a majority of our population mathematically illiterate: Equity has become an economic necessity.

The Council's goals also have particular meaning for the construction of 'identity', most visible in its general goals for all students:

(1) that they learn to value mathematics, (2) that they become confident in their ability to do mathematics, (3) that they become mathematical problem solvers, (4) that they learn to communicate mathematically, and (5) that they learn to reason mathematically.[15]

Presuming for the moment a linear connection among these goals, the obtainment of mathematical power, and finally the new social goals for education, we should ask just what this might mean for students. Should they accept current social and industrial trends as given and unmalleable, expecting the insecurity of a future filled with repeated job changes and the fear of unemployment due to a lack of competitive, ongoing retraining and skill updates? Should they satisfy demands for more years of schooling? Such demands are in many ways responses to the relatively recent increase in access opportunities for oppressed groups to high school and college diplomas; that is, the greater demand for certified education is possibly a form of 'hidden' racism and sexism following an oversupply of workers at previously acceptable qualification levels. At the same time, this contributes to the role of schooling and school mathematics in the construction of identity and knowledge even as many skills are unique to the task at hand and thus best learned on the job.

The work of Valerie Walkerdine was introduced in previous chapters precisely to emphasize the need for a continued rethinking of the history and object of mathematics education. Walkerdine's argument is particularly important because her analysis of practices undermines the theoretical base of 'the child' (or 'the student') as a 'rational unitary subject'. I reiterate an outline of her thoughts here, because they are vital to a discursive shift in the meaning of power. She starts with Cline-Cohen's history of mathematics education as one of 'calculation', pointing out that calculating the population to be governed and the idea of a calculating population (assisting the running of government and the emerging capitalist system) were intimately linked.[16] She continues by noting how this came to be extended, and to a certain extent supplanted, by the idea that bourgeois democracy was to be upheld, not by a coercive pedagogy, but by a 'natural' pedagogy of love, in which reason would unfold.

> Reason was to become the goal of a technology designed to provide reasoners who could govern and those who might, at least, be hoped to be reasonable, not pushed to rebellion by a repressive and coercive pedagogy. In that sense, then, such an approach is profoundly critical of any kind of universalism which understands reasoning as a quasi-natural phenomenon and the development of reasoning as following a pre-ordained naturalistic sequence ending with 'abstract' reasoning. The latter, while being a-historical, is also oppressive of the Other, the subject whose development does not appear to accord with the natural progression. Difference, in other words, becomes deviance and pathology.[17]

I recommend with Walkerdine rather different conceptions of power and identity than those offered by the National Council. I favor a formulation of power most recently rearticulated by Michel Foucault: a physics of power instead of an economics of power. Here power is understood as a property of all relationships, similar to gravitation among physical bodies. My notion of identity grows out of recent feminist theorizations on the multiply stranded nature of identity and subjectivity, theorizations that emphasize the politics of identity. For mathematics educators, attention would be drawn to the ways in which mathematics and mathematics education practice discursively construct possible fears and fantasies, contributing to the ongoing creation of identities that form an individual; the conflicts among these identities are crucial. In this analysis, all practices produced in and of the history of mathematics education become locations for the production of subjects. The 'regulated child' becomes a discursive position produced in the practices themselves. The representation of 'qualified workers' similarly drives educational practice even as educational practice clarifies this representation.

## From Critical Literacy to Popular Culture

Returning to the Council's fourth new educational goal, an 'informed electorate', I posit an opening for a more critically sensitive approach to mathematics education. "In particular, citizens must be able to read and interpret complex, and sometimes conflicting, information."[18] I add the creation of mathematics by citizens as well, in everyday life in addition to the workforce. In this respect, the relationships among popular culture, professional discourse, and 'the forces of commerce and profit' are highly problematic. For professional discourse in mathematics education, a stark association heavily weighted toward commerce and profit seems clear, as I have noted throughout this work. We might argue that this is the case because the (incorrectly) perceived immutability of mathematics makes it more likely to be consumed as a 'commodity' (a completed object to be accepted passively) than as a 'cultural resource' to be used. As John Fiske notes, "a number of important theoretical issues underlie the differences between a user of a cultural resource and a consumer of a commodity (which are not different activities, but ways of theorizing, and therefore of understanding, the same activity)."[19]

Mathematics and mathematics education swim in a murk of late capitalism characterized by commodities—"it is awash with them," writes Fiske, "it would be impossible to escape them, even if we wanted to." It is plausible, then, that we should be concerned with understanding commodities and the role they play in our cultural and political life, and there are a number of ways of doing so.

> In the economic sphere they ensure the generation and circulation of wealth, and they can vary from the basic necessities of life to inessential luxuries, and by extension, can include non-material objects such as television programs, a woman's appearance, or a star's name.

Fiske uses torn jeans to illustrate the difference between the material and cultural functions of commodities; building on his analysis, we can adapt these terms to the study of mathematics and mathematics education.

> The material function of jeans is to meet the needs of warmth, decency, comfort, and so on. The cultural function is concerned with meanings and values. All commodities can be used by the consumer to construct meanings of self, of social identity, and social relations. Describing a pair of jeans, or a TV program, as a commodity emphasizes its role in the circulation of wealth and tends to play down its separate, but related role, in the circulation of meaning. . . . [20]

If you, the reader, do not see an immediate connection to the view of 'mathematics' or 'parts' of mathematics as commodities, I have two suggestions. First, consider the role of mathematics in the creation and use of commodities, especially pervasive technological commodities. Second, consider the use of mathematics in the 'meaning' of nonmaterial commodities. In either case I propose the implications would only be expanded and elaborated. I indicate in this book how one can approach mathematics education in these terms through, for example, the commercial success of the life story of a great teacher of mathematics. Jaime Escalante became the subject of a mainstream Hollywood film and a profitable biography;

John Allen Paulos wrote a best-selling book and successor volume on the abysmal level of numeracy in the United States.

Further illustrations can be found in later chapters of this book as well. Problem solving and profit were inextricably linked on and off television, as discussed in the case of professional discourse and television game shows; curriculum mirrors consumerism as consumerism mirrors problem solving. Front-page news stories about the biological basis of the 'battle of the sexes' in mathematics ability helped sell numerous newspapers across the country (just as television sitcoms as in the *Donna Reed* episode mentioned in chapter 0 used the 'battle of the sexes' to help sell products advertised in commercials). I draw your attention moreover to the 1991–92 season of CTW's *Square One Television*, which, after successfully spoofing television genres in its initial season, began featuring commercials specifically designed to 'sell' various branches of mathematics, including algebra, statistics, and geometry. Indeed, the season premier, a two-hour prime-time episode of "Mathnet"—a popular sequence spoofing *Dragnet* found daily on *Square One*—became the pivot of a Sunday night pledge drive to 'sell' public television to its viewers. Most simply, however, mathematics is persistently advertised and sold as the key to success, on the job market and in social status.

## Mathematics as a Cultural Resource

The construction of mathematical power to be bought or won through schooling "emphasizes its role in the circulation of wealth and tends to play down its separate, but related role in the circulation of meaning."[21] It becomes difficult even to imagine mathematics as a cultural resource. In the research literature, the closest examples we have are in the work of Jean Lave on the mathematics of grocery shoppers or dieters.[22] In popular culture, the clearest illustration is the use of the variable $X$ by Malcolm X as a statement about identity in the aftermath of slavery and the institutionalization of racism. Even here, though, the resource is easily a commodity. We now have X-caps, X-shirts, X-jewelry, "X"-Brand potato chips, and so on; Malcolm's estate is in litigation over the royalties to the use of his name in the marketing of this paraphernalia.[23]

The difference of emphasis—money or meanings—carries with it a corresponding difference in the notion of 'power'. As Fiske remarks, the commodity-consumer approach places power with the producers of the commodity (factory owners, mathematicians/ mathematics teachers), because they make the profit out of its manufacture and sale. In one reading, the consumer gets to enjoy the benefits of the product (jeans, mathematics). A more critical reading describes the consumer as exploited insofar as the price he or she pays is inflated beyond the material cost to include as much profit as the producer is able to make. The exploitation can even take on a second dimension, as when the consumer is also a member of the workforce and so finds his or her labor exploited to contribute to the same profit.

Whether conservative or progressive, such a reading, when it begins to consider meaning, does so, according to Fiske, "through a theory of ideology that again situates power with the owners of the means of production." In the case of jeans, Fiske suggests someone might argue that jeans are so deeply imbued with the ideology of white capitalism that no one wearing them can avoid participating in it and therefore extending it. By wearing jeans we adopt the position of subjects within that ideology, become complicit with it, and therefore give it material expression. We "live capitalism through its commodities, and, by living it, we validate and invigorate it."[24] Even in the case of Malcolm's "X" the meaning might be lost in the process of commodification; it is less clear to us, either because we are still living the politics, or because the reading really is ambiguous.

We find similar arguments concerning ideology and power by some ethnomathematics proponents, who lament the imperialism of Amero-Euro-centric mathematics on, for example, Native Americans who perceive the world in an entirely different space-time frame,[25] or Africans whose mathematics is literally 'lived' in their own bodies.[26] Munir Fasheh is the most convincing of this sort of reader of mathematics and culture. He dramatically communicates the politics of 'Orientalism'[27] as implicated in the practice of teaching Palestinians 'Western' mathematics and its associated conceptions of identity, rationality, and technology.[28]

I agree with a parallel view of culture suggested by James Clifford. "The 'exotic' is uncannily close." But, at the same time, for those of us in the United States, there are no longer any distant places where the presence of 'modern' products, media, and power cannot be felt. "Cultural difference is no longer a stable, exotic otherness," writes Clifford; "self-other relations are matters of power and rhetoric rather than of essence. A whole structure of expectations about authenticity in culture and in art is thrown in doubt."

> Twentieth-century identities no longer presuppose continuous cultures or traditions. Everywhere individuals and groups improvise local performances from (re)collected pasts, drawing on foreign media, symbols, and languages.[29]

It is easier to register the loss of traditional orders of difference than to perceive the emergence of new ones, as Clifford notes. I suggest we adapt his 'ambiguous' yet attractive 'Caribbeanization of Culture', a creolized 'interculture' modeled after the 'neologistic' cultural politics of Aimé Césaire.

Such a culture, however, destabilizes the identification of 'intention' in power relationships, because any commodity can become a resource for political action. Fiske believes the producers and distributors of jeans do not 'intend' to promote capitalist ideology with their product: They are not deliberate propagandists. "X" crafts people further problematize the relationships expressed, because the politics of the X is what is so powerful in the marketing of the products, thus commodifying political action as well, even as consumer culture is politicized. I am not sure, however, that we can problematize mathematics educators in the same way. Many clearly argue the crucial importance of school mathematics for a capitalist economy; others, such as Bob Moses in his Algebra Project, intend to proselytize a particular form of the 'mastery of reason' within a local 'interculture'. The realization for us is that 'intention' need not be a focus of our investigations. The 'system' or 'the way things are' establishes commonsense notions of 'good' goals, which in a strong sense regulate the field of possibilities that can be imagined for practice; interrogating the naturalization of common sense is more crucial than placing blame.

'Reason' is an excellent example of this kind of commonsense naturalization of ideology. As Walkerdine writes, "the government of reason works by assuming both that reasoning is natural and that some sections of the population are themselves profoundly unnatural."

> Those Others, such as the working class, women, the mad and colonised peoples, were understood as being

less civilised and more animal, especially as when, in
some accounts, reason was understood as the highest
pinnacle of an evolutionary sequence of development.[30]

She traces femininity and reasoning from early accounts of
women's sexuality, that claimed the womb as the site of madness
and unreason—the very fact of the possession of a womb made
women unsuited to reasoning. Today we have arguments about a
lack of male hormones.[31] The idea of a natural femininity antithetical to reasoning is repeated again and again in data on gender differentiation in performance: girls' hard work and rule following are
compared with boys' natural talent or curiosity.

'Reason' is linked to 'power' by the National Council through
the cultivation of mathematical and logical thinking. It is through
this connection that the above sort of construction of difference
becomes an outcome of practice as a 'technology of power'. Developmental approaches to mathematics education provide further
examples of power implicated through practice as opposed to
'power' as an object produced in students. We are confronted continually with children and "difficult-to-teach" adults who do not fit
and who are often understood as somehow "both over-mature and
underdeveloped." A four-year-old middle-class white girl does not
understand that a window cleaner cleaning the windows of her
home has to be paid; she becomes for Tizard and Hughes[32] an
example of the 'power of the puzzling mind', in contrast to those
children who do not yet 'puzzle'. Several working-class children do
not puzzle over money; this is acknowledged by the researchers but
left unaccounted for in their description of the "generic four-year-
old."

> We must assume that it cannot possibly be the case that
> *they* could be more developed or that this evidence ques-
> tions the whole notion of a universal sequence of devel-
> opment itself.[33]

Walkerdine challenges a number of other research-based theories
as well. Williams and Shuard remark that 'exchange value' is an
'abstract concept' beyond the grasp of young children; they coun-
terpose abstract to concrete, but fail to engage with the idea of
'lived' practices and relations. Yet Terezinha Carraher and her colleagues give numerous examples of the skills of "third world" chil-

dren far ahead of their "first world" peers.[34] Finally, Walkerdine has argued extensively "that mathematics provides a clear fantasy of omnipotent control over a calculable universe, which the mathematician Brian Rotman called "Reason's Dream," a dream that things once proved stayed proved for ever, outside the confines of time and space."[35]

Analyzing mathematics education, then, in terms of discursive practices, raises the problematic nature of 'power' and 'intention' in a new light. It is not the point to find a scapegoat to blame for the propagation of 'reason'; but it is imperative to understand the origins of reason as a fantasy. This intellectual twist avoids the conflation of empowerment with traditional (often gendered) models of hypostasized power 'held', 'hoarded', or 'spent"; empowerment instead has more to do with imagined possibility (both 'good' and 'bad') than potential application or release. In other words, if we emphasize the study of commodities, we can become mired in pessimism, because the economic system (which determines mass production and mass consumption—of jeans and mathematics) reproduces itself ideologically in its commodities, whether indirectly or directly. A commodity is ideology made material. And ideology works in culture as economics does in its own sphere: It naturalizes the 'system' so that it appears to be the only one possible. An emphasis instead on cultural resources promotes readings that allow for agency on the part of subjects.

Where, then, can we find mathematics as a cultural resource? Fiske looks for a "refusal of commodification . . . an assertion of one's right to make one's own culture out of the resources provided by the commodity system."[36] This is Clifford's open and uncertain "local futures." Wearing torn jeans. Metaphorically 'tearing' or disfiguring the image of Judy Garland in order to create a heroine for the gay community in masquerade.[37] Similarly, we can look to a group of Minnesota college students who appropriated probability to form an alternative culture of fantasy games that later became known as *Dungeons and Dragons*.[38] We can consider the note-passing of eighth-grade girls in a mathematics classroom. They rate each potential class 'hunk' in a variety of categories, on a scale from one to 10, while also ranking the categories themselves; later, they determine their ideal boyfriend while simultaneously disappointing their teacher with their mathematics performance on tests.[39] Or the rigidly geometric and repeated patterns of skinheads and punks in 'alternative' dance clubs.[40] The symmetry of the 'peace sign'.

At these junctures, it is clear how mathematics can be part of what Fiske calls "excorporation," the process by which the subordinate make their own culture out of the resources and commodities provided by the dominant system;[41] Clifford's "compost for new orders of difference."[42] In an industrial society, this is central to popular culture, since virtually all resources available are those provided by the subordinating system. Because there is no 'authentic' folk culture to provide an alternative (as in Munir Fasheh's mother's weaving), popular culture is the "art of making do with what is available." This means that the study of popular culture requires not only the study of the commodities out of which it is made, but also the ways that people use them. Hence, the examination of how *Stand and Deliver* became implicated in a language about the role of meaning of school mathematics and, most importantly, the teacher of mathematics, needs to be enriched in further work by an examination of how people 'read' and transform this text. Such work would examine what this text might have meant for Latino identity, popular films originally sponsored by Public Television, the plausibility of films 'about' mathematics, or congressional support for CTW's *Square One Television*, which uses popular television and music video formats to foster an attraction to mathematics, much as Escalante used Latino culture to appeal to his students.

### Danger

I submit that a popular culture form of mathematics education enables consideration of such issues, while at the same time concerning itself with content and method: the content is the method. Furthermore, such an orientation addresses the politics of mathematics education via the centrality of mathematics conceived as a cultural resource. One theoretical danger that should be mentioned, however, is located in the conceptual terrain of 'incorporation' and 'containment'. These signs refer to the proposition that the vitality of groups is found in "the ways of using, not in what is used."[43]

Manufacturers quickly exploit the popularity of ragged jeans by producing factory-made tears or by "washing" or fading jeans before they are sold. This is a process of adopting the signs of resistance. They are incorporated into the dominant system and robbed of oppositional meanings; by depriving subordinate groups of the means to 'speak' their opposition, this theory suggests the opposition itself is lost. Containment occurs when controlled gestures of dissent are permitted to function as a safety valve; by coping with dissenters, the dominant system is strengthened. Foucault in fact argued that a certain minimal level of such dissent is necessary to the maintanence of the system, in order to clarify the borders of appropriate and inexcusable behaviors. Hence torn jeans and X potato chips become another range of commodities; they extend and enhance consumerism.

Similarly, *Dungeons and Dragons (D & D)* became a corporation for Dave Arneson and Gary Gygax. Teenagers were able to buy pre-planned fantasies and miniature theme-toys that weakened the element of imagination by allowing them to gaze upon the action rather than role-play it themselves. Probability was prepackaged so that no one knew what was behind the system of determining outcomes within the game. *D & D* clubs sprouted as officially sanctioned organizations in high schools around the country, thus containing the alternative quality of the subculture.[44]

The danger lies in the pessimism and lack of agency constructed by such a theory even of cultural resources. Thus, repeated comparisons of mathematics performance with that of other countries casts females as commodities, or commodified resources, to be bought by potential math courses, either on the remedial level, or at the advanced level—as potential workers in a new, increasingly mathematical industrial terrain. However, persistent attention by some educators to the need to "sell" mathematics to young people as a key element of cultural capital, i.e., as important job skills, enables an ongoing attempt to understand how school mathematics might have to change to "trick" female students into taking more of "it" in school. In the latter sense, 'women' as signifiers become crucial change agents in the field of professional discourse even as all women are, in the general public discourse, represented as lacking an essential biological maleness necessary for accomplishment in mathematics.

Regarding the consumer, then, it becomes important to question the nature of what is being consumed: The important issue for mathematics education is whether educators want to emphasize those aspects of mathematics that establish the subject matter as a commodity, or whether they choose to imagine it as a cultural resource. Mathematics tends to be perceived as a commodity mostly because common sense tells us it's a kind of platonic body of predefined already existing "stuff" to be used or sold as valuable on the job market. But if we could switch over to a focus on mathematics as a cultural resource, we might have a very different kind of mathematics—one in which mathematics is an ongoing dynamic form of communication among people, and which is malleable in the ongoing creation of meaning.

Thus, when we take Walkerdine's argument about fears and fantasies being the crucial entry into an understanding of the discursive practice of mathematics education, the most compelling fear evident in the Council's *Standards* is that of admitting that the nature of mathematics itself must change. We find teachers like "Queen Math Teacher" quoted at the beginning of this chapter, insisting that the mathematics has *not* changed at all, just the delivery system for the Platonic truths. Similarly, Diane Lang, a third-grade teacher in White Plains, New York, is quoted in a *New York Times* article on new teaching methods that put math into "real life": "Math concepts are the same, but the packaging is different."[45] Actually, the mathematics *has* changed in the classrooms of these two amazing 'superteachers'. "It's not enough to have the right answer anymore. You have to explain it and use it," says Ms. Lang.

> The way you and I learned math was meaningless. I had no concrete understanding, but these children do. They have a real foundation because math is connected to everything. That's something that we weren't taught.[46]

The question is whether the change is significant 'enough'. The article that uses Ms. Lang as a preeminent illustration reproduces examples of the distinction between "Old Math" and "New Math" provided by the National Council of Teachers of Mathematics. "Traditional math instruction," according to the Council, "emphasizes memorization, drill and practice." Problems typically focused on numerical solutions rather than understanding what the numbers mean. "New teaching methods," on the other hand, "use math as a way to reason, communicate and solve real problems," which often emphasize 'hands-on activities' and 'real-life applications'. Yet, while the problems printed do powerful things, such as ask for more than one possible answer or interpretation, they tend to combine several traditional problems in one question, or dress up the old ones in new words, instead of changing the 'mathematics' they construct:

> Problem 1 . . . I have six coins worth 42 cents; what coins do you think I have? Is there more than one answer?

> Problem 2 . . . I have some pennies, nickels and dimes in my pocket. I put three of the coins in my hand. How much money do you think I have? Can you list all the possible amounts I have when I pick three coins?[47]

Again we see ideology, hence hegemony, in action. A perceived choice is constructed, between 'old' and 'new' methods of teaching mathematics. John Saxon can be quoted as articulating the alarm ("The math standards are a disaster. . . . It won't become apparent for another 10 to 12 years, at which point it will be distressingly apparent."[48]) which many experimenting teachers fear ("Parents will come to me and say: 'I learned math this way. Why aren't my children learning the same way?'"[49]). In the end it becomes too risky for the 'new teaching methods' to do anything more than change the delivery system while maintaining the time-honored objectives.

Incorporation and containment leave out, for example, the social differentiation that remains between wearers of 'really' old jeans and Calvin Klein "Sports;" of dungeon masters who design their own worlds, and kids who buy prepackaged dungeons marketed by game publishers; between 'real *D & D* players', who learned from Arneson and Gygax, or their friend and coauthor Jeff Perren, at a gaming convention, and kids who buy the published rulebook at a local store. To a great extent, who is wearing an 'X'-cap, with whom, and how and where, all are crucial to the meaning expressed. We need to avoid the tendency to ignore the complexity and creativity by which the subordinate cope with the commodity system and its ideology in their everyday lives, and the degree to which the 'dominant' underestimate and thus devalue the conflict and struggle entailed in constructing popular culture. Thus, we have the example of my college roommate: a 'C' physics student who spent his entire out-of-class time reconstructing *Dungeons and Dragons* around a new, more 'realistic' sense of probability and outcome via logarithms. This was his 'secret' because it was his key to 'selling' his game on the market; it later led him to develop computer simulations of three-dimensional, real-time flight.[50]

In the case of gender, I now foreground for myself (as an educator) the attention of Shiela Tobias on what she calls the "second tier"—people (mostly women) who either: (a) later in life see a need for developing mathematical skills for their employment or political activism; or (b) demand at the high school and college levels more satisfactory courses in mathematics. I also find myself interested in the ways in which teachers and girls at very young ages begin to establish a politics of gender via their mathematics education experiences, a politics that is only read as significant too late, by early adolescence. In both of these cases, women and girls become political actors in the construction of both gender and mathematics. In both of these cases as well, the mathematics is used in political ways by these actors to effectively establish terrains of identity and possibility. In this manner, the female 'consumer' of mathematics and mathematics education courses is inherently a political concept, so it's not surprising that an application of the concept highlights the political nature of her consumption.

Malcolm's "X" appropriates the given mathematics for new means, challenging the 'system' in obvious, overt ways. We can compare such a cultural moment with the work of Jaime Escalante in the myth of "The Best Teacher in America"; here the efforts of the superteacher undermine societal expectations for urban Latino students yet fundamentally reaffirm the existing structure of mathematics education and its implication in a society that bestows esteem, comfort, and authority to professionals trained through calculus and beyond via a college education. Educators have generally accepted 'Black English' as a dialect inextricably connected to identity to the degree that it can not be denigrated or ignored by school; yet we still have to work hard to make the comparison with, in Escalante's terms, flipping tacos versus studying calculus. A similar message is sent by recent advertisements for the United Negro College Fund (UNCF) in the prestige press. A photograph of a typical standardized test used for college admission covers almost the entire page; the camera's focus is on problem 59: "If total costs are $13,000 a year, and Dad makes $19,000, how can Mike go to college?" "This is a tough problem even for bright kids," we are told.

> It's not math or science that's keeping bright kids out of college. It's home economics. That's why giving to the United Negro College Fund is so important.[51]

At once we find the reproduction of the traditional gendered mathematics of home finances, the reification of the standardized mathematics curriculum and its placement in an accepted image of educational success, and an acceptance of existing structures of support for higher education. "Dad makes $19,000," does not begin to suggest an awareness of the family demographics of the African-American students who will be the students at UNCF colleges. And the demands of the provocative question, with the directions "solve," belie its visual context within stereotypical algebraic formulas that require one merely to "solve for the indicated variable": The answer is, of course, not to challenge the system but to continue it by giving money to the UNCF, which in turn gives money to "historically black colleges." Thus is entrenched social inequality interwoven with received notions of what mathematics 'is'. The indicated variable here has a very different meaning from Malcolm's.

In other words, I am reiterating that the commodity/cultural resource conceptual distinction is inherently political. So using it seems to force a political reading of the consumer and the mathematics. I like this, because I want to emphasize the political nature of the issues; in the case of mathematics, I think we need an antidote to the commonsense construction of it as a neutral apolitical realm. But I also think using this approach makes us more aware of the inappropriateness of conceiving of an apolitical—possibly gendered apolitical—realm in contemporary cultural studies.

De Certeau[52] and Eco[53] write of military metaphors and 'semiotic guerilla warfare' as the key to understanding popular culture and its ability to resist the dominant ideology. This may be our most useful option. "The motor for social change," writes Fiske, "can come only from a sense of social difference that is based on conflict of interest, not a liberal pluralism in which difference is finally subordinate to a consensus whose function is to maintain those differences essentially as they are."[54] I argue for such tactics in the mathematics education community—what Foucault describes as "intellectual terrorism."[55] The 'power' of 'mathematical power' that I seek as a ground of my own professional practice is not the motor of reform advocated by the National Council of Teachers of Mathematics; it is the power relations of which popular culture is always a part. Queen Teacher, for example, might rap about issues important to her students; her students might rap for each other; or, together, they might discover the mathematics of the rap music they each find most powerful or entertaining. But who chooses the words and who creates their meaning is extremely important for the politics generated by this sort of mathematics education. The point, in de Certeau's terms, is to use the commodities for subcultural purposes, to become "tricksters" who appropriate the images and pleasures of mathematics for their own purposes. Like teen "shoppers" hanging out at a local mall, the student/teacher(s) of mathematics become purveyors of a 'new order of things'. Popular culture, again in the words of Fiske, "always bears traces of the constant struggle between domination and subordination, between power and various forms of resistance to it or evasions of it, between military strategy and evasions of it."[56]

> Evaluating the balance of power within this struggle is never easy: Who can say, at any one point, who is "winning" a guerilla war? The essence of guerilla warfare, as of popular culture, lies in not being defeatable. Structural change at the level of the system itself, in whatever domain—that of law, of politics, of industry, of the family—occur only after the system has been eroded and weakened by the tactics of everyday life.[57]
>
> This approach sees popular culture as potentially, and often actually, progressive (though not radical) and it is essentially optimistic. For it finds in the vigor and vitality of the people evidence both of the possibility of social change and of the motivation to drive it.[58]

### Homage to Whitty and Young

As a measure of 'academic progress', it would be useful at this point to reread Whitty and Young from 1976.[59] Searching for a new field they called the "politics" of school knowledge, they and their contributors "share[d] a profound dissatisfaction with the prevailing circumstances and definitions of schooling, and [saw] a need to redefine the sorts of experiences which have come to be regarded as 'educational'." They began, as did this current investigation 14 years later, by being "skeptical of attempts to justify current definitions of 'education' as intrinsically worthwhile."

The 'new sociology of education' that Whitty and Young founded focused on "the ways in which teachers and pupils make sense of their everyday classroom experiences, and on how educational 'reality' is continuously reconstructed in the interaction of individuals, rather than imposed upon them by mysterious external forces."

> Linked to this change of emphasis has been a refusal to regard definitions of what counts as 'education' as somehow neutral and irrelevant to the way in which inequality is produced in school and society. From such a perspective, what secretly keeps society going is crucially the practices of individual teachers and pupils, and the assumptions about knowledge, ability, teaching, and learning, which are embedded in them.[60]

Well, eighteen years later, I am still exploring "some of the assumptions which underlie both the explicit and the hidden curricula of schooling and the contribution which they make to the maintenance of the *status quo* in society" . . . because "they show it is both the values embodied in current conceptions of curricular knowledge and the styles of pedagogy and assessment adopted by teachers, which help to sustain existing social hierarchies."[61] What have we learned since Whitty and Young articulated this path of research? I have taken seriously their challenge to broaden my conception of 'educational institutions',[62] moving beyond schools to popular culture and mass media. Here I have attempted to more firmly establish their program for analyzing the wider political context of schooling.

> We have already implied that definitions of what counts as education and knowledge are sustained, not merely by the assumptions and activities of teachers but by the ideas and actions of a whole variety of other interests in society. Given the inadequate and abstract nature of many broad theories about the relationship between education and society, it becomes important to identify quite precisely the institutional practices which produce and sustain the constraints within which teachers work. It is only in the context of such work that we will be able to develop a more adequate understanding of the nature of that relationship and generate appropriate strategies for change.

So far so good. What, then, is the next step? As these pioneers so aptly pointed out,

> the implication that an invitation to teachers to suspend their taken-for-granted assumptions and to examine critically their own practices would produce a transformation in the nature of their activities was ludicrously naive. . . . The practices which keep society going and hide the ideological dimensions of prevailing notions of knowledge from public view are not just those of the classroom, but take place within a context as wide as capitalist society itself.[63]

Like the contributors to the volume edited by Whitty and Young, I offer here some suggestions for reconstructing educational practice. I do so particularly for mathematics education within a *discursive* practice that recognizes the importance of power and identity politics.

Both theory and practice are 'discursive practices'. Hence, viewing mathematics education as a technique of power/knowledge places this particular form of pedagogical experience within a theory of relations among practices-in-setting, ideologies of practice, and institutional arenas.[64] This approach does not perpetuate a 'commonsense' separation between theory and practice, but instead makes both accessible to discourse analysis. By making both popular culture and professional discourse (including in this 'new' sense, practice) at once the subjects of analysis, it is possible to understand professional discourse as part of popular culture, and popular culture as part of professional discourse. Because popular culture always bears traces of power and its relations, recent approaches to popular culture can be accommodated to mathematics education practice to achieve comparable goals.

There are at least three facets of mathematics education practice to which popular culture studies can be applied. First, as a form of preservice and professional development, a critical interrogation of popular culture can provide an evocative orientation to school and popular mathematics. Second, popular culture studies as a form of mathematics curriculum directly confronts issues of power and identity politics, reconstructing an undifferentiated content and method. The politics of mathematics education needs in this case to become part of the subject matter itself at all pedagogical levels. Finally, as a conceptual tool kit that can be used to develop strategies that affect curricula, the identification of mathematics as a cultural resource offers new organizational principles for mathematics education. Specifically, mathematics provides a particularly good location for critical inquiry into the mathematics implicit in the technological gadgets that have become artifacts of popular culture. More generally, the direction is away from the appropriation of the pleasure of popular culture as 'motivational' in instructional contexts, and toward a focus on that pleasure itself as the content and process of pedagogy. This allows for the ways in which 'pure abstract' mathematical puzzles can be tools of pleasure as well.

Such a pedagogy destabilizes individual/society dualisms. Popular culture studies links individual pleasure (the consumption of commodities) with the social texts of popular culture (mass produced and consumed by large enough numbers of people to make them 'popular'). Identity becomes social (and political) while the individual consumption of popular culture is fundamental to its ideological function. The mere confusion of the last sentence attests to the impossibility of a distillation.

## For(e)ward

Michael Young has recently written,

> In our context, it is the loss of credibility of the old curriculum that creates the possibility for a more genuinely democratic alternative. A politically aware mathematics education . . . must recognize the contradictory nature of the circumstances that we are in and identify the forces for and against attempts . . . to overcome inequalities. A time of great change and uncertainty is also a time of possibilities—in mathematics education as elsewhere.[65]

So we are to revel in the fears of impending economic and military decline and make use of these cultural resources for progressive change. Yet it is clear from the general tone of the National Council's position papers, the construction of superteacher myths, and the propagation of 'scientific' facts that ground professional practice, that populism is not automatically progressive. There is right-wing populism, conservative populism, and so on. Indeed, the story of the 1980s is to a large degree a narrative of the rise of such populism and the relative ineffectuality of liberal and progressive concerns about subordinated people "for some control over certain aspects of their lives, in particular over their culture."[66] As I indicate in chapter 0, Svi Shapiro's call for progressive educators to seize ideological needs is central to the reconstruction of mathematics education that I seek. Fiske is helpful here as well.

> The left's concern for the interests and well-being of the powerless and the weak, and its belief that such power-lessness and weakness are the results of the social system, and not of the inadequacies of the people within it, leads it to propose a political program of social action. The right has been eager to equate any such program with an increase in the power of the power-bloc and thus a reduction of people's ability to exercise control over their own lives. The right has been able to turn this popular desire for control to its own interests by articulating it with its own ideology of individualism. It has therefore been able to construct and have circulated a right-wing set of meanings of the opposition between the people and the power-bloc, a set of meanings that are relevant to popular culture because they align people with individualism and freedom and the power-bloc with state control. By its use of popular rhetoric the right has, in the domain of party politics at least, been able to define the left as anti-popular and itself as concerned with the interests of the people, and at the same time has been able to disguise the paradoxical nature of the definition.[67]

In Shapiro's more recent suggestion for a new kind of "back to basics" that cultivates a "politics of meaning,"[68] he indicates for us how Fiske's characterization can be applied in the areas of literacy, institutional organization, moral values, and discipline. It would seem therefore that mathematics education and curriculum in general might want to start with these terrains, taking advantage of the spade work already begun. Attention to numeracy that is more than mere technical skills for economic survival but that, as Shapiro suggests, "expands the definitions employed," requires that mathematics education seek those ways in which mathematical competencies and lenses of interpretation can help people "learn to decipher and discriminate among the complex, often confusing or deceptive messages of TV advertising, and other mass-mediated images." In this manner, numeracy can be expanded into a more comprehensive realm of mathematical literacy. Latching onto the National Council's emphasis on language and

> insisting that basic skills today means communicative competence gives a transformative twist to the existing public discourse on education, rooting the basic instructional work of schools in the work of empowering young people to cope with the complexity and confusions of the contemporary social world.[69]

Similarly, if we are serious about "unlearning the culture of narcissism" to develop a more progressive approach to discipline, as Shapiro recommends, then we are required to reflect on emerging theories of mathematics as an evolving language: theories which celebrate student-talk and the constructivist techniques of building mathematical knowledge on the competencies students bring with them to school. Merely sharing one's own strategies for solving a particular problem, for example, does not automatically develop one's disposition for learning from the talk of others. And initial teacher attempts to provide the transition necessary for students to enter such classroom discourse communities can come dangerously close to the vacuous "praise" touted by recent critiques of self-esteem curricula.[70] Here is one place for a serious attempt to comprehend the ongoing contestation over the meanings of individualism.

Most crucially, mathematics educators must examine the moral dimensions of their work. In this direction, I encourage renewed attention to the field of 'Problem-Posing' and its demand for attention to the morality of "deposing."[71] Epistemological and psychological 'attitudes' become entwined in the reproduction of mathematics education practice; it is in response to such attitudes that I list the following, suggested by Stephen Brown, as a sort of manifesto for the negation of common sense at which to target our 'intellectual terrorism':

1. It is necessary to have an outside authority to judge correctness of any alleged answer to a mathematical problem.

2. There is essentially one way of solving any mathematical problem.

3. One's job is to learn what the rules are and how to follow them. Deviation from them constitutes a moral sin.

4. All problems should come clearly posed or they are either incapable or unworthy of being analyzed.

5. One's job is to solve problems if possible. Posing belongs to the realm of experts.

6. In solving problems, one's focus ought to be constantly on the questions being asked.

7. The problems stand "out there," to be solved, and are not capable of shedding much light on the problem of understanding oneself.[72]

I also draw our attention to the warning posed by Sheila Tobias at the end of the previous chapter: Are we really serving the needs of students by training them in particular algorithms if those algorithms do not necessarily translate into useful job-related skills or meaningful forms of interpreting their world? The technologicization of society does not directly force a need for technical skills on the part of individuals, and in fact, as has been mentioned, it often means a widespread technical deskilling instead. The democratization of this sort of technical knowledge is of greater consequence. Hence, we need to find ways for students to perceive the mechanisms of obscurity that function through the use of mathematical language and the political implications of that obscurity, rather than train them in mechanical techniques. For example, the rhetorical use of units of measurement in the public discussion of radiation leakage from power plants or toxic waste dumps tends to make debate useless when people cannot understand the meaning of the numbers. Television and other 'news' media provide an excellent source of material for such curricula.[73]

The argument that mathematics skills are increasingly important for the job market is therefore absurd in the light of the technological mathematization of society. Indeed, the deskilling accomplished via the demathematization, and the lack of palpable connections between school and 'real life' experience in this respect, serves a function as a technology of power. Educational practice affects changes in the expectations of pupils and their teachers, and their aspirations and attitudes as well. That is, such educational practice structures the field of possibilities, for immediate action and for life trajectories. A recognition of this function allows a link between the content of mathematics, the practice of mathematics education, identity, and the politics of mathematics education. Deciding to deconstruct the boundaries between popular culture and educational discourse is one strategy for reconstructing a mathematics education which *begins* with this link rather than noting it as an observer, making the link central to mathematics education practice *as* a technology of power.

The focal element of a popular culture studies approach to education, however, is critique, which implies the evaluation of one's own practices in relation to the differentiations (and hence inequalities or hierarchies) that they create.[74] Individualism is one example of a place where we need to suspend our faith and examine the implications of our discourse. The uncritical appraisal of school mathematics as by definition essential for a basic education is another realm we must enter; for we will have a hard time transforming the nature of school mathematics if that very nature is the keystone to an unchallengable prestige and universality. Finally, the politics of mathematics education lies in its social mobilizations.[75] Tracing these mobilizations rather than the formal qualities of mathematics education will be the next step in a progressive reconstruction.

# Epilogue/Prologue

I have taken as a metaphor for the organization of this book what is known in mathematics as a cyclic group. My chapters have an ordering; but that ordering is not necessarily best represented by the current presentation. Taking Dewey's cycle of reflective thought seriously, I end as I begin—with questions. I do believe that my questions now, as I tentatively complete this version of my writing, are richer than those I started with. But there is another sense in which the last chapter should have been read before all of the others. It is a retrospective argument for doing what I have just done, a discourse analysis of popular culture and professional practice that merges the two together. Then again, I really do not think that the argument would be as strong or as useful if placed before chapter 0. Chapter (-1) belongs for me after the substantive chapters 1, 2, and 3, and before the 'introductory' chapter 0.

Keeping in mind the concern of my work for how mathematics is implicated in the construction of identity and knowledge, it is important for me to note how the labeling of my chapters with mathematical signs determines signifiers that group constellations of meanings. As I do so, I create a particular positioning of myself as viewed by the reader as well as a certain conception of my book as knowledge. Thank you for your indulgence. I hope you enjoy(ed) reading my book, and I encourage you to explore popular culture studies as a vehicle for educational research and practice.

## Questions

(0) Having destabilized the 'educative' qualities of formal and informal education, that is, having sublated the in-school/out-of-school dualism, what, then, is the role of formal schooling in terms of mathematics education? Using mathematics as a cultural resource in school would be the flip side of using school mathematics as a cultural resource outside of school. I see the work of Jean Lave and Terezinha Carraher as important with respect to the latter social practice. But I do not see much work being done in the former.

Hence, the placement of the video game *Tetris* or the Nintendo game *Yoshi's Cookie* in an arcade, a home, or a classroom introduces serious issues and questions. It may be best to 'flip-flop'.

(i) I believe 'power' and 'identity' can be focal signs for the introduction of a 'popular culture studies' approach to mathematics education. I believe as well that the approach and these specific terms would not be difficult to introduce into mainstream professional discourse, both for researchers and teachers. The implication is that this could be a common language bridging theory and practice, simply because the language itself strives to bridge the artificial distinction between these terms. How would this introduction best be accomplished? I suggest that studies such as I have done are one possibility. Teachers, preservice teachers, students, and others can do just as good a job as I did—except that I have more experience, having done it. To say this is to destabilize again the 'power' relations of education itself; I am comfortable equating myself—'the researcher'—, my students, and my teacher-colleagues.

(-i) Having established 'popular culture studies' as a fruitful approach to 'mathematics education', we should now ask, what 'social texts' are most efficacious for the exploration of 'power' and 'identity'? How do 'power' and 'identity' influence our decisions in this matter? How, in the end, does the commodification of mathematics promote or devalue its availability as a cultural resource?

# NOTES

## Chapter 0

1. Jay Rosen. "No content: The Press, Politics, and Public Philosophy." *Tikkun* 7, no. 3 (May/June, 1992): 11–14+. The quote, p. 11, is taken from the November 1991 issue of the *Los Angeles Times*.

2. Rosen, 13.

3. Rosen, 78.

4. Brian Rotman. *Signifying Nothing: The Semiotics of Zero* (London: Macmillan Press, 1987); this and all quotes following: 1. As Rotman does, I follow common mathematical texts and begin with a Chapter Zero; this mimickry is at once a gimmick and a strategy.

5. Jacques Derrida has emphasized the central pedagogical problem as the time lag between inquiry and presentation. Perhaps it is the way we represent this lag that is crucially significant to our pedagogical practice. Derrida wants to limit the delay and to bring educational practice in line with contemporary epistemology—to help pedagogy negotiate the same paradigm shift that altered the arts and sciences at the beginning of our century, but left pedagogy behind in the age of Hegel. See, e.g., his article, "L'age de Hegel," *Qui a peur de la Philosophie*, GREPH [Groupe de recherches sur l'enseignement de la philosophie], trans. Susan Winnett, ed. (Paris: Aubier-Flammarion: 73–107); and "The Age of Hegel,"*Glyph Textual Studies I* (Minneapolis: University of Minnesota Press, 1986). (This is the 'manifesto' of GREPH, of which Derrida was a founding member and long-time president.)

6. Rotman, 1.

7. This is not to construct a polarity between 'expert' and 'public' phenomena. 'Expertise' itself is a social phenomenon typi-

cally used, as Robert Welker has written, "to buttress professional privilege and to widen the distance between those who know and those who do not." See his article, "Expertise and the Teacher as Expert: Rethinking a Questionable Metaphor," *American Educational Research Journal* 28, no. 1 (Spring 1991): 19–35. I will return to this issue in chapter 1.

8. Len Barton and Stephen Walker, "Sociological Perspectives and the Study of Education," in Roland Meighan  (London: Holt, Rinehart & Winston, 1981).

9. Len Barton and Stephen Walker.

10. Maxine Greene, *Teacher As Stranger: Educational Philosophy for the Modern Age* (Belmont, Calif: Wadsworth Publishing Company, 1973), ii, 308: 70.

11. "Today, as before, some teachers assert that certain children 'aren't even human'. Some point to a child who cannot achieve and call him 'little animal'. They could not speak this way if they did not have in mind some abstract model of what they think a human being ought to be." Greene, 71.

12. Rene Thom, "Modern Mathematics: Does It Exist?" in A. G. Howson, ed., *Developments in Mathematics Education* (Cambridge: Cambridge University Press, 1972), 204.

13. Thomas J. Cooney, "A Beginning Teacher's View of Problem Solving," *Journal for Research in Mathematics Education* 16, no. 5 (1985): 324–336.

14. Stephen Lerman, "Alternative Perspectives of the Nature of Mathematics and Their Influence on the Teaching of Mathematics," *British Educational Research Journal* 16, no. 1 (1990): 53–61.

15. Alba Gonzalez Thompson, "The Relationship of Teachers' Conceptions of Mathematics and Mathematics Teaching to Instructional Practice," *Educational Studies in Mathematics* 15 (1984): 105–127.

16. Lerman, 53–54.

17. Imré Lakatos, *Proofs and Refutations: The Logic of Mathematical Discovery* (Cambridge: Cambridge University Press, 1976).

18. The philosophical move here is to make use of a method crafted by Ludwig Wittgenstein, which is to recognize philosophical conflicts as a matter of difference in language games. While I do not explicitly refer to Wittgenstein at any great length, his influence should be implicitly understood throughout.

19. 'Practice' has more than one meaning in this book: (a) practice as in the usual common usage of the word by educators, designates the work of practitioners as opposed to theory—what, for example, teachers do; and (b) practice as I use it suggests a complex of discursively organized thought and culturally proscribed action. The second meaning is what I mean to be referring to here, though the first can be understood as a special case.

20. Joan Wallach Scott, *Gender and the Politics of History* (New York: Columbia University Press, 1988), 3.

21. Here I refer mainly to Piagetian theories of mathematics learning and their descendents. A recent example is Pierre Van Hiele's *Structure and Insight: A Theory of Mathematics Education* (Orlando, Fla.: Academic Press, 1986).

22. Michel Foucault, *Discipline and Punish: The Birth of the Prison* (New York: Pantheon Books, 1977); *Power/Knowledge: Selected Interviews and Other Writings* (Brighton, England: Harvester Press, 1980). See also Stephen J. Ball, ed., *Foucault and Education: Disciplines and Knowledge* (London/New York: Routledge, 1990).

23. Elly Bulkin, Minnie Bruce Pratt, and Barbara Smith, *Yours in Struggle: Three Feminist Perspectives on Anti-Semitism and Racism* (Brooklyn, New York: Long Haul Press, 1984); Teresa de Lauretis, ed., *Feminist Studies, Critical Studies* (Bloomington: Indiana University Press, 1986); Mary Louise Adams, "There's No Place Like Home: On the Place of Identity in Feminist Politics," *Feminist Review* 31 (Spring 1989): 22–23; Leslie Wahl Rabine, "A Feminist Politics of Non-Identity," *Feminist Studies* 14 (Spring 1988): 11–31; Robert Snyder, "The Paterson Jewish Folk Chorus: Politics, Ethnicity and Musical Culture," *American Jewish History* 74 (September 1984): 27–

44; Mario T. Garcia, *Mexican Americans: Leadership, Ideology & Identity* (New Haven, Conn.: Yale University Press, 1989).

24.  As in Scott, 5.

25.  Because this is the main thrust of the project, I do not include references to 'popular culture studies' here. They will be introduced as appropriate throughout the book.

26.  David Parkin, "Controlling the U-Turn of Knowledge," in Richard Fardon, ed., *Power and Knowledge: Anthropological and Sociological Approaches* (Edinburgh: Scottish Academic Press, 1985), 49.

27.  See, e.g., Pierre Bourdieu and Jean-Claude Passeron, *Reproduction in Education, Society and Culture* (Beverly Hills, Calif: Sage, 1977); Samuel Bowles and Herbert Gintis, *Schooling in Capitalist America* (New York: Basic Books, 1976); Philip Cusick, *Inside High School* (New York: Holt, Rinehart & Winston, 1972); Richard Everhart, *Reading, Writing and Resistance* (Boston: Routledge & Kegan Paul, 1983); Philip Jackson, *Life in Classrooms* (New York: Holt, Rinehart & Winston, 1968); Ralph Larkin, *Suburban Youth in Cultural Crisis* (New York: Oxford University Press, 1979); Peter McLaren, *Schooling and Ritual Performance* (Boston: Routledge & Kegan Paul, 1985); Valerie Polakow, *The Erosion of Childhood* (Chicago: University of Chicago Press, 1982); Roger I. Simon, "Work Experience," in David W. Livingstone and contributors, *Critical Pedagogy and Cultural Power* (South Hadley, Mass.: Bergin & Garvey, 1987), pp. 155–177; James Walker, "Rebels with Our Applause," *Journal of Education*; Valerie Walkerdine, "Sex, Power and Pedagogy," *Screen Education* 38 (1981): 14–21; Willard Waller, *The Sociology of Teaching* (New York: John Wiley, 1965); Kathleen Weiler, *Women Teaching for Change* (South Hadley, Mass.: Bergin & Garvey, 1988); Lois Weis, *Working Class Without Work* (New York: Routledge, 1990); and Paul Willis, *Learning to Labor* (New York: Columbia University Press, 1981).

28.  See, e.g., Claude Levi-Strauss, *The Raw and the Cooked* (New York: Harper & Row, 1975).

29.  See Julian Henriques, et al., eds., *Changing the Subject: Psychology, Social Regulation and Subjectivity* (New York: Methuen, 1984).

30. A comparable approach would be to analyze rhetoric for significant 'public meanings' (i.e., meanings established as authoritative and normative). Here one reads meanings as elements contributing to the construction of a "symbolic order" (in which social phenomena are authoritatively defined and interpreted, and in which a field of legitimate action and choice is limited). See, e.g., Joseph Gusfield, *The Culture of Public Problems: Drinking-Driving and the Symbolic Order* (Chicago: University of Chicago Press, 1981). Michael Olneck adapts Gusfield's "symbolic order" to a comparison of early intercultural and recent multicultural education in "The Recurring Dream: Symbolism and Ideology in Intercultural and Multicultural Education," in *American Journal of Education* (February 1990): 147–174.

31. Jacob Neusner, *The Systemic Analysis of Judaism* (Atlanta: Scholars Press, 1988): 27.

32. Neusner, 27.

33. Stanley Aronowitz and Henry Giroux, *Education Under Siege* (South Hadley, Mass.: Bergin & Garvey, 1985), 52.

34. Christine Keitel, "Mathematics Education and Technology," *For the Learning of Mathematics* 9, no. 1 (February 1989): 103–120.

35. Philip Davis, "Applied Mathematics as a Social Contract," in *Mathematics, Education and Society,* Christine Keitel, Peter Damerow, Alan Bishop, and Paulus Gerdes, eds. (Paris: UNESCO document series no. 35, Science and Technology Education, 1989).

36. Of course, this is indeed increasingly done, as informatics is translated through word processing into aspects of textual production.

37. Ole Skovsmose, "Mathematical Education Versus Critical Education," *Educational Studies in Mathematics* 16, no. 4 (November 1985): 337–354.

38. Ole Skovsmose, *Towards a Philosophy of Critical Mathematics Education* (Dordrecht, Holland: Kluwer Academic, 1994), 96.

39. See, e.g., the work of Hans Freudenthal, especially, *Weeding and Sowing* and *Didactical Phenomenology of Mathematical Structures* (Dordrecht, Holland: D. Reidel, 1977 and 1983, respectively).

40. Stieg Mellin-Olsen, *The Politics of Mathematics Education* (Dordrecht, Holland: D. Reidel, 1987).

41. See, e.g., David Bloome, P. Puro, and E. Theodorou, "Procedural Display and Classroom Lessons," *Curriculum Inquiry* 19, no. 3 (1989): 265–291; David Bloome, "Toward a More Delicate Elaboration of Procedural Display," *Curriculum Inquiry* 20, no. 1 (1990): 71–73.

42. Skovsmose, 347.

43. This is important to me in terms of the 'politics of mathematics education' on a more traditional, professional level. I find the tendency in education to take one's research agenda from the perceived needs of policymakers and state-level mandates to be particularly damaging for the status and liveliness of education as a discipline. That is, if we take education to be a discipline in its own right, rather than as a collection of adaptations of disciplinary inquiry to (pre)-generated problems, then we have a better chance of establishing education as a legitimate self-constituted endeavor. We then can cultivate the possibility of borrowing 'in the other direction'—we can hope to see some day investigations in the pedagogy of sociology, philosophy, or anthropology, for example, in which subspecialties of other disciplines make use of empowering theorizations fostered by schools of education. Such an agenda underlies my project in its entirety.

44. Catherine Belsey, *Critical Practice* (New York: Methuen, 1980): 103.

45. Van Hiele, 8.

46. See, e.g., Michael Apple, "On Analyzing Hegemony," *in Ideology and Curriculum* (New York: Routledge & Kegan Paul, 1979), quotes from p. 16. See also Michael F. D. Young, ed., *Knowledge and Control* (London: Collier-Macmillan, 1971); Richard Brown, ed., *Knowledge, Education and Cultural Change* (London: Tavistock,

1973); Basil Bernstein*Towards a Theory of Educational Transmissions*, vol. 3 of , *Class, Codes and Control* (London: Routledge & Kegan Paul, 1977); Rachel Sharp and Anthony Green, *Education and Social Control: A Study in Progressive Education* (London: Routledge & Kegan Paul, 1975); John Eggleston, *The Sociology of the School* (London: Routledge & Kegan Paul, 1977).

47. Antonio Gramsci, *Selections from the Prison Notebooks* (London: Lawrence & Wishart, 1971). See also Raymond Williams, *The Long Revolution* (London: Chatto & Windus, 1961); *and Marxism and Literature* (Oxford: Oxford University Press, 1977).

48. Raymond Williams, "Base and Superstructure in Marxist Cultural Theory," in *Schooling and Capitalism: A Sociological Reader*, Roger Dale, et al., eds. (London: Routledge & Kegan Paul, 1976): 205.

49. Williams, *Base and Superstructure*, 205.

50. See, e.g., Louis Althusser. *Lenin and Philosophy and Other Essays* (London: New Left Books, 1971).

51. Apple, 22.

52. See, e.g., Michael Apple, *Education and Power* (Boston: Ark Paperbacks, 1982); Nicholas Burbules, "A Theory of Power in Education," *Educational Theory* 36, no. 2 (1986): 95–114.

53. See, e.g., Michel Foucault, *Discipline and Punish* (New York: Random House, 1979) and *Power/Knowledge* (New York: Pantheon Books, 1980). This conception of power was also introduced in English much earlier by Bertrand Russell, who claimed power as "the fundamental concept in social science . . . in the same sense in which energy is the fundamental concept in physics." See Russell's *Power: A New Social Analysis* (New York: Norton, 1938).

54. This paragraph is taken from Valerie Walkerdine, "Subjectivity, Discourses and Practice," in *Political Dimensions of Mathematics Education: Action and Critique: Proceedings of the First International Conference*, Richard Noss, et. al., eds. (London: Department of

Mathematics, Statistics and Computing, Institute of Education, University of London [no page numbers]).

"Discourses are perhaps best understood as practices that systematically form the objects of which they speak." Madan Sarup, *Post-Structuralism & Post-Modernism* (Athens, Ga.: University of Georgia Press, 1989), 70.

55. See "Subjectivity, Discourses and Practice," above; and Walkerdine's *The Mastery of Reason: Cognitive Development and the Production of Meaning* (New York: Routledge, 1987).

56. Walkerdine, "Subjectivity, Discourses and Practice," p. 2 of article.

57. Apple, 22.

58. David Nyberg, *Power Over Power* (Ithaca, New York: Cornell University Press, 1981); Maxine Greene, *The Dialectic of Freedom* (New York: Teachers College Press, 1988).

59. Hannah Arendt, *The Human Condition* (Chicago: University of Chicago Press, 1958).

60. Of course, both Arendt and Gray are well known for discussions of how such cooperative power can lead to atrocious forms of collective power and identity, i.e., fascism, as well as emancipatory change; an application of this sort of notion of power to education will need to keep this in mind.

61. Greene, *Dialectic*, 134.

62. Greene, *Dialectic*, 115–116.

63. Here the idea is that an action which maintains a given structure on a given field of actions is actually interpreted as actively reconstructing that structure. Power relations may give the appearance that there is no choice; but 'genuine' power relations within this definition of power are those that structure possible actions rather than manipulating or forcing other actions.

64. Philip Wexler, *Social Analysis of Education: After the New Sociology* (London/New York: Routledge & Kegan Paul, 1987). See also Walker, above.

65. Svi Shapiro, "Educational Theory and Recent Political Discourse: A New Agenda for the Left?" *Harvard Educational Review* 89, no. 2 (1987): 171–200.

66. Shapiro, 190.

67. His agenda for schools was very similar to that espoused early in this century by Antonio Gramsci.

68. Shapiro, 185.

69. As Shapiro put it, "One wonders if there is a message here to Democrats"; 187.

70. On the strength of this strategy, see, e.g., Peter M. Appelbaum, *The Power of Individual Subjectivity and the Subjectivity of Power in Education*, Program on the Comparative Study of Social Transformations, Working Paper Series no. 30 (Ann Arbor, Mich.: University of Michigan, 1989).

71. Henry Giroux, "Citizenship, Public Philosophy, and the Struggle for Democracy," *Educational Theory* 37, no. 2 (1987): 103–120.

72. Richard Ohmann, *The Politics of Letters* (Middletown, Conn.: Wesleyan University Press, 1987), p. 205. For more on popular and mass culture studies, see Stanley Aronowitz and Henry A. Giroux, "Mass Culture and Critical Pedagogy," in *Education Under Siege* (South Hadley, Mass.: Bergin & Garvey, 1985).

73. Carlos E. Cortes, "Empowerment Through Media Literacy: A Multicultural Approach," in Christine E. Sleeter, ed., *Empowerment Through Multicultural Education* (Albany, N.Y.: State University of New York Press, 1991), 143–157. The following discussion of media as educators is taken directly from this excellent chapter.

74. Cortes, 156–157.

75.  Herbert J. Gans, "The Mass Media as an Educational Institution," *Television Quarterly* 6 (1967): 20–37; quote, p. 21–22, taken and edited from Cortes, p. 144.

76.  Alexis Jetter, "Mississippi Learning," *The New York Times,* 21 February 1992, VI, 20–35. See also "College Board's Equity 2000 Program," in the same magazine section of *The New York Times,* in which the board's President, Donald M. Stuart, describes mathematics as the gatekeeper to the "academic track."

77.  Alan J. Bishop, *Mathematical Enculturation: A Cultural Perspective on Mathematics Education* (Boston: Kluwer Academic, 1988).

78.  David Bloor, *Wittgenstein: A Social Theory of Knowledge* (New York: Columbia University Press, 1983); Terezinha N. Carraher, David W. Carraher, and Analucia D. Schliemann, "Mathematics in the Streets and in Schools," *British Journal of Developmental Psychology* 3 (1985): 21–29; Carraher, Schliemann, and Carraher, "Mathematical Concepts in Everyday Life," in Geoffrey B. Saxe and Maryl Gearhart. eds., *Children's Mathematics* (San Francisco: Jossey-Bass, 1988); Jean Lave.

79.  *Action in Teacher Education* IXX, no. 2 (Summer 1987).

80.  Michael F. D. Young, "An Approach to the Study of Curricula as Socially Organized Knowledge," in Michael F. D. Young, ed., *Knowledge and Control* (London: Collier-Macmillan, 1971).

81.  Landon E. Beyer and Michael W. Apple, *The Curriculum: Problems, Politics, and Possibilities* (Albany, N.Y.: State University of New York Press, 1988). They label the eight sets of questions epistemological, political, economic, ideological, aesthetic, ethical, and historical.

82.  Joseph Schwab, *The Practical: A Language for Curriculum* (Washington: National Education Association. Center for the Study of Instruction, 1970).

83.  James R. C. Leitzel, ed., *A Call for Change: Recommendations for the Mathematical Preparation of Teachers of Mathematics,* publication of the Committee on the Mathematical Education of

Teachers, The Mathematical Association of America (Reston, Va.: National Council of Teachers of Mathematics, 1991.

84. Bishop, 6.

85. Bishop, 7.

86. Rachel Sharp, *Knowledge, Ideology and the Politics of Schooling: Towards a Marxist Analysis of Education* (Boston: Routledge & Kegan Paul, 1980), 10.

## Chapter 1

1. The Holmes Group, *Tomorrow's Teachers* (East Lansing, Mich.: The Holmes Group, 1986).

2. National Council of Teachers of Mathematics, Commission on Teaching Standards for School Mathematics, *Professional Standards for Teaching Mathematics* (Reston, Va.: NCTM, 1991).

3. James T. Fey, "Surveying Today's Mathematics Teaching," *Mathematics Teacher* LXXI (October 1979): 490–504. Also printed in condensed form in *Education Digest* 45, no. 4 (1979): 19–22; quote, p. 21. The NSF commissioned studies were: Iris Weiss, *Report of the 1977 National Survey of Science, Mathematics and Social Studies Education* (Research Triangle Park, N.C.: Research Triangle Institute, 1978); Marilyn N. Suydam and Alan Osborne, *Mathematics Education*, volume II of *The Status of Pre-College Science, Mathematics, and Social Science Education: 1955–1975* (Columbus, Ohio: Ohio State University Center for Science and Mathematics Education, 1977); and Robert E. Stake and Jack Easley, eds., *Case Studies in Science Education* (Urbana, Ill.: University of Illinois, 1978).

4. Fey, 21.

5. Janet Hook, "House Clears Bill Allowing Prayer Meetings in Schools; Attached to Math-Science Aid," *Congressional Quarterly Weekly* 42 (28 July 1984): 1807–8. See also Michael S. Knapp, et al., "The Eisenhower Mathematics and Science Education Program: An Enabling Resource for Reform. Summary Report," National Study of

the Education for Economic Security Act (EESA) Title II Program (Washington, D.C.: Planning and Evaluation Service, Office of Planning, Budget and Evaluation, U.S. Department of Education, February 1991).

6. See, e.g., Clyde Paul, "Suggestions for Solving the Mathematics Teacher Shortage," *Education Digest* 46, no. 9 (May 1981): 42–44; Michael W. Heikkinen, "On the Supply of Science and Math Teachers in Idaho," *Phi Delta Kappan* 64 (December 1982): 288; E. McGrath, "Low-Tech Teaching Blues," *Time* 120 (27 December 1982): 67.

7. See, e.g., Denis P. Doyle, "Why Johnny's Teacher Can't Do Algebra," *Across the Board* 26 (June 1989): 34–38+.

8. See, e.g., David C. Berliner, "Math Teaching May Favor Boys Over Girls," *Instructor* (October 1987). Also in condensed form in *Education Digest* 53, no. 5 (January 1988): 29.

9. See, e.g., "Studying Math Development," *Children Today* 10, no. 6 (November–December 1981): 25–26.

10. See, e.g., George Neill, "NAEP at Age 10 Says: Schools Are in Trouble," *Phi Delta Kappan* 61 (November 1979): 157; "Skill Shortages Threaten Technological Prowess," *Futurist* 18, no. 1 (February 1984): 79–80.

11. Ian McNett, "Teaching Math by the Socratic Method," *Education Digest* 45, no. 7 (March 1980): 43.

12. McNett, 42.

13. John Saxon, "Al-ge-bra- Made . . . Understandable," *National Review* 33, no. 10 (29 May 1981): 584.

14. John Saxon, "Breakthrough in Algebra," *National Review* 33, no. 20 (16 October 1981): 1206.

15. Saxon, "Breakthrough," 1206.

16. John Saxon, "Save Our Mathematics!" *National Review* 35 (August 19, 1983): 1016. See also Trevor Armbrister, "The Teacher Who Took On the Establishment," *Readers Digest* 126 (March 1985): 23–28.

17. Saxon, "Breakthrough," 1206.

18. Henrietta Wexler, "The Man Who Loves Junior High," *American Educator* 18 (July 1982): 29–31.

19. John Allen Paulos, *Innumeracy: Mathematical Illiteracy and Its Consequences* (New York: HIll & Wang, 1988).

20. Chris Goodrich, "Big Numbers for Innumeracy: Hill & Wang's first bestseller heralds a new direction," *Publishers Weekly* 235 (2 June 1989): 46–48.

21. D. Chu, "An Eminent Math Professor Says 'Innumeracy' Rivals Illiteracy as a Cause for Concern in America," *People Weekly* 31(23 January 1989): 95–96+; Stefan Kanfer, "To Conquer Fear of Counting," *Time* (30 January 1989): 66; Kay Bartlett, "Are You Innumerate?" *The Saturday Evening Post* 261 (September 1989): 36.

22. Kim Hubbard, "Beating Long Odds, Jaime Escalante Stands and Delivers, Helping to Save a Faltering High School," *People Weekly* 29 (11 April 1988): 57.

23. *Los Angeles Times,* 7 December 1982.

24. Jay Matthews, *Escalante: The Best Teacher in America* (New York: Henry Holt, 1988).

25. A 'discourse' is a domain of language use, a particular way of talking (and writing and thinking). Later I will expand the notion of discourse to suggest that educational practices are themselves "discursive." For an elaboration, within the post-Saussurean theoretical perspective I am using, see Catherine Belsey, *Critical Practice* (New York: Methuen, 1980).

26. Matthews; see also Randy Fitzgerald, "The Teacher They Call the 'Champ'," *Readers Digest* (August 1983): 119–122.

27. Sarah Lawrence Lightfoot, *The Good High School: Portraits of Character and Culture* (New York: Basic Books, 1983).

28. See, e.g., Marilyn Cohn, Robert B. Kottkamp, and Eugene F. Provenzo, Jr., *To Be a Teacher: Cases, Concepts, Observation Guides* (New York: Random House, 1987).

29. In 1989, for example, debate over House Bill H.R. 996 centered on college scholarships for future mathematics and science teachers. See Phil Kuntz, "Science and Math Training Stirs Concern on Hill," *Congressional Quarterly Weekly* 47, no. 33 (19 August 1989): 2179–2183.

30. Doyle, op. cit.

31. Doyle, 41.

32. Andrew Kupfer, "Turning Students on to Science," *Fortune* 121, no. 12 (Spring 1990): 82–83+; quote, p. 82.

33. Deborah P. Britzman, "Cultural Myths in the Making of a Teacher: Biography and social structure in teacher education," *Harvard Educational Review* 56, no. 4 (November 1986): 442–456. She is writing in the context of professional training of teachers; I am adapting her insights for the critical reading of fictional or truth-based narratives about teachers. But I would also argue that there is little relevant difference, within the interpretation I am developing, between fictional accounts of teachers, projected fantasies of student-teachers within personal biographies, or reports of teachers within educational research. See, e.g., Willard Waller's early insight that educational sociology requires the tools and techniques of the realist novelist as well as that of the trained anthropologist, in *The Sociology of Teaching* (New York: Russell & Russell, 1932/1961).

34. McNett, 43.

35. McNett, 44.

36. In 1983 *The Mathematics Teacher* and *The Arithmetic Teacher*, publications of the National Council of Teachers of Mathematics, refused to print any more of his advertisements, accusing

him of being too vitrioloic and accusatory. This of course bolstered Saxon's image as bucking the experts in the establishment.

37. D. Chu, "An Eminent Math Professor Says 'Innumeracy' Rivals Illiteracy as a Cause for Concern in America" [interview], *People Weekly* 31 (29 May 1989): 95–96+; "The Odds are You're Innumerate," *The New York Times*, 1 January 1989, 1+; Joe Garofalo, "Metacognition and School Mathematics," *Arithmetic Teacher* 34, no. 9 (May 1987): 22–23. On self-regulating individuals, see the discussion of Walkerdine in chapters 0 and (-1).

38. Ferdinand de Saussure, *Course in General Linguistics* (London: Duckworth, 1983).

39. As Jacques Derrida wrote:

What was it that Saussure in particular reminded us of? That "Language [which consists only of differences] is not a function of the speaking subject." This implies that the subject (self-identical or even conscious of self-identity, self-conscious) is inscribed in the language, that he [sic] is a "function" of the language. He becomes *a speaking* subject only by conforming his speech . . . to the system of linguistic prescriptions taken as the system of differences.

Jacques Derrida, *Speech and Phenomena*, trans. David B. Allison (Evanston, Ill.: Northwestern University Press, 1973).

In this book, I have indicated a sign in my written work by single quotes; standard double quotes indicate their usual meaning of words taken from someone else.

40. Belsey, p. 42.

41. Here I am applying the work of Murray Edelman. See, for example, his book *Constructing the Political Spectacle* (Chicago: University of Chicago Press, 1988). More on the construction of public problems will be addressed in chapter 3.

42. Roland Barthes, *Mythologies* (New York: Hill and Wang, 1972).

43. Belsey, 104.

44. Warren Colburn, *First Lessons in Arithmetic, on the Plan of Pestalozzi, With Some Improvements* (Boston: Cummings, Hilliard & Co., 1825), quote, x.

45. Colburn, x11.

46. Anne Meek, "On Creating *Ganas*: A conversation with Jaime Escalante," *Educational Leadership* (February 1989): 47.

47. McNett, 45.

48. I am using here *Webster's New Collegiate Dictionary* (Springfield, Mass.: G & C Merriam, 1977), p. 536. Because Webster's Dictionary is a summary of contemporary usage, rather than of 'correct' definitions, it is helpful in establishing the degree to which Escalante satisfies all possible meanings of a hero.

49. Paul Farber, and Gunilla Holm, "Teacher as Hero: Commercial Films of the 1980s." Paper presented at the annual meeting of the American Educational Studies Association, Orlando, Fla., 1990.

50. Farber and Holm could not recall any main characters other than Escalante in their extensive database—personal communication.

51. See, e.g., Denis P. Doyle, "Escalante: A classroom hero," *Across the Board* 26 (1989): 39.

52. Matthews, back cover.

53. Jack Kroll, "To Señor, With Love, Brains and Ganas," *Newsweek* (March 14, 1988): 62.

54. Tom O'Brien, "Two Heroes: 'Cry of Reason' & 'Deliver'," *Commonweal* 115 (3 June 1988): 342.

55. Mona Charen, "Bush Sets Right Education Goals," *The Ann Arbor News*, 1 May 1991, A9.

56. Fitzgerald, p. 120; see also Matthews' biography.

57. See, e.g., "Stand and Deliver," *Glamour* 86 (May 1988): 215–216.

58. Stefan Ulstein, "Great Teachers Rock the Boat," *Christianity Today* 32, no. 61 (2 September 1988): 61. Ulstein compares great teachers with prophets: " . . . if Jesus was history's greatest teacher, the Pharisees were history's quintessential school board."

59. James Lardner, "Stand and Deliver; The Milagro Beanfield War," *The Nation* 246 (30 April 1988): 619.

60. Pat Aufderheide, "Reel Life," *Mother Jones* 13 (April 1988): 45.

61. Aufderheide, 26.

62. Matthews, p. vii. It is important to note that Jay Matthews was a prominent *Washington Post* newswriter whose interest in Escalante can be understood as an indicator of Escalante's importance. Indeed, Matthews won a national award for his reporting on the Calculus A.P. Test controversy. His biography of Escalante, begun long before the film was conceived, was a five-year project.

63. Matthews, vii–ix.

64. Matthews, ix.

65. See, e.g., the numerous quotes on the book's cover. Jonathan Kozol, noted author, states, "It pares away the myth and leaves the real man."

66. David Denby, "Welcome to East L.A.," *New York* 21 (18 April 1988): 102.

67. Doyle, "Escalante," 39. I presume the noted expert to be *Lee* Shulman; it was printed *Les*. See also the Shulman article below.

68. Meek, 46.

69. Meek, 47.

70. Lee S. Shulman, "Toward a Pedagogy of Substance," *AAHE Bulletin* (June 1989): 8–13.

71. Leonard Gillman, "Teaching Programs that Work," *Focus: The newsletter of the Mathematical Association of America* 10, no. 1 (January–February 1990): 7.

72. Fitzgerald, 121.

73. There were no female superteachers of mathematics. Note, however, my discussion of this in chapters 3 and (-1).

74. Jay Matthews, "Miracle Worker of Garfield High," *Readers Digest* 134 (January 1989): 196.

75. Ulstein, 61.

76. Denby, 101.

77. Kroll, 62.

78. Fitzgerald, 121.

79. See, e.g., Denby, 101.

80. Fitzgerald, 121.

81. Fitzgerald, 120, 121.

82. Kroll, 62.

83. *Glamour*, 215.

84. Matthews, 6.

85. Hubbard, 58.

86. Matthews, 5.

87. I base the following paragraph on Robert Welker. Expertise and the Teacher as Expert: Rethinking a questionable metaphor. *American Educational Research Journal* 28, no. 1 (Spring 1991): 19–35.

88. See, e.g., Matthews' discussions of Escalante helping Ben Jimenez with his early discipline problems, 95-98.

89. Again, a good example is in Matthew's discussion of how Jimenez perfects his own craft. See, e.g., p. 116: "The younger teacher had discovered that simply remaining in his classroom at noon and after school [like Escalante] brought enormous benefits. Even his laziest and most disruptive students were more willing to try if he was available and showed he cared." Of course, by mimicking this particular practice, Jimenez further isolated his own teaching from other teachers and the wider community, preferring instead to spend more time as the only adult in his classroom. The practice moreover reinforced the notion that everything depends on the teacher who alone provides the resources for academic success within his classroom. We might wonder how students would react if *all* their teachers were so motivating and demanding!

90. Welker, 21.

91. Welker, 28.

92. Matthews, back cover.

93. Matthews, 3.

94. Aufderheide, 26. Curiously, like the genuine hero that he was, Escalante publicly expressed little direct interest in being used as a political symbol: In the film as in the classroom, noted Aufderheide, his focus was on his students. Compare also the mythical portrayal of high school principal Joe Clark, also depicted as battling the education establishment in order to bring discipline to his students. Clark was typically represented as a serious, well-dressed professional carrying a baseball bat as if he intended to use it when necessary. Another feature film was loosely based on him; here the film altered possible racial aspects of the myth by casting white James Belushi in the title role, while Clark was black. A good refer-

ence on Clark is the *Time* magazine cover story of 1 February 1988, "Getting Tough: New Jersey principal Joe Clark kicks up a storm about discipline in city schools," by Ezra Bowen, 52–58; and "President Reagan says Clark has the right stuff," p. 3, in the table of contents. The cover photo from Matthews' book, *Escalante: The Best Teacher in America,* was reproduced in this article, in which he was grouped with other 'get tough' educators that were making the new difference in urban schooling.

95. Matthews, 4.

96. Matthews, 162.

97. Kroll, 62.

98. Aufderheide, 26.

99. Kroll, 62.

100. Matthews, 13.

101. Matthews, 3.

102. Matthews, 5.

103. Matthews, 6.

104. Matthews, 2.

105. Matthews, 12–13.

106. Matthews, 2.

107. Matthews, 3.

108. R. Corliss, "Stand and Deliver," *Time* (4 April 1988): 77.

109. Matthews, 4.

110. Matthews, 5.

111. Meek, 47.

112. Matthews, 5.

113. Meek, 47.

114. Lardner, 618.

115. *Stand and Deliver.*

116. "We Will Rock You," complete with hand-clapping as pupils ceremoniously dropped homework into a basket. Bowen, 57.

117. Lardner, 618.

118. For example, should one answer a related rate problem about toxic waste seapage? Would the better question be, why do you want to know this information? Do you plan on designating a nearby location as a toxic waste dump? Would you rather I determine the minimum production of toxic waste possible?

119. Denby, 102.

120. O'Brien, 342.

121. Valerie Richardson, "Make It 3 Rs and a T as Test Mania Thrives," *The Washington Times* (3 May 1988): A1. "We don't just practice every once in a while—we practice every day," fifth grade teacher Jacqueline Chandler said. A similar *Education Life* cover story by Edward Fiske, "America's Test Mania," *The New York Times* 12 (10 April 1988): 16–20, collected concerns expressed by Gregory Anrig, president of the Educational Testing Service, Archie LaPointe, executive director of the National Assessment of Educational Progress, Chris Pipho of the Education Commission of the States, superintendents of schools in Connecticut, Arkansas, Georgia, Texas, and Lousiana, educational historian Diane Ravitch of Columbia University, and Larry Cuban, associate dean of education at Stanford University, among others. The National Education Association's Mid-Atlantic Chapter held a conference to discuss testing in September of 1988. This is a full decade after the Education Commission of the States expressed identical concerns in its

1979 report 09–MA–01, *Changes in Mathematical Achievement, 1973–78,* summarized as "Analyzing Changes in Students Math Achievement: Study by the National Assessment of Educational Progress, in *Education Digest* 45, no. 4 (1979): 15–18.

122. Michael F. D. Young, "An Approach to the Study of Curricula as Socially Organized Knowledge," in Michael F. D. Young, ed., *Knowledge and Control* (London: Collier-Macmillan, 1971).

123. Landon E. Beyer and Michael W. Apple, *The Curriculum: Problems, Politics, and Possibilities* (Albany, N.Y.: State University of New York Press, 1988).

124. Beyer and Apple, 5.

125. Michael J. Streibel, "A Critical Analysis of Three Approaches to the Use of Computers in Education," in *The Curriculum: Problems, Politics, and Possibilities,* Landon E. Beyer and Michael W. Apple, eds. (Albany, N.Y.: State University of New York Press, 1988), 259–288; quote, p. 263.

126. Streibel, 264.

127. These criteria are adapted as well from Streibel, 264.

128. See also Adelaida R. Del Castillo, Jeanie Frederickson, Teresa McKenna and Flora Ida Ortiz, "An Assessment of the Status of the Education of Hispanic American Women," in McKenna, and Ortiz, eds., *The Broken Web: The Educational Experience of Hispanic American Women* (Berkeley: Floricanto Press, 1988). They argue that national commissions gave a backseat to the issue of equality in educational opportunity by stressing a return to 'excellence'. The issue of 'achievement motivation' was a central part of the Tomas Rivera Center study on Hispanic women, which culminated in a symposium and the subsequent book referred to here.

129. See, e.g., Henry Gradillas' letter to the testing service, in which he appeals to the presumed universality of mathematics in an argument for the particular inappropriateness of challenging the credibility of Hispanic students. Matthews, 160–164.

130. Note the similarity between Escalante's slogan, "You can become whatever you want to be," and the contemporaneous army television commercial, "be all you can be . . . in the army."

131. Streibel, 265.

132. For example, students were not allowed to drop Escalante's course or switch to another teacher.

133. Escalante fed his students, found money for them so they could tutor instead of working at less academic jobs, etc.

134. Max Weber, *On Charisma and Institution Building,* Shmuel Noah Eisenstadt, ed. (Chicago: University of Chicago Press, 1968).

135. Even the book's cover photograph cultivates a missionary image: Escalante is 'giving' his students the 'word', as he gestures toward the camera amidst these beatific students.

136. Welker, 34.

137. Lynn Olson, "Goodlad on Teacher Education: Low status, unclear mission," *Education Week* 28, no. 1 (February 1990): 27–28.

138. Britzman, 454.

139. Alan R. Tom, *Teaching as a Moral Craft* (New York: Longman, 1984).

140. See, e.g., Stanley Aronowitz and Henry A. Giroux, *Education Under Siege: The Conservative, Liberal, and Radical Debate Over Schooling* (South Hadley, Mass.: Bergin & Garvey Press, 1985); Henry A. Giroux, *Teachers as Intellectuals: Toward a Critical Pedagogy of Learning* (Granby, Mass.: Bergin & Garvey Press, 1988).

141. Here, too, I owe some insight to Britzman, who came to parallel conclusions in the study of student teachers.

Chapter 2

1. Henry A. Giroux and Roger I. Simon, "Popular Culture and Critical Pedagogy," in Henry A. Giroux and Peter McLaren, eds., *Critical Pedagogy, the State, and Cultural Struggle* (Albany, N.Y.: State University of New York Press, 1989), 236–251; quote, p. 236.

2. See, e.g., Allan Bloom, *The Closing of the American Mind: How Higher Education Has Failed Democracy and Impoverished the Souls of Today's Students* (New York: Simon and Schuster, 1987); E. D. Hirsch, *Cultural Literacy: What Every American Needs to Know* (Boston: Houghton Mifflin, 1987).

3. Edwin Kiester, Jr. and Sally Valente Kiester, "Everyday Math for Grownups," *Reader's Digest* 135 (October 1989): 43–48. Matthew Weinstein recently described the mutually affirming hegemony of professional and popular culture in terms of popular and "official" conceptions sharing a basic ethos. See his "Robot World: Crossing the Borders Between Official and Popular Culture," a paper presented at the annual meeting of the American Educational Research Association, New Orleans, 1994.

4. Giroux and Simon, 237. After Bennett resigned from the Department of Education shortly before the 1988 election, Reagan called him "the best thing to happen to American education since the McGuffy reader." *New York Times*, 10 August 1988, A12; quoted in Maurice Berube, *American Presidents and Education* (New York: Greenwood Press), 103. Berube also notes that Bennett's proposed curriculum for his ideal James Madison High School appeared to be a sound model for the college bound; but nonetheless, it revealed the secretary of education's cultural biases. The suggested syllabus for American literature, for example, reflected Bennett's adherence to "New Criticism": of the American authors recommended only one was a woman—Emily Dickinson—and only one was an African American—Ralph Ellison; none of the authors represented had published significant work after the 1950s (p. 106).

5. Giroux and Simon, 238.

6. Philip S. Jones and Arthur F. Coxford, eds., *A History of Mathematics Education in the United States and Canada* (Washington,

D.C.: The National Council of Teachers of Mathematics, 1970). See especially pp. 41–45.

7. David Eugene Smith, *The Teaching of Junior High School Mathematics* (Boston: Ginn, 1927).

8. Jacob William Albert Young, *The Teaching of Mathematics in the Elementary and Secondary School* (New York: Longmans, Green & Co., 1907, 1914, 1931). Mathematicians continued to contribute the discussion of mathematics education throughout the 1980s as well. See, e.g., Serge Lang, *Math! Encounters with High School Students* (New York: Springer-Verlag, 1985); Philip J. Davis, *The Mathematical Experience* (Boston: Birkhauser, 1980); Philip J. Davis, "Mathematics as a Social Contract," in Christine Keitel, ed., *Mathematics, Education, and Society* (Paris: UNESCO Document Series No. 35, 1989).

9. Although the authors of this book did not necessarily intend this interpretation; we may instead consider their reading of history as a gauge of the persistence of such an approach to mathematics education.

10. Jones, 43–44.

11. Escalante, "A Classroom Hero," *Across the Board* 26 (1989): 39.

12. See, e.g., Progressive Education Association, *Mathematics in General Education: A Report of the Committee on the Function of Mathematics in General Education for the Commission on Secondary School Curriculum* (New York: D. Appleton Century Company, 1938). This seminal work in the incorporation of concerns for individual growth within a social context focused on the ways in which mathematics might contribute to such growth; it called attention to valuable aspects of problem solving. However, it had little influence during the war years, and was mostly forgotten in the postwar period.

13. See, e.g., Zoltan P. Dienes, comp., *Mathematics in Primary Education: Learning of Mathematics by Young Children* (Hamburg, Germany: UNESCO International Studies in Education Series No. 164, 1966); Zoltan P. Dienes and M. A. Jeeves, *Thinking in Structures*

(London: Hutchinson Educational, 1965); Jerome S. Bruner, *Toward a Theory of Instruction* (Cambridge, Mass.: Belknap Press, 1966).

14. See, e.g., Pierre Van Hiele, *Structure and Insight: A Theory of Mathematics Education* (Orlando, Fla.: Academic Press, 1986); David Fuys, "Van Hiele Levels in Geometry," *Education and Urban Society* 17, no. 4 (August 1985): 447–462. Fuys characterized Van Hiele as shifting Piagetian theory to the role of the teacher in effecting transitions from one level of geometric thinking to the next.

15. Robert B. Davis, *Learning Mathematics: The Cognitive Science Approach to Mathematics Education* (Norwood, N.J.: Ablex, 1984). Davis is now at Rutgers, in New Jersey.

16. See, e.g., Stieg Mellin-Olsen *The Politics of Mathematics Education* (Dordrecht, Holland: D. Reidel, 1987); Alan J. Bishop, *Mathematical Enculturation: A Cultural Perspective on Mathematics Education* (Dordrecht, Holland: Kluwer, 1988).

17. William Higginson, "On the Foundations of Mathematics Education," *For the Learning of Mathematics* 1, no. 2 (November 1980): 3–7.

18. Further discussion of mathematics education as a professional and evolving discipline will be found in chapter 3.

19. National Council of Teachers of Mathematics, *A General Survey of Progress in the Last 25 Years*, first yearbook (Reston, Va.: NCTM, 1926/1966).

20. National Council, *General Survey*.

21. Alan H. Schoenfeld, "Some Thoughts on Problem-solving Research and Mathematics Education," in Frank K. Lester and Joe Garofalo, eds., *Mathematical Problem Solving: Issues in Research* (Philadelphia: The Franklin Institute Press, 1982); *Mathematical Problem Solving* (New York: Academic Press, 1983).

22. The largest and most comprehensive curriculum project of the 1980s was implemented by The University of Chicago School Mathematics Project. UCSMP was motivated by the injection of a

"reality orientation towards both the selection of content and the approaches allowed the student in working out the problems. . . . Real-life situations motivate ideas and provide additional settings for practice." UCSMP began in 1983 with a six-year grant from the Amoco Foundation. Additional funding was provided by the Ford Motor Company, the Carnegie Corporation of New York, the National Science Foundation, the General Electric Foundation, GTE, and Citicorp. The result of the project was a series of text books that reorganized the presentation and content of the curriculum within the goals of "reality." See, e.g., Zalman Usiskin et al., *Transition Mathematics* (Glenview, Ill.: Scott, Foresman, 1990), quote, p. v.

23. See, e.g., Robert M. Gagne, *Principles of Instructional Design* (New York: Holt, Rinehart & Winston, 1974); Robert M. Gagne and Robert A. Reiser, *Selecting Media for Instruction* (Englewood Cliffs, N.J.: Educational Technology Publications, 1983).

24. David Parkin, "Controlling the U-Turn of Knowledge," in Richard Fardon, ed., *Power and Knowledge: Anthropological and Sociological Approaches* (Edinburgh: Scottish Academic Press, 1985), quote, p. 49.

25. See chapter 1 and chapter (-1) on power.

26. Please note my use of 'practice' as discussed in chapter 0. I am using the second theoretical or anthropological notion of practice rather than the commonsense notion of practice as distinguished from theory.

27. See, e.g., Valerie Walkerdine, "Subjectivity, Discourse and Practice in Mathematics Education," in Richard Noss, Andrew Brown, et. al., eds., *Political Dimensions of Mathematics Education: Action & Critique* (London: Department of Mathematics, Statistics and Computing, Institute of Education, University of London, 1990); Jean Lave, *Cognition in Practice* (Cambridge: Cambridge University Press, 1988); Terezinha N. Carraher, "Negotiating the Results of Mathematical Computations," *International Journal of Educational Research* 13, no. 6 (1989): 637–646; Terezinha N. Carraher, "Street Mathematics and School Mathematics," International Conference of Psychology of Mathematics Education (Hungary,

1988); Terezinha N. Carraher, Analucia D. Schliemann, and David W. Carraher, "Mathematical Concepts in Everyday Life," in Geoffrey B. Saxe and Maryl Gearhart, eds., *Children's' Mathematics* (San Francisco: Jossey-Bass, 1988).

28. For a parallel argument based in the psychological activity theory of Vygotsky, see Stieg Mellin-Olsen.

29. See, e.g., J. Henriques, et al., *Changing the Subject* (London: Methuen, 1984).

30. Philip J. Davis and Reuben Hersh, *The Mathematical Experience* (Boston: Houghton Mifflin Co., 1981).

31. George Polya, *How to Solve It: A New Aspect of Mathematical Method* (Princeton, N.J.: Princeton University Press, 1945/46/71/73), quotes, pp. v, 1, 21. See also Polya, *Mathematics and Plausible Reasoning* (Princeton, N.J.: Princeton University Press, 1954); *Mathematical Discovery: On Understanding, Learning, and Teaching Problem Solving* (New York: Wiley, 1962).

32. National Council of Teachers of Mathematics (NCTM), *An Agenda for Action* (Reston, Va.: NCTM, 1980).

33. See, e.g., Zalman Usiskin, "We Need Another Revolution in Secondary School Mathematics." In *The Secondary School Mathematics Curriculum,* edited by Christian R. Hirsch and Marilyn J. Zweng, 1–21. Reston, Va.:" NCTM, 1985.

34. D. E. Knuth, *Surreal Numbers: How Two Ex-students Turned on to Pure Mathematics and Found Total Happiness* (Reading, Mass.: Addison-Wesley, 1974). For another "novel" approach to mathematics education, see Raffaella Borasi and Stephen I. Brown, "Communications: A 'Novel' Approach to Texts," *For the Learning of Mathematics* 5, no. 1 (February 1985): 21–23. Frederique Papy's Frederique's Stories (St. Louis, Mo.: Cemrel [Central Midwestern Regional Laboratory]) is an example of an elementary-level story form.

35. This and following quotes from Knuth, 113.

36. Knuth, 114.

37. Seymour Papert, *Mindstorms: Children, Computers, and Powerful Ideas* (New York: Basic Books, 1980).

38. Marge Kosel and Mike Fish, *The Factory: Strategies in Problem Solving* (Pleasantville, N.Y.: Sunburst Communications, 1983); Marge Kosel, Jay Carlson, and Melissa Verber, *The Incredible Laboratory: Strategies in Problem Solving* (Pleasantville, N.Y.: Sunburst Communications, 1984); Sharon Dugdale and David Kibbey, *Green Globs and Graphing Equations* (Pleasantville, N.Y.: Sunburst Communications, 1986); Judah L. Schwartz and Michal Yerushalmy, *The Geometric Supposer* (Newton, Mass: Education Development Center, 1986).

39. Imré Lakatos, *Proofs and Refutations: The Logic of Mathematical Discovery* (Cambridge: Cambridge University Press, 1976).

40. Rene Thom, "Modern Mathematics: Does It Exist?, in A. G. Howson, ed., *Developments in Mathematics Education* (Cambridge: Cambridge University Press, 1972): 204. See chapter 0 for a list of research following this agenda.

41. Ruth E. Parker, *Mathematical Power: Lessons from a Classroom* (Portsmouth, N.H.: Heinemann, 1993).

42. Parker, 4.

43. National Council of Teachers of Mathematics. Curriculum and Evaluation Standards for School Mathematics. Reston, Va.: NCTM.

44. Lawrence Cremin, *Public Education* (New York: Basic Books, 1976).

45. Cremin, 62. The persistence of all educational reform being formulated in terms of curriculum was noted as maintained by Secretary of Education Bennett. See, e.g., Berube, p. 106.

46. Elizabeth Fennema, "Justice, Equity, and Mathematics Education," in Elizabeth Fennema and Gilah C. Leder, eds., *Mathe-*

*matics and Gender* (New York: Teachers College Press, 1990): 1–9, quote, p. 6.

47. Carraher, Lave, Pinxtin.

48. D'Ambrosio, Munir Fasheh, Claudia Zaslavsky.

49. Lauren B. Resnick, "Learning In School and Out," *Phi Delta Kappan* (December 1987): 13–19.

50. Giroux and Simon, 237–238. I expanded the quote to include teachers; I would also include administrators, policy-makers, and the general public as well.
You may notice that I am breaking form with established research paradigms by dissolving any distance between me and my subject. I am embracing a particular discursive position within the educational debate of the 1980s while simultaneously claiming to represent and analyze this debate. I make no apology for this strategy; I instead suggest that this is an important element in the kind of critical reflection on public discourse I aim to promote.

51. Allan Bloom, *The Closing of the American Mind.*

52. Giroux and Simon, 238.

53. Richard Zoglin, "Game Shows Hit the Jackpot," *Time* (24 February 1986), 78.

54. Michael Pollan, "Jackpot! The Biggest, Shrewdest, Money-makingest Little Show on Earth," *Channels of Communications* 6 (June 1986): 22.

55. Pollan, 23. See also Harry F. Waters, "What a Deal!, *Newsweek* (9 February 1987): 62–68, and Todd Gold, "Behind the Scenes of America's #1 Game Show," *McCall's* (October 1986): 162–165; forty-three million viewers tuned in to *Wheel* each day. Gold referred to one critic's declaration that *Wheel* was "the hottest game show in the history of Western civilization. "If *Wheel* continues to hang in there," said King World Chairman Roger King, "it will do better business than *Star Wars*"—Zoglin, 79.

56. Lewis Grossberger, "Triumph of the Wheel," *Rolling Stone* (4 December 1986): 64. See also Harry F. Waters, "What a Deal!" *Newsweek* (9 February 1987): 64.

57. John Fiske, *Television Culture* (New York: Methuen, 1987). See especially chapter 14, "Quizzical Pleasures," 265–280. Again, I am not trying to argue a "truth" about education here, but am characterizing a pervasive and often used generalization. Schooling differentiates, but the educational system does not uniquely or singly channel people into jobs. We should note two aspects of social reproduction: agents of reproduction and places within the productive process. Practical ideology within schooling is centrally concerned with the first; but an understanding of the second is necessary for comprehending the changing ideological forms of schooling given that social formations are constantly reconstructing an inbuilt dynamism that alters the labor market while it is itself transformed. See Rachel Sharp, *Knowledge, Ideology and the Politics of Schooling* (Boston: Routledge & Kegan Paul, 1980).

58. Fiske, 265.

59. This works quite differently from state lotteries, which establish the image of 'equal' opportunity for everyone to get their lucky break despite their circumstances or natural abilities, even as they sap the minimal resources of those most in need of luck.

60. Fiske, 276.

61. There are no female game show hosts. *Wheel of Fortune* broke ground by declaring Vanna White a "hostess" and billing her as equal with Pat Sajak, despite the fact that her job was similar to many female nonentities on other programs, i.e., to "tease" the prizes (see her autobiography, photo section). The declaration of equality at once with the glorification of her beauty and largely unskilled job has much in common with what Linda Street has called the "postfeminist woman" common to 1980s television.

62. Dick Clark, host for *$64,000 Pyramid*, was described as "everyone's ideal teacher." Waters, 62.

63. Zoglin, 79.

64. Pollan, 22.

65. "*Wheel of Fortune* creates the illusion for the hard-work-ing, treadmill-trotting Middle American yearner (the show's great-est strength is outside the major media markets) that he or she is in the big game." Grossberger, 68.

66. Grossberger, 68.

67. Fiske, 272.

68. See, e.g., Pollan, 26; Ginny Swinson and Peter Haines, "How I (And the Taxman) Won $27,000 In Prizes On *Wheel of For-tune*," *Good Housekeeping* 204 (May 1987): 72; Jean Sherman, "I Took a Turn On Wheel of Fortune," *Seventeen* 46 (July 1987): 28; Marjorie Rosen, "I Tri-d T- B-at Th- -h—l -f F-rt-n-," *Glamour* 85 (September 1987): 178. Grossberger, 68.

69. Grossberger, 68. Another example: "'A Shot in the Dark,' I guessed aloud when I saw the *Wheel of Fortune* puzzle on my TV. 'You got it *again*, Mom! And hardly any letters are showing!' My teenage sons, Paul and Gregg, were amazed. . . . Every night we competed with the contestants to see who could guess the puzzle first." Susan Soffer, "I Got Behind The Wheel of Fortune," *Redbook* (January 1986): 26.

70. Pollan, 26. "The producers of *Wheel* have accurately taken the nation's mental measure, and they're making 40 million Amer-icans feel good about their intelligence every day."

71. Pollan, 26; Gold, 164.

72. More than 40,000 people tried to become contestants each year, said *Wheel's* producer Nancy Jones; of them, only about 1000 were selected. Gold, 164. Soffer reported that only three out of every 100 would-be contestants were selected. Gold, 32. See also Rosen, 184–185.

73. Fiske, 273.

74. Fiske, 273. See also George Lipsitz, *Time Passages: Collective Memory and Popular Culture* (Minneapolis: University of Minnesota Press, 1991), for another related issue. The powerful apparati of contemporary commercial electronic mass communications dominate discourse in the modern world. Yet the "content" can appear as another novelty and diversion within the seemingly autonomous realms of commercialized leisure. Sometimes we forget (or do not know) that the creators or artists have origins or intentions at all, because the stimuli are so pervasive.

75. Soffer, 26.

76. Richard Fiddler, Conversation.

77. That is, the player had the chance to choose varying techniques of spinning the wheel to influence the outcome of a spin. He or she needed to actively generate hypotheses regarding force and speed of spin and then test them within the limits of turn-taking. In this respect, the wheel had more in common with, for example, old-fashioned (pin-based) slot machines than modern electronic ones that no longer allow physical interaction to adjust the odds of "winning."

78. Waters, 63. See also Vanna White, *Vanna Speaks* (New York: Warner Books, 1987), chapter 2.

79. *Wheel's* annual production costs for 1987: $7 million; annual gross revenue: $120 million. Merv Griffin sold *Wheel* along with *Jeopardy!* to Coca-Cola for approximately $250 million. Waters, 63.

80. Fiske, 270.

81. The hostess Vanna White is the embodiment of the myth of luck. The daughter of a poor Southern mother and a drunken father who left her at a very young age, she happened to be at the right time and place for Merv Griffin to select her. Her opportunity to be on *Wheel of Fortune* then enabled her to become a national phenomenon. "My life changed on Thanksgiving Eve, 1982, with a phone call from the producer of *Wheel of Fortune* announcing "You've got the job!"; White's autobiography, *Vanna Speaks*, photo

section. Her ordinariness and folksiness were continually played up as part of her celebrity (e.g., providing knitting, dieting, and cooking hints in her autobiography). See also Fiske, 270; Vernon Scott. "Vanna White and Me," *Good Housekeeping* 205 (November 1987): 34+; Vernon Scott, "The Millionaire Who Made Vanna White a Star," *Good Housekeeping* (May 1987): 66+. Another excellent example of this presentation is in the Pictorial/Cover, *Playboy* (May 1987): 134+.

82.  Again compare state lotteries, in which no winner means the promise of an even bigger winner eventually.

83.  Pollan, 26.

84.  Zoglin, 78.

85.  See, e.g., Arthur F. Coxford and Joseph N. Payne, *HBJ Algebra 2: With Trigonometry* (New York: Harcourt Brace Jovanovich, 1983/1987). (Note especially Section 1-6, "From Words to Symbols," 22–25.) John Saxon, *Algebra I: An Incremental Development* (Norman, Okla.: Grassdale, 1982). (Here note Lesson 31 Word Problems: 90–92.) Mary P. Dolciani, William Wooton, Edwin F. Beckenbach, and Sidney Sharron, *Algebra 2 and Trigonometry* (Boston: Houghton Mifflin, 1980). (One example in this text is Section 4-4. "Using Two Variables to Solve Problems," 119–124.)

86.  "Rules just clutter up the game and confuse people," said Alex Trebek, host and producer of *Jeopardy!* "People should be able to understand the show in the first half-hour, even if it's their first time watching." Zoglin, 78.

87.  Pollan, 25.

88.  Just as school word problems avoided the complexity of their everyday, evolving articulation (Perla Nesher, "A Research Programme for Mathematics Education," *For the Learning of Mathematics* 1, no. 3 (March 1981): 47–50; Perla Nesher, "The Stereotyped Nature of School Word Problems," *For the Learning of Mathematics* 2, no. 1 (Jully 1980): 27–28), so *Wheel's* game 'solved' puzzles without interrogating where the mystery phrases came from, when people said them, and how they came to be generally well known. For

a lone critique of problem solving in favor of a more active and reflective form of problem 'posing' during this period, see Stephen I. Brown and Marion I. Walter, *The Art of Problem Posing* (Philadelphia: The Franklin Institute Press, 1983).

89. See, e.g., Stephen I. Brown, "The Logic of Problem Generation: From Morality and Solving to De-posing and Rebellion," *For the Learning of Mathematics* 4, no. 1 (February 1984): 9–20; Stephen I. Brown, "Ye Shall Be Known By Your Generations," *For the Learning of Mathematics* 1, no. 3 (March 1981): 27–36; Stephen I. Brown, "The Right to Be Wrong," *For the Learning of Mathematics* 1, no. 3 March 1981): 27–36.

90. "Surely he did not know what a craze this deceptively simple-looking cube would create." Scientific American columnist Douglas R. Hofstadter called the cube "a model and metaphor for all that is profound and beautiful in science." David Singmaster, *Rubik's Magic Cube* (Hillsdale, N.J.: Enslow, 1981), cover jacket.

91. See, e.g., Mark Driscoll, *Research Within Reach: Secondary School Mathematics* (Reston, Va.: NCTM, 1982/1983), 59. Driscoll noted an exemplary problem from the National Assessment of Educational Progress (NAEP). Nearly a quarter of the 13 year-olds tested solved the following word problem by multiplying 2 X 5 X 52 = 520: "One rabbit eats 2 pounds of food each week. There are 52 weeks in a year. How much food will 5 rabbits eat in one week?"

92. See, e.g., Goldin and McClintock, 1984.

93. See, e.g., Donald L. Zalewski, "A study of Problem-solving Performance Measures," in John G. Harvey and Thomas A. Romberg, eds., *Problem-Solving Studies in Mathematics* (Madison, Wisc.: Research and Development Center for Individualized Schooling, 1980), 67–91.

94. See, e.g., Jack Lochhead, *An Anarchistic Approach to Teaching Problem Solving Methods* (paper read at the annual meeting of the American Education Research Association, *Symposium: Can We Teach Problem Solving?* San Francisco, April 1989); Lochhead, "Research Synthesis on Problem Solving," *Educational Leadership* 39 (1981): 68–70.

95. See, e.g., Stanley Aronowitz and Henry A. Giroux, *Postmodern Education: Politics, Culture, & Social Criticism* (Minneapolis: University of Minnesota Press, 1991), which contains updated versions of various articles from the late 1980s.

96. Aronowitz and Giroux, 16.

97. Alan J. Bishop, *Mathematical Enculturation: A Cultural Perspective on Mathematics Education* (Boston: Kluwer Academic, 1988); Douglas Campbell, "Developing Mathematical Literacy in a Bilingual Classroom," in Jenny Cook-Gumperz, ed., *The Social Construction of Literacy* (Cambridge: Cambridge University Press, 1986): 156–184; Ubiratan D'Ambrosio, "Ethnomathematics and Its Place in the History and Pedagogy of Mathematics," *For the Learning of Mathematics* 5, no. 1 (February 1985): 44–48; Ubiratan D'Ambrosio, *Sociocultural Bases for Mathematics Education* (Campinas, Brazil: UNICAMP, 1985).

98. Stuart Hall, 1977; Fiske, 273.

99. "Thus, when MTV is articulated with the record industry, its meanings are commercial and economic, but when it is articulated with the domain of youth, possible with a drug-subculture, its glossy, rapid, consumerist images may articulate (speak) meanings of opposition or evasion," Fiske, 274.

100. Fiske, 274.

101. Fiske, 275.

102. Using game shows wasn't only limited to the incorporation of their format; sometimes the show itself was an intentional pedagogical intervention. "I can't remember when I wasn't fascinated by word games like Hangman and Scrabble, but I didn't get hooked on *Wheel of Fortune* until I discovered it could help me be a better teacher. About 10 years ago, while teaching a special class of teenagers with serious discipline problems, I found I could hold their attention by tuning in to daytime's *Wheel of Fortune* and having them play along. Like the contestants, they would try to complete a word or a phrase with only a few letters as clues. It was a

great way to teach the kids spelling, phonics, and pronunciation," Swinson, 72.

103. Richard Zoglin, "Multiple Fun on Square One," *Time* 129 (23 February 1987): 86.

104. Fiske, 276.

105. See, e.g., the U.S. Department of Education 1986 publication, *What Works: Research About Teaching and Learning*, 29. "Children in early grades learn mathematics more effectively when they use physical objects in their lesson." References cited include articles by L. Carmody, Elizabeth Fennema, D. Jamison, P. Suppes, Jean Piaget, and Marilyn Suydam. The argument here and subsequent paragraphs are based on research by Valerie Walkerdine reported in her book, *The Mastery of Reason: Cognitive Development and the Production of Rationality* (New York: Routledge, 1988).

106. Walkerdine, *Mastery*, 148. Walkerdine noted however that the commonsense theory is possibly more accurate for middle-class children. Her studies of working-class children in Britain consistently identified abstract skills normally presumed unavailable to young people. In this way educational practice devalued the skills of some students while positioning them in specific class-based ways. One of Walkerdine's points is that pedagogical theory is based heavily on the experiences of middle-class children. Working-class children, however, typically have a more elaborate and abstract comprehension of money and its role than their middle-class peers. Unfortunately, this is not valued in their early school experiences; and by the time it is valued, these students have learned well the lesson that such comprehension is irrelevant to school mathematics.

107. Waters, 64.

108. Grossberger, 68.

109. Pollan, 26.

110. Pollan, 26.

111. Pollan, 26.

112. Pollan, 26. "Merv himself once said, 'It's like being let loose on Rodeo Drive.'" Grossberger, 68. *"Wheel of Fortune* is more than a game show: it's an electronic shopping mall." Waters, 64.

113. Sherman, 28.

114. Pollan, 26.

115. Pollan, 26.

116. Thomas Mulkeen, introduction, special issue on new trends in mathematics education, *Education and Urban Society* 17, no. 4 (August 1985): 371–376; quote, 373.

117. More on professional practice as the construction of public problems will be found in the next chapter.

118. National Council of Teachers of Mathematics, *Curriculum and Evaluation Standards for School Mathematics* (Reston, Va.: NCTM, 1989).

119. National Council of Teachers of Mathematics, *Professional Standards for Teaching Mathematics* (Reston, Va.: NCTM, 1991).

### Chapter 3

1. Lorelei Brush, *Encouraging Girls in Mathematics: The Problem and the Solution* (Cambridge, Mass.: Abt Books, 1980).

2. Brush, 1–2.

3. Brush, 19.

4. See, e.g., Valerie Walkerdine, "On the Regulation of Speaking and Silence: Subjectivity, Class and Gender in Contemporary Schooling," in Carolyn Steedman, Cathy Urwin, and Valerie Walkerdine, eds., *Language, Gender and Childhood* (London: Rout-

ledge & Kegan Paul, 1985), 203–241; Valerie Walkerdine, "It's Only Natural: Rethinking Child-Centered Pedagogy," in Ann-Marie Wolpe and James Donald, eds., *Is There Anyone Here from Education? Education after Thatcher* (London: Pluto Press, 1983).

5. Gilah C. Leder, "Gender Differences in Mathematics: An Overview," in Elizabeth Fennema and Gilah C. Leder, eds., *Mathematics and Gender* (New York: Teachers College, 1990), 10–26.

6. See Margaret R. Meyer and Mary Schatz Koehler, "Internal Influences on Gender Influences in Mathematics," in Elizabeth Fennema and Gilah C. Leder, eds., *Mathematics and Gender* (New York: Teachers College, 1990), 60–95. Two different models are discussed: the Autonomous Learning Behaviors model, and the Model of Academic Choice.

7. Critics have noted that attending to individual differences also has the effect of easing the teaching task. John Goodlad, for example, discussed the widespread practice of "tracking" or "ability grouping" as having as its primary objective reducing the range of individual differences present in a single classroom. See , John I. Goodlad, *A Place Called School: Prospects for the Future* (New York: McGraw-Hill, 1983). He defines tracking as "an organizational arrangement by means of which students observed to be making varied progress in school are grouped so as to reduce the apparent range of achievement and performance in any one group"; p. 151. He argues that grouping or tracking practices are justified "by resorting, on the one hand, to the myth of inevitable and irrevocable human variability and, on the other, to the popular rhetoric of providing for individual differences in learning"; p. 165. Observing that many of these "differences" were associated with economic status and racial identification, Goodlad suggests that tracking and grouping are "widely practiced by educators as a device for endeavoring to reduce the range of differences in a class and therefore the difficulty and complexity of the teaching task"; p. 151.

8. Mark Driscoll, *Research Within Reach: Secondary School Mathematics. A Research-Guided Response to the Concerns of Educators* (Reston, Va.: National Council of Teachers of Mathematics, 1982).

9. Driscoll, 15.

10. Driscoll, 15.

11. Driscoll, 19. For comparison, see J. P. Keeves, "Sex Differ-ence in Ability and Achievement," *The International Encyclopedia of Education* (New York: Pergamon Press, 1985), 4538–4544. Keeves argues that differences by gender are related to the sex-role stereo-typing of the society in which young people are undertaking their schooling. Nevertheless, he does not rule out origins of difference in abilities between the sexes. He lists intelligence, verbal, quanti-tative, and spatial abilities as areas of research; the origins of these differences are said to lie in biological factors including genetic, maturational, hormonal, and brain laterization influences; social-ization factors including effects that are transmitted by parents, teachers, or the peer group and are related to sex roles in society; and affective factors including expectancy of success, attitudes, and values. For problems with such research, see J. A. Sherman, *Sex-related Cognitive Differences: An Essay on Theory and Evidence* (Spring-field, Ill.: Thomas, 1978).

12. See, e.g., Mary Schatz Koehler, "Classrooms, Teachers, and Gender Differences in Mathematics," in Fennema and Gilah C. Leder, eds., *Mathematics and Gender* (New York: Teachers College, 1990), 128–148; Sheila Riddell, "Pupils, Resistance and Gender Codes: A study of classroom encounters," *Gender and Education* 1, no. 2 (1989): 183–197; Rosie Walden and Valerie Walkerdine, *Girls and Mathematics: The Early Years* (London: University of London Institute of Education, Bedford Way Papers 8, 1982). This blaming of teachers' expectations and unconscious yet inequitable treat-ment of girls has a long history; for a good summary of research in the 1970s, see, e.g., Lynn H. Fox, "The Effects of Sex Role Socializa-tion on Mathematics Participation and Achievement," in Lynn H. Fox, Elizabeth Fennema, and Julia Sherman, *Women and Mathemat-ics: Research Perspectives for Change* (Washington, D.C.: National Institute of Education, 1977), 1–78.

13. Elizabeth Fennema, "Teachers' Beliefs and Gender Differ-ence in Mathematics," in Fennema and Gilah C. Leder, eds., *Math-ematics and Gender* (New York: Teachers College, 1990), 169–187.

14. Fennema, 172. See also Alba Gonzalez Thompson, "The relationship of Teachers' Conceptions of Mathematics and Mathe-

matics Teaching to Instructional Practice," *Educational Studies in Mathematics* 15 (1984): 105–127: "Teachers develop patterns of behavior that are characteristic of their instructional practice. In some cases, these patterns may be manifestations of consciously held notions, beliefs, and preferences that act as 'driving forces' in shaping the teacher's behavior. In other cases, the driving forces may be unconsciously held beliefs or intuitions that may have evolved out of the teacher's experience"; p. 105. Thompson welcomed the interest in teacher cognition as a long-awaited correction to a legacy of orthodox behaviorism.

15. See chapter 2 for how I define power/knowledge following Foucault. There will be further discussion of the limitations of this working definition in the next chapter, chapter (-1).

16. See, e.g., reports of research done by Harold Stevenson of the University of Michigan. Edward B. Fiske, "U.S. Pupils Lag in Math Ability, 3 Studies Find," *The New York Times*, 11 January 1987, 1; "Lessons: Behind Americans' problems with math, a question of social attitudes" (June 15, 1988): 8. Similar arguments were made in popular journals in their advice to parents. Reporting on studies that attempted to explain why Japanese children performed better on standardized tests than their American counterparts, these journals implored parents to avoid creating a bad "attitude" in the home. They linked achievement in mathematics with the mother's attitudes about mathematics. Mary H. Futrell, president of the National Education Association, was quoted in *Jet* contrasting the typical Japanese mother's "successful" view that effort results in achievement, with the "common American mother's unsuccessful view" that achievement is the result of ability. "Children's Math Aptitude Linked to Mom's Attitude," *Jet* 71 (9 Februrary 1988): 39.

17. Joan Wallach Scott, *Gender and the Politics of History* (New York: Columbia University Press, 1988).

18. Walkerdine, *Counting Girls Out* (London: Virago Press, 1989). Secretary of Education William Bennett provided a good example of this in his publication *First Lessons*, intended to promote reform in elementary schooling. A condensed version of his report printed in *Phi Delta Kappa* in 1986 included the admonition that "Just as important as a good foundation of knowledge, skills,

and interests is a foundation of good habits. The elementary school that trains a young girl to read instructions carefully and to check her work when she is finished is shaping the habits that distinguish good students from bad. 'It makes no small difference,' Aristotle wrote, 'whether we form habits of one kind or another from our very youth; it makes a great deal of difference, or rather all the difference.'" Walkerdine noted that girls already learn this lesson well, which accounts for the tendency to favor females in achievement in the early grades. They are often described as hard working and neat. In the later grades, these very skills are labels for a lack of natural ability, evidenced by challenging the teacher, or not attending to irrelevant features of work such as neatness. Bennett quote found in First Lessons. *Phi Delta Kappan* (October 1986): 125–134; p. 129.

19. Elizabeth Fennema, "Justice, Equity, and Mathematics Education," in Fennema and Gilah C. Leder, eds., *Mathematics and Gender* (New York: Teachers College, 1990), 1–9; quote, 6.

20. See, e.g., Robert M. Hashway, "Sex Differences in Mathematics Achievement—Are They Real?, *Phi Delta Kappan* 63 (October 1981): 139–140. About 98 percent of the differences between individuals in mathematics achievement could be attributed to some characteristic other than sex; sex differences accounted for less than 1.5 percent of variation between individuals. Hashway also argued that, since the variable "sex" could not be altered in the classroom or through counseling, it was not of practical importance to teachers: They should address other variables.

21. It should be clear, however, from my discussion of gender, that I believe "sex differences" to be culturally and socially constructed through practice; thus I find it absurd to imagine biologically fundamental differences to be pertinent.

22. For a similar argument from a British perspective on gender and mathematics education, see Rosie Walden and Valerie Walkerdine, "Characteristics, Views and Relationships in the Classroom," in Leone Burton, ed., *Girls Into Maths Can Go* (New York: Holt, Rinehart & Winston, 1986), 122–146. Concerning statistical significance, see, e.g., R. P. Carver, "The Case Against Significance Testing," *Harvard Educational Review* 48 (1978): 378–399; D. E. Mor-

rison and R. E. Henkle, eds., *The Significance Test Controversy* (Chicago: Aldine, 1970).

23. Gilah C. Leder and Elizabeth Fennema, "Gender Difference in Mathematics: A Synthesis," in Fennema and Gilah C. Leder, eds., *Mathematics and Gender* (New York: Teachers College, 1990), 188–199; quote, 197.

24. Fennema, "Justice, Equity and Mathematics Education," 1. The following argument is a paraphrase of Fennema.

25. Mathematics educators do have a natural interest in the increase in students of mathematics and mathematics courses in schools, and this could be a plausible 'explanation' for gender-related research: increasing the market for mathematics education.

26. These arguments are based in essentialist conceptions of gender as a fundamental fact of reality. They argue that there are basic cognitive differences by gender (meaning 'sex'), and that female 'ways of thinking' would change the nature of mathematics. See Carol Gilligan, *In a Different Voice* (Cambridge, Mass.: Harvard University Press, 1982), for an argument that could be used to support this essentialist view (even though Gilligan herself does not support biological essentialism). On gender and mathematics as a field of knowledge, see R. Mura," "Feminist Views on Mathematics," *International Organization of Women and Mathematics Newsletter* 3, no. 2 (1987): 6–11; and Leone Burton, "Mathematics as a Cultural Experience: Whose Experience?," in Christine Keitel, ed., *Mathematics, Education, and Society* (Paris: UNESCO Science and Technology Education Document Series No. 35, 1989), 16–18. On expanding notions of problem solving and problem posing via Gilligan's study of moral decision making, see Stephen I. Brown, "The Logic of Problem Generation: From Morality and Solving to De-Posing and Rebellion," *For the Learning of Mathematics* 4, no. 1 (Feburary 1984): 9–20.

27. This argument has been made by Mary Antony in the context of science education in India in her article, "Knowledge and Control: A Sociohistorical Analysis of Sexism and Science Education in India," *Michigan Feminist Studies* 6 (Fall 1991): 187–201.

28. Lynn Friedman, "Mathematics and the Gender Gap: A meta-analysis of recent studies on sex differences in mathematical tasks," *Review of Educational Research* 59, no. 2 (Summer 1989): 185–213.

29. Gila Hanna, "Girls and Boys About Equal in Mathematics Achievement in Eighth Grade: Results From Twenty Countries," *Educational Studies in Mathematics* 20, no. 2 (May 1989): 225–232; Erika Kuendiger, "Mathematics—A Male Subject?," in Christine Keitel, ed., *Mathematics, Education, and Society* (Paris: UNESCO Science and Technology Education Document Series No. 35, 1989), 134–138. See also Corinna A. Ethington, "Gender Differences in Mathematics: An international perspective," *Journal for Research in Mathematics Education* 21 no. 1 (January 1990): 74–80.

30. Fennema, "Justice, Equity," 1. She is referring to Gilligan's *Different Voice*, noted above.

31. See also Anne C. Petersen, et al., "Sex Differences," in H. E. Mitzel, ed., *Encyclopedia of Educational Research*, fifth edition (New York: Free Press, 1982), 1696–1712. Nancy Russo, director of Women's Programs for the American Psychological Association and president of Organizations for Professional Women, was reported as responding to research on sex differences with the important point that most research on sex differences would be biased because of the very social context in which it was conducted. "It would be funny," [she said,] "if such research were not used to justify the status quo that keeps women from pursuing math and science careers." "Researchers Dispute Role of Genetics in Math Achievements By the Sexes," *Phi Delta Kappan* 63 (March 1982): 435–436.

32. Valerie Walkerdine, comp., *Counting Girls Out* (London: Virago Press, 1989); quote, 1–2.

33. Murray Edelman, *Constructing the Political Spectacle* (Chicago: University of Chicago Press, 1988).

34. See, e.g., "Problems! Math skills are down again," *Time* (24 September 1979): 55.

35. See, e.g., "U.S. Report Fears Most Americans Will Become Scientific Illiterates," *The New York Times*, 23 October 1980, 3.

36. Patricia McCormack, "The Lasting Crisis in Math, Science: U.S. Education Droops in the Era of High Technology," *Los Angeles Times*, December 1982, 3

37. McCormack, 12.

38. See, e.g., Dennis A. Williams, Marsha Zabarsky, and Barbara Burgower, "Bait for Science Teachers," *Newsweek* (14 Feburary 1983): 79.

39. McCormack, 12.

40. In 1981 there was reported a 22 percent gap between the supply of teachers and the demand for them. A National Council of Supervisors of Mathematics survey found 26 percent of mathematics teachers nationwide either had no certification or only temporary certification in mathematics. See "Math Curriculum Drives Students, Teachers Away," *Phi Delta Kappan* 63 (March 1982): 436; "Science and Math Education," *Technology Review* 93 (November–December 1990): 61; United States Senate Committee on Governmental Affairs "Crisis in Science and Math Education" Hearings February 28, 1990 and November 1989, Supt. Docs. Y4.Sci2: 1-1/94 1990 and Y4G74/95. hrg 101–561 1990.

41. Williams, 79.

42. Michael W. Apple, "National Reports and the Construction of Inequality," *British Journal of Sociology of Education* 7, no. 2 (1986): 171–190. The argument for this paragraph is based in Apple's assessment.

43. Education Commission of the States Task Force on Education for Economic Growth, *Action for Excellence* (Denver, Colo.: Education Commission of the States ED 235 588, 1983): 1.

44. A. Harry Passow, *Reforming Schools in the 1980s: A Critical Review of the National Reports* (New York: ERIC Clearinghouse on

Urban Education No. 84, Institute for Urban and Minority Education, Teachers College, Columbia University, 1984), 28.

45. Goodlad, 291.

46. Apple, 172.

47. Svi Shapiro, "Educational Theory and Recent Political Discourse: A New Agenda For the Left?," *Harvard Educational Review* 89, no. 2 (1987): 171–200; quote, 185.

48. Apple, 172.

49. See, e.g., John H. Martin, chair, *The Education of Adolescents* (Washington, D.C.: National Panel on High School and Adolescent Education, U.S. Government Printing Office, 1974).

50. National Commission, 26.

51. A poll found voucher systems favored by a majority, 51 percent to 38 percent. John Bunzel, ed., *Challenge to American Schools* (New York: Oxford University Press, 1985), 7.

52. Bunzel reported a substantial majority (75 percent) in favor of promotion based on examinations rather than "social" promotion, growing support for lengthening the school day and the school year, and a two-to-one margin in favor of merit plans for teachers, where teachers would be paid for results. Bunzel, 8; also reported in Apple, 173.

53. See also Henry Giroux's discussion of patriotism in his essay on popular films of the 1980s: "Citizenship, Public Philosophy, and the Struggle for Democracy," *Educational Theory* 37, no. 2 (1987): 1103–1120. Giroux argues that the "new right" did not "select the discourse," but by resonating with the desires and experiences of many people, it enabled the formation of a "public philosophy" that distorted the desires and experiences themselves, thus becoming more entrenched, while systematically ignoring major social problems and promoting hazardous levels of militarism. "Celluloid patriotism" in Hollywood films and TV programming spoke to the need for reaffirmation, to the need to have a

voice and to create larger-than-life figures who articulated the frustrations and despair experienced by many people. Citizenship in this case combined an appeal to "traditional values" with an ideology that legitimated "hypernationalism"; this ideology reinforced forms of institutional authority that refused to tolerate dissent while promoting social relations in which chauvinism and modern forms of neosexism together redefined the meaning of masculinity and power.

54. I will discuss this further below.

55. Edelman, 22. Edelman notes his conclusion is somewhat similar to the premise of the "garbage can theory" of administrative decision making suggested by James March and Johan Olsen in *Ambiguity and Choice in Organization* (Bergen, Norway: Universitetsforlaget, 1976).

56. Bunzel, 6–7. See also the film *The Principal*, which told the story of an "I mean business" principal battling these very crises in a school with strict discipline and high expectations.

57. Apple, 173.

58. Apple, 173. I have included Michael Apple's representation as an indication of counterdiscourse present in professional education journals.

59. The National Commission on Excellence in Education, *A Nation at Risk: The Imperative for Educational Reform* (Washington, D.C.: U.S. Government Printing Office, April 1983), 5.

60. Mathematical Sciences Education Board of the National Research Council, *Counting on You: Actions supporting mathematics teaching standards* (Washington, D.C.: National Academy Press, 1991).

61. *Counting on You*, 4.

62. Apple, 174. The indicated shift is from a language of subsistence or person rights to one of property rights. Apple discussed the work of Frances Fox Piven and Richard A. Cloward, *The New*

*Class War* (New York: Pantheon Books, 1982). Piven and Cloward identified an ideological context for the 1980s, in which the gains made by working men and women, minority and poor groups, and others in employment, health and safety, welfare programs, affirmative action, legal rights, and education had to be rescinded because they were "too expensive" in the wake of the greatest structural economic crisis since the great depression.

63. Ezra Bowen, "Bad News About Math," *Time* (26 January 26 1987): 65.

64. Denis P. Doyle, "Why Johnny's Teacher Can't Do Algebra," *Across the Board* 26 (June 1989): 34–8+; quote, 34.

65. Andrew Kupfer, "Turning Students on to Science," *Fortune* (Special Save Our Schools Issue) (Spring 1990): 82-3+.

66. Compare also Julian C. Stanley an Camilla P. Benbow, who conducted well-publicized research on "precocious youth." Government agencies and private foundations should consider more financial support for the descriptive and long-term follow-up aspects of longitudinal studies that characterize talented youth identification learning and what happens to them, they argued. As well, they further suggested research should be pursued on the causes of "the great hostility toward precocious intellectual achievement that is endemic in this country and on ways to counteract it." Students such as those studied in Stanley and Benbow's research "form[ed] the major basis for our country's scientific and technological future." Julian C. Stanley and Camilla P. Benbow, "Educational Policy Recommendations for Mathematically Precocious Youths," *Educational Researcher* (May 1982). Reprinted in *Educational Digest* 48, no. 3 (November 1982): 40–42. Stanley and Benbow are discussed below.

67. Kathleen Weiler, *Women Teaching for Change* (South Hadley, Mass.: Bergin & Garvey, 1988).

68. Weiler, 28.

69. Madeleine Arnot, "Male Hegemony, Social Class and Women's Education," *Journal of Education* 164, no. 1 (1982): 64–89; quote, 68. Also quoted in Weiler, 28.

70. Zalman Usiskin, "We Need Another Revolution in Secondary School Mathematics," in Christian R. Hirsch and Marilyn J. Zweng, eds., *The Secondary School Mathematics Curriculum*, 5.

71. Edward W. Said, *Covering Islam: How the Media and the Experts Determine How We See the Rest of the World* (New York: Pantheon Books, 1981); quote, xi.

72. Edelman, 1.

73. Edelman, 2.

74. Edelman, 11. Edelman elaborates: "A crisis, like all news developments, is a creation of the language used to depict it; the appearance of a crisis is a political act, not a recognition of a fact or rare situation." Page 31.

75. Edelman, 34.

76. Sheila Tobias, *Overcoming Math Anxiety* (New York: Houghton Mifflin, 1978): 13. Lucy Sells published an article based on this research in 1978, "Mathematics—A Critical Filter (The Forum)," *The Science Teacher* 45, no. 2 (February 1978): 28–29.

77. Tobias, 14. The review she referred to is: E. E. Maccoby and C. N. Jacklin, *The Psychology of Sex Differences* (Stanford University Press, 1974).

78. Tobias, 15.

79. Tobias, 16.

80. Tobias, 15.

81. Jane Byrne, "Math X Ignorance - Fear = Anxiety," *The New York Times*, 17 February 1980, 3.

82. Marlene Cimons, "Solving the Equation of Math Anxiety," *Los Angeles Times*, 23 October 1980, 1: 6.

83. Cimons, 26.

84. Eloise Salholz and Rosalyn Jones, "Curing Math Anxiety," *Newsweek* (23 August 1982): 71.

85. "Girls Could Equal Boys at Math, Study Asserts," *Detroit News*, 15 April 1980, A-3:3. The report was titled "Women in Mathematics."

86. "Women in Math: A rising trend," *Los Angeles Times*, 17 April 1980, V-28: 1.

87. Camilla Persson Benbow and Julian C. Stanley, "Sex Differences in Mathematical Ability: Fact or Artifact?," *Science* 210 (12 December 1980): 1262–1264.

88. A selection of late 1980 titles: The gender factor in math—a new study says males may be naturally abler than females; Do males have a math gene?; New study finds boys beat girls at math; Boys beat girls in math: why?; Are boys better at math? Compare a selection of early 1980 titles: Study shows women are equally qualified; Girls could equal boys at math; Women in math: a rising trend.

89. "Gender Factor"—*Time* article.

90. "Are Boys Better At Math?" *The New York Times*, 7 December 1980, 102: 1. See also "Boys Beat Girls in Math Study: Why?," *The Detroit News*, 18 December 1980, CD12: 1; "New Study Finds Boys Beat Girls at Math," *Los Angeles Times*, 21 December 1980, 1-A: 7: 1; Dennis A. Williams and Patricia King, "Do Males Have a Math Gene?," *Newsweek* (15 December 1980): 73; "The Gender Factor in Math," *Time* (15 December 1980): 57.

91. Williams and King, 73.

92. *Los Angeles Times* article.

93. Williams and King, 73.

94. Williams and King, 73.

95. Caryl Rivers, "Got Good Math Genes?" *The New York Times,* 30 May 1981, I-23: 2. For a discussion of contemporaneous "biosocial" debates in a more global context, see Cynthia Fuchs Epstein, *Deceptive Distinctions: Sex, Gender, and the Social Order* (New Haven Conn.: Yale University Press, 1988).

96. Mildred G. Goldberger, "Figuring the Odds Against Women," *Los Angeles Times,* 28 January 1982, V-8: 1.

97. "Who Is Really Better at Math?" *Time* (22 March 1982): 64.

98. See, e.g., Harold M. Schmeck, Jr., "Boys Better Than Girls In Math Test," *The New York Times,* 29 November 1983, III-2: 1.

99. Lee Dembart. "Biological Basis for Math Ability Suggested By Study," *Los Angeles Times,* 6 January 1984, 1: 1; "Math Skills Linked to Hormone," *The Detroit News,* 27 May 1986, A-1: 2. See also the full-length feature article by Daniel Goleman, "Girls and Math: Is biology really destiny?" *The New York Times* Special Education Life Section, 27 August 1987, XII, 42: 1.

100. Dembart. The most plausible biological basis for declining test scores I have found was made by Ira Shor in *Culture Wars: School and Society in the Conservative Restoration, 1969–1984* (Boston: Routledge & Kegan Paul, 1986). He reports research that links the decline with the increase in radiation levels since the advent of nuclear testing. Populations of test-takers in Utah, in which the testing occurred, had the most dramatic declines.

101. Betty Ann Kevles, "Do Boys' Superior Math Skills Add Up?" *Los Angeles Times,* 29 August 1984, V-10: 1.

102. Kevles.

103. Kevles.

104. Goleman,: 42.

105. Sheila Tobias, *They're Not Dumb, They're Different: Stalking the Second Tier* (Tucson, Ariz.: Research Corporation, 1990).

106. *Visible Language* XI, no. 3 (1982). See also Garth Boomer, "From Catechism to Communication: Language learning and mathematics," *The Australian Mathematics Teacher* 42, no. 1 (April 1986): 1-7; G. Corran and Valerie Walkerdine, "Reading the Signs of Mathematics," in *The Practice of Reason*, volume 1 (London: University of London Institute of Education, 1981); David Pimm, *Speaking Mathematically—Communicating in Mathematics Classrooms* (London: Routledge & Kegan Paul, 198?). It is true that most of this work was done in the United Kingdom. Yet its reputation could not have gone unnoticed in the entire mathematics education community. Indeed, the Cockcroft Report, which altered the entire British mathematics curriculum, was well-referenced in American journals, and it was particularly noted for its introduction of literacy-oriented curricula and evaluation methods.

107. I know of none. And I have found no references to any.

108. Valerie Walkerdine, "Sex, Power, and Pedagogy," *Screen Education* 38 (1981): 14–21; Walkerdine, ed., *Counting Girls Out*.

109. Elsie Moore, quoted in Goleman, 43.

110. Tobias, *Not Dumb*; Perla Nesha, "The Stereotyped Nature of School Word Problems," *For the Learning of Mathematics* 1, no. 3 (March 1981): 47–50.

111. Darrell Block and Elsie Moore, authors of *Advantage and Disadvantage*, quoted in Goleman, 43.

112. *Counting Girls Out*.

113. Kevles.

114. Goleman, 43.

115. "A Raft of Plans That Try to Dispel Math Anxieties," *The New York Times*, 2 August 1987, XII, 43: 3.

116. "Students' Hesitance to Study Science, Math Examined," *Los Angeles Times,* 7 December 1984, A-7: 1.

117. Pat Rogers, "Gender Differences in Mathematical Ability—Perceptions vs. Performance," *Association for Women in Mathematics Newsletter (AMM Newsletter)* 19: 4: 6–10. Reprinted in Leone Burton, ed., *Gender and Mathematics: An International Perspective* (Strand, England: Cassell Educational Limited, 1990): 38–46.

118. Rogers: 8.

119. Rogers, 8.

120. Rogers, 10.

121. See, e.g., Lynda Richardson, "Up Tempo Teaching by Rapping Right Triangles," *The New York Times,* 17 November 1993, 143, no. 49, B7; William Celis III, "New Teaching Methods Puts Math in Real Life," *The New York Times,* 16 June 1993, B7.

122. Janice A. Leroux and Cheeying Ho, "Success and Mathematically Gifted Female Students: The Challenge Continues," *Feminist Teacher* 7, no. 2 (1993): 42–48; quote, p. 42.

123. Leroux and Ho, 47.

124. Leroux and Ho, 47.

125. Jane Gross, "To Help Girls Keep Up: Math Class Without Boys," *The New York Times,* 24 November 1993, B9.

126. Tobias, *Not Dumb,* 83.

Chapter (-1)

1. "Queen Math Teacher" Beverly Davidman, quoted in Lynda Richardson, "Up Tempo Teaching by Rapping Right Triangles," *The New York Times,* 17 November 1993, B7.

2. National Council of Teachers of Mathematics. Commission on Standards for School Mathematics, *Curriculum and Evaluation Standards for School Mathematics* (Reston, Va.: NCTM, 1989); quote, 11; *Professional Standards for Teaching Mathematics* (Reston, Va.: NCTM, 1991).

3. See my discussion of power in chapter 0.

4. *Professional Standards*, 1.

5. The concept 'cultural capital' owes its origin to Pierre Bourdieu. See, e.g., Pierre Bourdieu, *Reproduction in Education, Society and Culture* (Beverly Hills, Calif.: Sage Publications, 1977); Pierre Bourdieu, *Outline of a Theory of Practice* (Cambridge: Cambridge University Press, 1977). Michael Apple, in *Education and Power*, makes extensive use of 'cultural capital' for a development of power that could be contrasted with my own (Boston: Routledge & Kegan Paul, 1982). As I mention in chapter 0, the major difference is my abandonment, with Foucault, of power as a hypostasized, i.e., reified, idea.

6. Rudy Rucker, *Mind Tools: The Five Levels of Mathematical Reality* (Boston: Houghton Mifflin, 1987): 99.

7. Nyberg. See chapter 0.

8. *Professional Standards*, 3.

9. See Rucker's chapter on "Math Space and Real Space."

10. Conrad W. Worrill, "Teaching math and science," *Chicago Defender*, 9 May 1990, 10:1.

11. Harold E. Charles, "Innumeracy and Illiteracy," *Chicago Defender*, 4 March 1989, 28:1.

12. *Curriculum and Evaluation Standards*, 3.

13. *Curriculum and Evaluation Standards*, 3.

14. *Curriculum and Evaluation Standards*, 3.

15. *Curriculum and Evaluation Standards*, 5.

16. P. Cline-Cohen, *A Calculating People: The Spread of Numeracy in Early America* (Berkeley, Calif.: University of California Press, 1982).

17. Valerie Walkerdine, "Subjectivity, Discourse and Practice in Mathematics Education," paper presented at the First International Conference on the Political Dimensions of Mathematics Education: Action & Critique (London: Department of Mathematics, Statistics and Computing, Institute of Education, University of London, April 1–4, 1990): no page numbers. See also her book, *The Mastery of Reason: Cognitive Development and the Production of Rationality* (London/New York: Routledge, 1988).

18. *Curriculum and Evaluation Standards*, 5.

19. John Fiske, *Understanding Popular Culture* (Boston: Unwin Hyman, 1989).

20. Fiske, 11.

21. Fiske, 11. Here I am continuing to adapt Fiske's argument for my own purposes.

22. Jean Lave, *Cognition in Practice: Mind, Mathematics, and Culture in Everyday Life* (Cambridge/New York: Cambridge University Press, 1988); Jean Lave, *Situated Learning: Legitimate Peripheral Participation* (New York: Cambridge University Press, 1991).

23. Phil Patton, "Who Owns 'X'?" *The New York Times,* 8 November 1992, IX, 1: 9: 1.

24. Fiske, 11–14.

25. Rik Pinxten, Ingrid van Dooren, and Frank Harvey, *Anthropology of Space* (Philadelphia: University of Pennsylvania Press, 1983); Rik Pinxten, I. van Dooren, and E. Soberon, *Towards a Navajo Geometry* (Ghent, Belgium: K.K.I., 1987).

26. Claudia Zazlavsky, *Africa Counts: Number and Pattern in African Culture* (Boston: Prindle, Weber & Schmidt, 1973; paperback, Chicago: L. Hill, 1979). See also: Ubiratan D'Ambrosio, "Ethnomathematics and Its Place in the History and Pedagogy of Mathematics," *For the Learning of Mathematics* 5, no. 1 (February 1985): 44–48; Ubiratan D'Ambrosio, *Sociocultural Bases for Mathematics Education* (Campinas, Brazil: UNICAMP, 1985); Alan Bishop, *Mathematical Enculturation* (Dordrecht, Holland: Kluwer Academic Publishers, 1988). Paul Gerdes, "Conditions and Strategies for Emancipatory Mathematics Education in Underdeveloped Countries," *For the Learning of Mathematics* 5, no. 1: 15–20.

27. See Edward Said, *Orientalism* (New York: Pantheon Books, 1978).

28. Munir Fasheh, "Community Education: To Reclaim and Transform What Has Been Made Invisible," *Harvard Educational Review* 60, no. 1 (1990): 19–35; Munir Fasheh, "Mathematics in a Social Context: Math Within Education as Praxis Versus Within Education as Hegemony," in Christine Keitel, ed., *Mathematics, Education, and Society* (Paris: UNESCO Document Series No. 35, 1989); Munir Fasheh, "Mathematics, Culture and Authority," *For the Learning of Mathematics* 3, no. 1 (1982): 2–8.

29. James Clifford, *The Predicament of Culture: Twentieth-Century Ethnography, Literature, and Art* (Cambridge: Harvard University Press, 1988); quotes, 14–15.

30. Walkerdine, 3.

31. See chapter 3.

32. British researchers whose work Walkerdine has reexamined.

33. Walkerdine, 4.

34. Terezinha Nunas Carraher, "Negotiating the Results of Mathematical Computations," *International Journal of Educational Research* 13, no. 6 (1989): 637–646; Terezinha Nunas Carraher and P. E. Bryant, *Addition and Subtraction as Everyday and Mathematical*

*Concepts* (International Society for the Study of Behavior Development, China Satellite Conference, Beijing, 1987). T. Carraher, "From Drawings to Buildings: Mathematical Scales at Work," *International Journal of Behavioral Development* 9 (1986): 527–544; T. Carraher, "Material Embodiments of Mathematical Models in Everyday Life," in Keitel, ed. See also Philip J. Davis and Reuben Hersh, *Descartes' Dream: The World According to Mathematics* (San Diego: Harcourt Brace Jovanovich, 1986).

35. Walkerdine, 6. She is referring to Brian Rotman, *Mathematics: An Essay in Semiotics* (Bristol, England: University of Bristol Mimeo, 1980).

36. Fiske, 15.

37. Fiske, 15.

38. See Lawrence Schick, *Heroic Worlds: A History and Guide to Role-Playing Games* (Buffalo: Prometheus Books, 1991).

39. Peter Appelbaum, "Mathematics as a Social Semiotic: Lemke and Halliday Come to America" (Ann Arbor: The University of Michigan, 1988).

40. Dick Hebdige, *Subculture: The Meaning of Style* (London: Methuen, 1979). See also Seymour Papert's recent discussion of *Dirty Dancing* in *The Children's Machine* (New York: Basic Books, 1993).

41. Fiske, 15.

42. Clifford, 15.

43. Fiske, 15.

44. Schick.

45. William Celis III, "New Teaching Methods Put Math in Real Life," *The New York Times*, 16 June 1993, B7.

46. Celis, B7. A noteworthy professional call for legitimizing such change can be found in Stephen Lerman's "Constructivism, Mathematics and Mathematics Education," *Educational Studies in Mathematics* 20, no. 2 (May 1989): 211–223.

47. Celis, B7.

48. Celis, B7.

49. Diane Lange, quoted in Celis, B7.

50. Ned Lerner, *Chuck Yaeger Flight Simulator* (Calif.: Electronic Arts).

51. See, e.g., "United Negro College Fund. A Mind is a Terrible Thing To Waste," *The New York Times,* 17 October 1993, N.J. 14.

52. Michel de Certeau, *Heterologies: Discourse on the Other* (Minneapolis: University of Minnesota Press, 1986); *The Practice of Everyday Life* (Berkeley: University of California Press, 1984).

53. Umberto Eco, "Social Life as a Sign System," in David Robey, ed., *Structuralism: An Introduction* (Oxford: Clarendon Press, 1973); Umberto Eco, *The Role of the Reader: Explorations in the Semiotics of Texts* (London: Hutchinson, 1981). Fiske uses de Certeau and Eco to make a similar point.

54. Fiske, 19.

55. Michel Foucault, *Power/Knowledge.*

56. Fiske, 19.

57. Fiske, 20.

58. Fiske, 21.

59. Geoff Whitty and Michael Young, eds, *Explorations in the Politics of School Knowledge* (Nafferton, Driffield, England: Nafferton Books, 1976); quotes this paragraph, 1.

60. Whitty and Young, 2.

61. Whitty and Young, 2.

62. Whitty and Young, 5.

63. Whitty and Young, 2.

64. Jean Lave.

65. Michael Young, foreword in Andrew Brown and Paul Dowling, *Towards a Critical Alternative to Internationalism and Monoculturalism in Mathematics Education* (London: Centre for Multicultural Education, Institute of Education, University of London, Working Paper No. 10, 1989), 7.

66. Fiske, 164.

67. Fiske, 164.

68. Svi Shapiro, "Back to Basics: A Politics of Meaning for Education," *Tikkun* 8, no. 1 (January/Feburary 1993): 46–50, 75–76.

69. Shapiro, "Back to Basics," 47.

70. See, e.g., Lilian G. Katz, "Reading, Writing, Narcissism," *The New York Times,* 15 July 1993, A25; William Celis III, "Down From the Self-Esteem High," *The New York Times,* 1 August 1993, D3; Richard Cohen, "Self Esteem: Sorry, No Extra Credit," *The Washington Post,* 12 June 1991, A23; Jayne E. Stake and Joan M. Singer, "Mathematics and Self-Esteem: Implications for Women's Career Choice," *Psychology of Women Quarterly* (December 1986): 339–351.

71. Stephen I. Brown and Marion I. Walter, *The Art of Problem Posing* (Philadelphia: The Franklin Institute Press, 1983); and *Problem Posing: Reflections and Applications* (Hillsdale, N.J.: Lawrence Erlbaum, 1993).

72. Stephen I. Brown, "Mathematics and Humanistic Themes: Sum Considerations," in Brown and Marion I. Walter, eds,

*Problem Posing: Reflections and Applications* (Hillsdale, N.J: Lawrence Erlbaum, 1993).

73. See also Iris Rotberg's "Math and Science Education: A New Perspective," adapted in *Education Digest* 50, no. 6 (February 1989): 24–27; or *Phi Delta Kappan* 65 (May 1984): 668–673.

74. Andrew Brown and Paul Dowling, *Towards a Critical Alternative to Internationalism and Monoculturalism in Mathematics Education* (London: Centre for Multicultural Education, Institute of Education, University of London, Working Paper No. 10, 1989), 29.

75. See Fiske, 165.

# BIBLIOGRAPHY

"A Raft of Plans That Try to Dispel Math Anxieties," *The New York Times,* 2 August 1987: XII, 43: 3.

*Action in Teacher Education* IXX, no. 2 (Summer 1987).

Adams, Mary Louise. "There's No Place Like Home: On the Place of Identity in Feminist Politics." *Feminist Review* 31 (Spring 1989): 22–23.

Althusser, Louis. *Lenin and Philosophy and Other Essays.* London: New Left Books, 1971.

Antony, Mary. "Knowledge and Control: A Sociohistorical Analysis of Sexism and Science Education in India." *Michigan Feminist Studies* 6 (Fall 1991): 187–201.

Appelbaum, Peter M. "Mathematics as a Social Semiotic: Lemke and Halliday Come to America." Ann Arbor, Mich.: The University of Michigan, 1988.

Appelbaum, Peter M. *The Power of Individual Subjectivity and the Subjectivity of Power in Education.* Program on the Comparative Study of Social Transformations, Working Paper Series #30. Ann Arbor, Mich.: The University of Michigan, 1989.

Apple, Michael W. *Education and Power.* Boston: Ark Paperbacks, 1982.

Apple, Michael W. "National Reports and the Construction of Inequality." *British Journal of Sociology of Education* 7, no. 2 (1986): 171–190.

Apple, Michael W. *On Analyzing Hegemony. In Ideology and Curriculum.* New York: Routledge & Kegan Paul, 1979.

"Are Boys Better At Math?" *The New York Times,* 7 December 1980: 102: 1.

Arendt, Hannah. *The Human Condition*. Chicago: University of Chicago Press, 1958.

Armbrister, Trevor. "The Teacher Who Took On the Establishment." *Readers Digest* 126 (March 1985): 23–28.

Arnot, Madeleine. "Male Hegemony, Social Class, and Women's Education." *Journal of Education* 164, no. 1 (1982): 64–89.

Aronowitz, Stanley, and Henry A. Giroux. *Education Under Siege: The Conservative, Liberal, and Radical Debate Over Schooling*. South Hadley, Mass.: Bergin & Garvey Press, 1985.

Aronowitz, Stanley, and Henry A. Giroux. *Postmodern Education: Politics, Culture, & Social Criticism*. Minneapolis: University of Minnesota Press, 1991.

Aufderheide, Pat. "Reel Life." *Mother Jones* 13 (April 1988): 45.

Ball, Stephen J., ed. *Foucault and Education: Disciplines and Knowledge*. London/New York: Routledge, 1990.

Barthes, Roland. *Mythologies*. New York: Hill and Wang, 1972.

Bartlett, Kay. "Are You Innumerate?" *The Saturday Evening Post*, September 1989, 36.

Barton, Len, and Stephen Walker. "Sociological Perspectives and the Study of Education." In *A Sociology of Educating*, edited by Roland Meighan. London: Holt, Rinehart & Winston, 1981.

Belsey, Catherine. *Critical Practice*. New York: Methuen, 1980.

Benbow, Camilla Persson, and Julian C. Stanley. "Sex Differences in Mathematical Ability: Fact or Artifact?" *Science* 210 (12 December 1980): 1262–1264.

Bennett, William. "First Lessons." *Phi Delta Kappan* (October 1986): 125–134; p. 129.

Berliner, David C. "Math Teaching May Favor Boys Over Girls."

*Instructor* (October 1987). Also published in *Education Digest* 53, no. 5 (January 1988): 29.

Bernstein, Basil. *Towards a Theory of Educational Transmissions.* Vol. 3 of *Class, Codes and Control.* London: Routledge & Kegan Paul, 1977.

Berube, Maurice. *American Presidents and Education.* New York: Greenwood Press, 1991.

Beyer, Landon E., and Michael W. Apple. *The Curriculum: Problems, Politics, and Possibilities.* Albany, New York: State University of New York Press, 1988.

Bishop, Alan J. *Mathematical Enculturation: A Cultural Perspective on Mathematics Education.* Boston: Kluwer Academic, 1988.

Bloom, Allan. *The Closing of the American Mind: How Higher Education Has Failed Democracy and Impoverished the Souls of Today's Students.* New York: Simon and Schuster, 1987.

Bloome, David. "Toward a More Delicate Elaboration of Procedural Display." *Curriculum Inquiry* 20, no. 1 (1990): 71–73.

Bloome, David, P. Puro, and E. Theodorou. "Procedural Display and Classroom Lessons." *Curriculum Inquiry* 19, no. 3 (1989): 265–291.

Bloor, David. *Wittgenstein: A Social Theory of Knowledge.* New York: Columbia University Press, 1983.

Boomer, Garth. "From Catechism to Communication: language learning and mathematics." *The Australian Mathematics Teacher* 42, no. 1 (Apilr 1986): 1–7.

Borasi, Raffaella, and Stephen I. Brown. "Communications: A 'Novel' Approach to Texts." *For the Learning of Mathematics* 5, no. 1 (February 1985): 21–23.

Bourdieu, Pierre, and Jean-Claude Passeron. *Reproduction in Education, Society and Culture.* Beverly Hills, Calif.: Sage, 1977.

Bourdieu, Pierre. *Outline of a Theory of Practice.* Cambridge: Cambridge University Press, 1977.

Bowen, Ezra. "Bad News About Math." *Time* (26 January 1987): 65.

Bowles, Samuel, and Herbert Gintis. *Schooling in Capitalist America.* New York: Basic Books, 1976.

"Boys Beat Girls in Math Study: Why?" *The Detroit News,* 18 December 1980, CD12: 1.

Britzman, Deborah P. "Cultural Myths in the Making of a Teacher: Biography and social structure in teacher education." *Harvard Educational Review* 56, no. 4 (November 1986): 442–456.

Brown, Andrew, and Paul Dowling. "Towards a Critical Alternative to Internationalism and Monoculturalism in Mathematics Education." London: Centre for Multicultural Education, Institute of Education, University of London, Working Paper No. 10, 1989.

Brown, Richard, ed. *Knowledge, Education, and Cultural Change.* London: Tavistock, 1973.

Brown, Stephen I. "Reflections on a Letter of Acceptance." *For the Learning of Mathematics* 2, no. 1 (July 1981): 46–49.

Brown, Stephen I. "The Logic of Problem Generation: From Morality and Solving to De-Posing and Rebellion." *For the Learning of Mathematics* 4, no. 1 (February 1984): 9–20.

Brown, Stephen I. "The Right to Be Wrong." *For the Learning of Mathematics* 1, no. 3 (March 1981): 27–36.

Brown, Stephen I. "Ye Shall Be Known By Your Generations." *For the Learning of Mathematics* 1, no. 3 (March 1981): 27–36

Brown, Stephen I., and Marion I. Walter. *The Art of Problem Posing.* Philadelphia: The Franklin Institute Press, 1983.

Brown, Stephen I., and Marion I. Walter (eds.). *Problem Posing:*

*Reflections and Applications.* Hillsdale, N.J.: Lawrence Erlbaum, 1993.

Bruner, Jerome S. *Toward a Theory of Instruction.* Cambridge, Mass.: Belknap Press, 1966.

Brush, Lorelei. *Encouraging Girls in Mathematics: The Problem and the Solution.* Cambridge, Mass.: Abt Books, 1980.

Bulkin, Elly, Minnie Bruce Pratt, and Barbara Smith. *Yours in Struggle: Three Feminist Perspectives on Anti-Semitism and Racism.* Brooklyn, N.Y.: Long Haul Press, 1984.

Bunzel, John, ed. *Challenge to American Schools.* New York: Oxford University Press, 1985.

Burbules, Nicholas. "A Theory of Power in Education." *Educational Theory* 36, no. 2 (1986): 95–114.

Burton, Leone. "Mathematics as a Cultural Experience: Whose Experience?" *Mathematics, Education, and Society,* edited by In Christine Keitel. Paris: UNESCO Science and Technology Education Document Series No. 35, 1989.

Byrne, Jane. "Math X Ignorance - Fear = Anxiety." *The New York Times* 17 February 1980, 20: 3.

Campbell, Douglas. "Developing Mathematical Literacy in a Bilingual Classroom." In *The Social Construction of Literacy,* edited by Jenny Cook-Gumperz. Cambridge: Cambridge University Press, 1986.

Carraher, Terezinha N. "Negotiating the Results of Mathematical Computations." *International Journal of Educational Research* 13, no. 6 (1989): 637–646.

Carraher, Terezinha N., Analucia D. Schliemann, and David W.Carraher. "Mathematical Concepts in Everyday Life." In *Children's Mathematics,* edited by Geoffrey B. Saxe and Maryl Gearhart. San Francisco: Jossey-Bass, 1988.

Carraher, Terezinha N., and Analucia D. Schliemann. "Culture, Arithmetic and Mathematical Models." *Cultural Dynamics* 1, no. 2 (1988): 180–194.

Carraher, Terezinha N., David W. Carraher, and Analucia D. Schliemann. "Mathematics in the Streets and in the Schools." *British Journal of Developmental Psychology* 3 (1985): 21–29.

Carraher, Terezinha. "From Drawings to Buildings: Mathematical Scales at Work." *International Journal of Behavioral Development* 9 (1986): 527–544.

Carraher, Terezinha. "Material Embodiments of Mathematical Models in Everyday Life." In *Mathematics, Education, and Society,* edited by Christine Keitel. Paris: UNESCO Science and Technology Education Document Series No. 35, 1989.

Carver, R. P. "The Case Against Significance Testing." *Harvard Educational Review* 48 (1978): 378–399.

Celis, William III. "New Teaching Methods Put Math in Real Life." *The New York Times*, 16 June 1993, B7.

Celis, William III. "Down From the Self-Esteem High." *The New York Times* 1 August 1993, D3.

Certeau, Michel de. *Heterologies: Discourse on the Other.* Minneapolis: University of Minnesota Press, 1986.

Certeau, Michel de. *The Practice of Everyday Life.* Berkeley, Calif.: University of California Press, 1984.

Charen, Mona. "Bush Sets Right Education Goals." *The Ann Arbor News,* 1 May 1991, A9.

Charles, Harold E. "Innumeracy and Illiteracy." *Chicago Defender* 4 March 1989, 28: 1.

"Childrens' Math Aptitude Linked to Mom's Attitude." *Jet* 9 February 1988, 39.

Chu, D. "An Eminent Math Professor Says 'Innumeracy' Rivals Illiteracy as a Cause for Concern in America." *People Weekly* 31 (23 January 1989): 95–96+.

Cimons, Marlene. "Solving the Equation of Math Anxiety." *Los Angeles Times*, 23 October 1980, 1: 6.

Clifford, James. *The Predicament of Culture: Twentieth-Century Ethnography, Literature, and Art*. Cambridge, Mass.: Harvard University Press, 1988; quotes: 14–15.

Cline-Cohen, Patricia. *A Calculating People: The Spread of Numeracy in Early America*. Berkeley, Calif.: University of California Press, 1982.

Cohen, Richard. "Self Esteem: Sorry, No Extra Credit." *The Washington Post*, 12 June 1991, 114: A23, col 5.

Cohn, Marilyn, Robert B. Kottkamp, and Eugene F. Provenzo, Jr. *To Be a Teacher: Cases, Concepts, Observation Guides*. New York: Random House, 1987.

Colburn, Warren. *First Lessons in Arithmetic, on the Plan of Pestalozzi, with Some Improvements*. Boston: Cummings, Hilliard & Co., 1825.

Cooney, Thomas. "A Beginning Teacher's View of Problem Solving." *Journal for Research in Mathematics Education* 16, no. 5 (1985): 324–336.

Corliss, R. "Stand and Deliver." *Time*, 4 April 1988, 77.

Corran, G., and Valerie Walkerdine. "Reading the Signs of Mathematics." *In The Practice of Reason*, vol. 1. London: University of London Institute of Education, 1981.

Cortes, Carlos E. "Empowerment Through Media Literacy: A Multicultural Approach." In *Empowerment Through Multicultural Education*, edited by Christine E. Sleeter, 143–157. Albany: State University of New York Press, 1991.

Coxford, Arthur F., and Joseph N. Payne. *HBJ Algebra 2: With Trigonometry.* New York: Harcourt Brace Jovanovich, 1983/1987.

Cremin, Lawrence. *Public Education.* New York: Basic Books, 1976.

Cusick, Philip. *Inside High School.* New York: Holt, Rinehart & Winston, 1972.

D'Ambrosio, Ubiratan. "Ethnomathematics and Its Place in the History and Pedagogy of Mathematics." *For the Learning of Mathematics* 5, no. 1 (February 1985): 44–48.

D'Ambrosio, Ubiratan. *Sociocultural Bases for Mathematics Education.* Campinas, Brazil: UNICAMP, 1985.

Davis, Philip J., and Reuben Hersh. *Descartes' Dream: The World According to Mathematics.* San Diego: Harcourt Brace Jovanovich, 1986.

Davis, Philip J., and Reuben Hersh. *The Mathematical Experience.* Boston: Birkhauser, 1980.

Davis, Philip. "Applied Mathematics as a Social Contract." *In Mathematics, Education and Society,* edited by Christine Keitel. Paris: UNESCO document series no. 35, Science and Technology Education, 1989.

Davis, Robert B. *Learning Mathematics: The Cognitive Science Approach to Mathematics Education.* Norwood, N.J.: Ablex, 1984.

de Lauretis, Teresa, ed. *Feminist Studies, Critical Studies.* Bloomington, Ind.: Indiana University Press, 1986.

Del Castillo, Adelaida R., Jeanie Frederickson, Teresa McKenna, and Flora Ida Ortiz. "An Assessment of the Status of the Education of Hispanic American Women." In *The Broken Web: The Educational Experience of Hispanic American Women,* edited by Teresa McKenna and Flora Ida Ortiz. Berkeley, Calif.: Floricanto Press, 1988.

Dembart, Lee. "Biological Basis for Math Ability Suggested By Study." *Los Angeles Times,* 6 January 1984, 1: 1.

Denby, David. "Welcome to East L.A." *New York,* 18 April 1988, 102.

Derrida, Jacques. "L'age de Hegel." *In Qui a peur de la philosophie,* edited by GREPH [Group de recherches sur l'enseignement de la philosophie]. Paris: Aubier-Flammarion: 73–107.

Derrida, Jacques. *Speech and Phenomena.* Translated by David B. Allison. Evanston, Ill.: Northwestern University Press, 1973.

Dienes, Zoltan P., comp. *Mathematics in Primary Education: Learning of Mathematics by Young Children.* Hamburg, Germany: UNESCO International Studies in Education Series No. 164, 1966.

Dienes, Zoltan P., and M. A. Jeeves. *Thinking in Structures.* London: Hutchinson Educational, 1968.

Dolciani, Mary P., William Wooton, Edwin F. Beckenbach, et al. *Algebra 2 and Trigonometry.* Boston: Houghton Mifflin, 1980.

*Donald Duck in Mathmagicland.* Burbank, Calif.: Walt Disney Home Videos, 1969.

Doyle, Denis P. "Escalante: A classroom hero." *Across the Board* 26 (1989): 39.

Doyle, Denis P. "Why Johnny's Teacher Can't Do Algebra." *Across the Board* 26 (June 1989): 34–38+.

Driscoll, Mark. *Research Within Reach: Secondary School Mathematics. A research-guided response to the concerns of educators.* Reston, Va.: National Council of Teachers of Mathematics, 1982.

Dugdale, Sharon, and David Kibbey. *Green Globs and Graphing Equations.* Pleasantville, N.Y.: Sunburst Communications, 1986.

Eco, Umberto. "Social Life as a Sign System." In *Structuralism: An Introduction,* edited by D. Robey. Oxford: Clarendon, 1973.

Eco, Umberto. *The Role of the Reader: Explorations in the Semiotics of Texts.* London: Hutchinson, 1981.

Edelman, Murray. *Constructing the Political Spectacle*. Chicago: The University of Chicago Press, 1988.

Education Commission of the States Task Force on Education for Economic Growth. *Action for Excellence*. Denver, Colo.: Education Commission of the States ED 235 588, 1983.

Eggleston, John. *The Sociology of the School*. London: Routledge & Kegan Paul, 1977.

Epstein, Cynthia Fuchs. *Deceptive Distinctions: Sex, Gender, and the Social Order*. New Haven, Conn.: Yale University Press, 1988.

"Escalante: A Classroom Hero." *Across the Board* 26 (1989): 39.

Ethington, Corinna A. "Gender Differences in Mathematics: An international perspective." *Journal for Research in Mathematics Education* 21, no. 1 (January 1990): 74–80.

Everhart, Richard *Reading, Writing and Resistance*. Boston: Routledge & Kegan Paul, 1983.

Farber, Paul, and Gunilla Holm. "Teacher as Hero: Commercial Films of the 1980s." Paper presented at the annual meeting of the American Educational Studies Association, Orlando, Fla., 1990.

Fasheh, Munir. "Community Education: To Reclaim and Transform What Has Been Made Invisible." *Harvard Educational Review* 60, no. 1 (1990): 19–35.

Fasheh, Munir. "Mathematics in a Social Context: Math Within Education as Praxis Versus Within Education as Hegemony." In *Mathematics, Education, and Society*, edited by Christine Keitel. Paris: UNESCO Document Series No. 35, 1989.

Fasheh, Munir. "Mathematics, Culture and Authority." *For the Learning of Mathematics* 3, no. 2 (November 1982): 2–8.

Fennema, Elizabeth. "Justice, Equity, and Mathematics Education." In *Mathematics and Gender*, edited by Elizabeth Fennema and Gilah C. Leder. New York: Teachers College Press, 1990.

Fennema, Elizabeth. "Teachers' Beliefs and Gender Difference in Mathematics." In *Mathematics and Gender*, edited by Elizabeth Fennema and Gilah C. Leder. New York: Teachers College, 1990.

Fey, James T. "Surveying Today's Mathematics Teaching." *Mathematics Teacher* LXXI (October 1979): 490–504. Also published in *Education Digest* 45, no. 4 (1979): 19–22.

Fiske, Edward B. "Lessons: Behind Americans' problems with math, a question of social attitudes." *The New York Times*, 15 June 15 1988, 8.

Fiske, Edward B. "U.S. Pupils Lag in Math Ability, 3 Studies Find." *The New York Times*, 11 January 1987, 1.

Fiske, John. *Television Culture*. New York: Methuen, 1987.

Fiske, John. *Understanding Popular Culture*. Boston: Unwin Hyman, 1989.

Fitzgerald, Randy. "The Teacher They Call the 'Champ'." *Readers Digest* August 1983, 119–122.

Foucault, Michel. *Discipline and Punish: The Birth of the Prison*. New York: Pantheon Books, 1977.

Foucault, Michel. *Power/Knowledge: Selected Interviews and Other Writings*. Brighton, England: Harvester Press, 1980.

Fox, Lynn H. "The Effects of Sex Role Socialization on Mathematics Participation and Achievement." In *Women and Mathematics: Research Perspectives for Change*, edited by Lynn H. Fox, Elizabeth Fennema and Julia Sherman, 1–78. Washington, D.C.: National Institute of Education, 1977.

Freudenthal, Hans. *Didactical Phenomenology of Mathematical Structures*. Dordrecht, Holland: Dreidel, 1983.

Freudenthal, Hans. *Weeding and Sowing*. Dordrecht, Holland: Dreidel, 1977.

Friedman, Lynn. "Mathematics and the Gender Gap: A meta-analysis of recent studies on sex differences in mathematical tasks." *Review of Educational Research* 59, no. 2 (Summer 1989): 185–213.

Fuys, David. "Van Hiele Levels in Geometry." *Education and Urban Society* 17, no. 4 (August 1985): 447–462.

Gagne, Robert M., and Robert A. Reiser. *Selecting Media for Instruction*. Englewood Cliffs, N.J.: Educational Technology Publications, 1983.

Gagne, Robert M. *Principles of Instructional Design*. New York: Holt, Rinehart & Winston, 1974.

Gans, Herbert J. "The Mass Media as an Educational Institution." *Television Quarterly* 6 (1967): 20–37.

Garcia, Mario T. *Mexican Americans: Leadership, Ideology & Identity*. New Haven, Conn.: Yale University Press, 1989.

Garofalo, Joe. "Metacognition and School Mathematics." *Arithmetic Teacher* 34, no. 9 (May 1987): 22–23.

"The Gender Factor in Math." *Time,* 15 December 1980: 57.

Gerdes, Paul. "Conditions and Strategies for Emancipatory Mathematics Education in Underseveloped Countries." *For the Learning of Mathematics* 5, no. 1: 15–20.

Gilligan, Carol. *In a Different Voice*. Cambridge, Mass: Harvard University Press, 1982.

Gillman, Leonard. "Teaching Programs that Work." *Focus: The Newsletter of the Mathematical Association of America* 10, no. 1 (January–February 1990): 7.

"Girls Could Equal Boys at Math, Study Asserts." *Detroit News,* 15 April 1980, A-3:3.

Giroux, Henry A. "Citizenship, Public Philosophy, and the Struggle for Democracy." *Educational Theory* 37, no. 2 (1987): 1103–1120.

Giroux, Henry A. *Teachers as Intellectuals: Toward a Critical Pedagogy of Learning*. Granby, Mass.: Bergin & Garvey Press, 1988.

Giroux, Henry A., and Roger I. Simon. "Popular Culture and Critical Pedagogy." In *Critical Pedagogy, the State, and Cultural Struggle*, edited by Henry A. Giroux and Peter McLaren. Albany, N.Y.: State University of New York Press, 1989.

Gold, Todd. "Behind the Scenes of America's #1 Game Show." *McCall's* (October 1986): 162–165.

Goldberger, Mildred G. "Figuring the Odds Against Women." *Los Angeles Times*, 28 January 1982, V-8: 1.

Goleman, Danial. "Girls and Math: Is biology really destiny?" *The New York, Times* Special Education Life Section, 27 August 1987, 42: 1.

Goodlad, John I. *A Place Called School: Prospects for the Future*. New York: McGraw-Hill, 1983.

Goodrich, Chris. "Big Numbers for Innumeracy: Hill & Wang's first bestseller heralds a new direction." Publishers Weekly 235 (2 June 1989): 46–48.

Gramsci, Antonio. *Selections from the Prison Notebooks*. London: Lawrence & Wishart, 1971.

Greene, Maxine. *Teacher As Stranger: Educational Philosophy for the Modern Age*. Belmont, Calif.: Wadsworth Pub. Co., 1973.

Greene, Maxine. *The Dialectic of Freedom*. New York: Teachers College Press, 1988.

Gross, Jane. "To Help Girls Keep Up: Math Class Without Boys." *The New York Times*, 24 November 1993, B9.

Grossberger, Lewis. "Triumph of the Wheel." *Rolling Stone*, 4 December 1986, 64.

Gusfield, Joseph. *The Culture of Public Problems: Drinking-Driving and the Symbolic Order.* Chicago, University of Chicago Press, 1981.

Hall, Stuart. "Culture, the Media and the 'Ideological Effect'." In *Mass Communication and Society,* edited by James Curran. Beverly Hills, Calif.: Sage, 1977.

Hanna, Gila. "Girls and Boys About Equal in Mathematics Achievement in Eighth Grade: Results from Twenty Countries." *Educational Studies in Mathematics,* 20, no. 2 (May 1989): 225–32.

Hashway, Robert M. "Sex Differences in Mathematics Achievement—Are They Real?" *Phi Delta Kappan* 63 (October 1981): 139–140.

Hebdige, Dick. *Subculture: The Meaning of Style.* London: Methuen, 1979.

Heikkinen, Michael W. "On the Supply of Science and Math Teachers in Idaho." *Phi Delta Kappan* 64 (December 1982): 288.

Henriques, Julian, et al. *Changing the Subject: Psychology, Social Regulations and Subjectivity.* London: Methuen, 1984.

Higginson, William. "On the Foundations of Mathematics Education." *For the Learning of Mathematics* 1, no. 2 (November 1980): 3–7.

Hirsch, E. D. *Cultural Literacy: What Every American Needs to Know.* Boston: Houghton Mifflin, 1987.

Holmes Group, The. *Tomorrow's Teachers.* East Lansing, Mich.: The Holmes Group, 1986.

Hook, Janet. "House Clears Bill Allowing Prayer Meetings in Schools; Attached to Math-Science Aid." *Congressional Quarterly Weekly* 42 (28 July 1984): 1807–1808.

Hubbard, Kim. "Beating Long Odds, Jaime Escalante Stands and Delivers, Helping to Save a Faltering High School." *People Weekly* 29 (11 April 1988): 57.

Jackson, Philip. *Life in Classrooms.* New York: Holt, Rinehart & Winston, 1968.

Jetter, Alexis. "Mississippi Learning." *The New York Times*, 21 February 1992, VI: 28: 1–35.

Jones, Philip S., and Arthur F. Coxford, eds. *A History of Mathematics Education in the United States and Canada*. Washington, D.C.: The National Council of Teachers of Mathematics, 1970.

Kanfer, Stefan. "To Conquer Fear of Counting." *Time*, 30 January 1989, 66.

Katz, Lilian G. "Reading, Writing, Narcissism." *The New York Times*, 15 July 1993, A25.

Keeves, J. P. "Sex Difference in Ability and Achievement." *The International Encyclopedia of Education*, 4538–4544. New York: Pergamon Press, 1985.

Keitel, Christine, ed. *Mathematics, Education, and Society*. Paris: UNESCO Document Series No. 35, 1989.

Keitel, Christine. "Mathematics Education and Technology." *For the Learning of Mathematics* 9, no. 1 (February 1989): 103–120.

Kevles, Betty Ann. "Do Boys' Superior Math Skills Add Up?" *Los Angeles Times*, 29 August 1984, V-10: 1.

Kiester, Edwin, Jr., and Sally Valente Kiester. "Everyday Math for Grownups." *Readers Digest*, October 1989, 43–48.

Knapp, Michael S., Andrew Zucker, Nancy Adelman, and Mark St. John. *The Eisenhower Mathematics and Science Education Program: An Enabling Resource for Reform. Summary Report*. National Study of the Education for Economic Security Act (EESA) Title II Program. Washington, D.C.: Planning and Evaluation Service, Office of Planning, Budget and Evaluation, U.S. Department of Education, February 1991.

Knuth, Donald E. *Surreal Numbers: How Two Ex-Students Turned on to Pure Mathematics and Found Total Happiness*. Reading, Mass: Addison-Wesley, 1974.

Koehler, Mary Schatz. "Classrooms, Teachers, and Gender Differences in Mathematics." In *Mathematics and Gender*, edited by Elizabeth Fennema and Gilah C. Leder, 128–148. New York: Teachers College, 1990.

Kosel, Marge, and Mike Fish. *The Factory: Strategies in Problem Solving*. Pleasantville, N.Y.: Sunburst Communications, 1983.

Kosel, Marge, Jay Carlson, and Melissa Verber. *The Incredible Laboratory: Strategies in Problem Solving*. Pleasantville, N.Y.: Sunburst Communications, 1984.

Kroll, Jack. "To Señor, With Love, Brains and Ganas." *Newsweek*, 14 March 1988.

Kuendiger, Erika. "Mathematics—A Male Subject?" In *Mathematics, Education, and Society*, edited by Christine Keitel. Paris: UNESCO Science and Technology Education Document Series No. 35, 1989: 134–138.

Kuntz, Phil. "Science and Math Training Stirs Concern on Hill." *Congressional Quarterly Weekly* 47, no. 33 (19 August 1989): 2179–2183.

Kupfer, Andrew. "Turning Students on to Science." *Fortune*, Special Save Our Schools Issue (Spring 1990): 82–83+.

Lakatos, Imré. *Proofs and Refutations: The Logic of Mathematical Discovery*. Cambridge: Cambridge University Press, 1976.

Lang, Serge. *Math! Encounters with High School Students*. New York: Springer-Verlag, 1985.

Lardner, James. "Stand and Deliver; The Milagro Beanfield War." *The Nation* 246 (30 April 1988): 619.

Larkin, Ralph. *Suburban Youth in Cultural Crisis*. New York: Oxford University Press, 1979.

Lave, Jean. *Cognition in Practice: Mind, Mathematics, and Culture in Everyday Life*. Cambridge/New York: Cambridge University Press, 1988.

Lave, Jean. *Situated Learning: Legitimate Peripheral Participation*. New York: Cambridge University Press, 1991.

Leder, Gilah C. Gender Differences in Mathematics: An Overview. In *Mathematics and Gender*, edited by Elizabeth Fennema and Gilah C. Leder, 10–26. New York: Teachers College, 1990.

Leder, Gilah C., and Elizabeth Fennema. "Gender Differences in Mathematics: A Synthesis." In *Mathematics and Gender*, edited by Elizabeth Fennema and Gilah C. Leder, 188–199. New York: Teachers College, 1990.

Leitzel, James R. C., ed. Committee on the Mathematical Education of Teachers, The Mathematical Association of America. *A Call for Change: Recommendations for the Mathematical Preparation of teachers of Mathematics*. Reston, Va.: National Council of Teachers of Mathematics, 1991.

Lerman, Stephen. "Alternative Perspectives of the Nature of Mathematics and Their Influence on the Teaching of Mathematics." *British Educational Research Journal* 16, no. 1 (1990): 53–61.

Lerman, Stephen. "Constructivism, Mathematics and Mathematics Education," *Educational Studies in Mathematics* 20, no. 2 (May 1989): 211–223.

Lerner, Ned. *Chuck Yaeger Flight Simulator*. Calif.: Electronic Arts.

Leroux, Janice A., and Cheeying Ho. "Success and Mathematically Gifted Female Students: The Challenge Continues." *Feminist Teacher* 7, no. 2 (1993): 42–48.

Levi-Strauss, Claude. *The Raw and the Cooked*. New York: Harper & Row, 1975.

Lightfoot, Sarah Lawrence. *The Good High School: Portraits of Character and Culture*. New York: Basic Books, 1983.

Lipsitz, George. *Time Passages: Collective Memory and American Popular Culture*. Minneapolis: University of Minnesota Press, 1991.

Lochhead, Jack. "An Anarchistic Approach to Teaching Problem-Solving Methods." Paper read at the annual meeting of the American Education Research Association, Symposium: Can We Teach Problem Solving? San Francisco, April 1989.

Lochhead, Jack. "Research Synthesis on Problem Solving." *Educational Leadership* 39 (1981): 68–70.

Maccoby, Eleanor E., and Carol N. Jacklin. *The Psychology of Sex Differences*. Stanford University Press, 1974.

March, James, and Johan Olsen. *Ambiguity and Choice in Organization*. Bergen, Norway: Universitetsforlaget, 1976.

Martin, John H., chair. *The Education of Adolescents*. Washington, D.C.: National Panel on High School and Adolescent Education, U.S. Government Printing Office, 1974.

"Math Skills Linked to Hormone." *The Detroit News*, 27 May 1986, A-1: 2.

Mathematical Sciences Education Board of the National Research Council. *Counting on You: Actions Supporting Mathematics Teaching Standards*. Washington, D.C.: National Academy Press, 1991.

Matthews, Jay. *Escalante: The Best Teacher in America*. New York: Henry Holt, 1988.

Matthews, Jay. "Miracle Worker of Garfield High." *Readers Digest*, January 1989, 196. Condensed from Matthews' book.

McCormack, Patricia. "The Lasting Crisis in Math, Science: U.S. Education Droops in the Era of High Technology." *Los Angeles Times*, 27 December 1982, V, 12: 3.

McGrath, E. "Low-Tech Teaching Blues." *Time*, 27 December 1982, 67.

McLaren, Peter. *Schooling and Ritual Performance*. Boston: Routledge & Kegan Paul, 1985.

McNett, Ian. "Teaching Math by the Socratic Method." *Education Digest* 45, no. 7 (March 1980): 43.

Meek, Anne. "On Creating Ganas: A conversation with Jaime Escalante." *Educational Leadership* (February 1989).

Mellin-Olsen, Stieg. *The Politics of Mathematics Education*. Dordrecht, Holland: D. Reidel, 1987.

Meyer, Margaret R., and Mary Schatz Koehler. "Internal Influences on Gender Influences in Mathematics." *In Mathematics and Gender*, edited by Elizabeth Fennema and Gilah C. Leder, 60–95. New York: Teachers College, 1990.

Morrison, D. E., and R. E. Henkle, eds. *The Significance Test Controversy*. Chicago: Aldine, 1970.

Mulkeen, Thomas. "Introduction, Special Issue on New Trends in Mathematics Education." *Education and Urban Society* 17, no. 4 (August 1985): 371–376.

Mura, R. "Feminist Views on Mathematics." *International Organization of Women and Mathematics Newsletter* 3, no. 2 (1987): 6–11.

National Council of Teachers of Mathematics (NCTM). *An Agenda for Action*. Reston, Va.: NCTM, 1980.

National Council of Teachers of Mathematics. Commission on Standards for School Mathematics. *Curriculum and Evaluation Standards for School Mathematics*. Reston, Va.: NCTM, 1989.

National Council of Teachers of Mathematics. *A General Survey of Progress in the Last 25 Years*. First Yearbook. Reston, Va.: NCTM, 1926/1966.

National Council of Teachers of Mathematics. Commission on Teaching Standards for School Mathematics. *Professional Standards for Teaching Mathematics*. Reston, Va.: NCTM, 1991.

National Council of Teachers of Mathematics. *Curriculum and Evaluation Standards for School Mathematics*. Reston, Va.: NCTM.

Neill, George. "NAEP at Age 10 Says: Schools Are in Trouble." *Phi Delta Kappan* 61 (November 1979): 157.

Nesher, Perla. "A Research Programme for Mathematics Education." *For the Learning of Mathematics* 1, no. 3 (March 1981): 47–50.

Nesher, Perla. "The Stereotyped Nature of School Word Problems." *For the Learning of Mathematics* 2, no. 1 (July 1980): 27–28.

Neusner, Jacob. *The Systemic Analysis of Judaism*. Atlanta, Georgia: Scholars Press, 1988.

"New Study Finds Boys Beat Girls at Math." *Los Angeles Times*, 21 December 1980, 1-A: 7: 1.

Nyberg, David. *Power Over Power*. Ithaca, N.Y.: Cornell University Press, 1981.

O'Brien, Tom. "Two Heroes: 'Cry of Reason' & 'Deliver'." *Commonweal* 115 (3 June 1988): 342.

Ohmann, Richard. *The Politics of Letters*. Middletown, Conn.: Wesleyan University Press, 1987.

Olneck, Michael. "The Recurring Dream: Symbolism and Ideology in Intercultural and Multicultural Education." *American Journal of Education* (February 1990): 147–174.

Olson, Lynn. "Goodlad on Teacher Education: Low status, unclear mission." *Education Week* 28, no. 1 (February 1990): 27–28.

Papert, Seymour. *The Children's Machine*. New York: Basic Books, 1993.

Papert, Seymour. *Mindstorms: Children, Computers, and Powerful Ideas*. New York: Basic Books, 1980.

Papy, Frederique. *Frederique's Stories*. St. Louis: CEMREL (Central Midwestern Regional Laboratory).

Parker, Ruth E. *Mathematical Power: Lessons From a Classroom*. Portsmouth, N.H.: Heinemann, 1993.

Parkin, David. "Controlling the U-Turn of Knowledge." In *Power and Knowledge: Anthropological and Sociological Approaches*, edited by Fardon, Richard. Edinburgh: Scottish Academic Press, 1985.

Passow, A. Harry. *Reforming Schools in the 1980s: A Critical Review of the National Reports*. New York: ERIC Clearinghouse on Urban Education No. 84, Institute for Urban and Minority Education, Teachers College, Columbia University, 1984.

Patton, Phil. "Who Owns 'X'?" *The New York Times.*, 8 November 1992, 9: 1.

Paul, Clyde. "Suggestions for Solving the Mathematics Teacher Shortage." *Education Digest* 46, no. 9 (May 1981): 42–44.

Paulos, John Allen. *Innumeracy: Mathematical Illiteracy and Its Consequences*. New York: Hill & Wang, 1988.

Petersen, Anne C., et al. "Sex Differences." In *Encyclopedia of Educational Research*, fifth edition, edited by H. E. Mitzel, 1696–1712. New York: Free Press, 1982.

Pictorial/Cover Story. *Playboy*. May 1987, 134+.

Pimm, David. *Speaking Mathematically—Communication in Mathematics Classrooms*. London: Routledge & Kegan Paul, 1987.

Pinxten, Rik, I. van Dooren, and E. Soberon. *Towards a Navajo Geometry*. Ghent, Belgium: K.K.I., 1987.

Pinxten, Rik, Ingrid van Dooren, and Frank Harvey. *Anthropology of Space*. Philadelphia: University of Pennsylvania Press, 1983.

Piven, Frances Fox, and Richard A. Cloward. *The New Class War*. New York: Pantheon Books, 1982.

Polakow, Valerie. *The Erosion of Childhood*. Chicago: University of Chicago Press, 1982.

Pollan, Michael. "Jackpot! The biggest, shrewdest, moneymakingest little show on earth." *Channels of Communications* 6 (June 1986): 22.

Polya, George. *How to Solve It: A New Aspect of Mathematical Method.* Princeton, N.J.: Princeton University Press, 1945/46/71/73.

Polya, George. *Mathematical Discovery: On Understanding, Learning, and Teaching Problem Solving.* New York: Wiley, 1962.

Polya, George. *Mathematics and Plausible Reasoning.* Princeton, N.J.: Princeton University Press, 1954.

"Problems! Math skills are down again." *Time,* 24 September 1979, 55.

Progressive Education Association. *Mathematics in General Education: A Report of the Committee on the Function of Mathematics in General Education for the Commission on Secondary School Curriculum.* New York: D. Appleton Century Company, 1938.

Rabine, Leslie Wahl. "A Feminist Politics of Non-Identity." *Feminist Studies* 14 (Spring 1988): 11–31.

*Readers' Guide to Periodical Literature.* New York: H. W. Wilson Co.

"Researchers Dispute Role of Genetics in Math Achievements By the Sexes." *Phi Delta Kappan* 63 (March 1982): 435–436.

Resnick, Lauren B. "Learning In School and Out." *Phi Delta Kappan* (December 1987): 13–19.

Richardson, Lynda. "Up Tempo Teaching by Rapping Right Triangles." *The New York Times,* 17 November 1993, B7.

Riddell, Sheila. "Pupils, Resistance, and Gender Codes: A study of classroom encounters." *Gender and Education* 1, no. 2 (1989): 183–197.

Rivers, Caryl. "Got Good Math Genes?" The New York Times, 30 May 1981, I-23: 2.

Rogers, Pat. "Gender Differences in Mathematical Ability—Perceptions vs. Performance." *Association for Women in Mathematics Newsletter (AMM Newsletter)* 19, no. 4: 6–10. Reprinted in Leone Burton, ed., *Gender and Mathematics: An International Perspective.* Strand, England: Cassell Educational Limited, 1990, 38–46.

Rosen, Marjorie. "I Tri-d T- B-at Th- -h—l -f F-rt-n-." *Glamour,* September 1987, 178.

Rotberg, Iris C. "Math and Science Education: A New Perspective." *Education Digest* 50, no. 6 (February 1985): 24–27.

Rotberg, Iris C. "Math and Science Education: A New Perspective." *Phi Delta Kappan* 65 (May 1984): 668–673.

Rotman, Brian. "Mathematics: An Essay in Semiotics." Bristol, England: University of Bristol Mimeo, 1980.

Rotman, Brian. *Signifying Nothing: The Semiotics of Zero.* London: Macmillan Press, 1987.

Rucker, Rudy. *Mind Tools: The Five Levels of Mathematical Reality.* Boston: Houghton Mifflin, 1987.

Russell, Bertrand. *Power: A New Social Analysis.* New York: Norton, 1938.

Said, Edward W. *Covering Islam: How the Media and the Experts Determine How We See the Rest of the World.* New York: Pantheon Books, 1981.

Said, Edward. *Orientalism.* New York: Pantheon Books, 1978.

Salholz, Eloise, and Rosalyn Jones. "Curing Math Anxiety." *Newsweek* 23 August 1982, 71.

Saussure, Ferdinand de. *Course in General Linguistics.* London: Duckworth, 1983.

Saxon, John. "Al-ge-bra- Made . . . Understandable." *National Review* 33, no. 10 (29 May 1981): 584.

Saxon, John. *Algebra I: An Incremental Development*. Norman, Okla.: Grassdale, 1982.

Saxon, John. "Breakthrough in Algebra." *National Review* 33, no. 20 (16 October 1981): 1206.

Saxon, John. "Save Our Mathematics!" *National Review* 35 (19 August 1983): 1016.

Schick, Lawrence. *Heroic Worlds: A History and Guide to Role-Playing Games*. Buffalo, N.Y.: Prometheus Books, 1991.

Schmeck, Harold M., Jr. "Boys Better Than Girls In Math Test." *The New York Times*, 29 November 1983, III-2: 1.

Schoenfeld, Alan H. *Mathematical Problem Solving*. New York: Academic Press, 1983.

Schoenfeld, Alan H. "Some Thoughts on Problem-solving Research and Mathematics Education." In *Mathematical Problem Solving: Issues in Research*, edited by Frank K. Lester and Joe Garofalo. Philadelphia: The Franklin Institute Press, 1982.

Schwab, Joseph. *The Practical: A Language for Curriculum*. Washington, D.C.: National Education Association. Center for the Study of Instruction, 1970.

Schwartz, Judah L., and Michal Yerushalmy. *The Geometric Supposer*. Newton, Mass.: Education Development Center, 1986.

Scott, Joan Wallach. *Gender and the Politics of History*. New York: Columbia University Press, 1988.

Scott, Vernon. "The Millionaire Who Made Vanna White a Star." *Good Housekeeping* 204 (May 1987): 66+.

Scott, Vernon. "Vanna White and Me." *Good Housekeeping* 205 (November) 1987: 34+.

Sells, Lucy. "Mathematics—a Critical Filter." The Science Teacher 45, no. 2 (February 1978): 28–29.

Shapiro, Svi. "Back to Basics: A Politics of Meaning for Education." *Tikkun* 8, no. 1 (January/February 1993): 46–50, 75–76.

Shapiro, Svi. "Educational Theory and Recent Political Discourse: A new agenda for the left?" *Harvard Educational Review* 89, no. 2 (1987): 171–200.

Sharp, Rachel, and Anthony Green. *Education and Social Control: A Study in Progressive Education.* London: Routledge & Kegan Paul, 1975.

Rachel Sharp, *Knowledge, Ideology, and the Politics of Schooling: Towards a Marxist Analysis of Education.* Boston: Routledge & Kegan Paul, 1980.

Sherman, Jean. "I Took a Turn On Wheel of Fortune." *Seventeen* (July 1987): 28.

Sherman, Julia A. *Sex-related Cognitive Differences: An Essay on Theory and Evidence.* Springfield, Ill.: Thomas, 1978.

Shor, Ira. *Culture Wars: School and Society in the Conservative Restoration, 1969–1984.* Boston: Routledge & Kegan Paul, 1986.

Shulman, Lee S. "Toward a Pedagogy of Substance." *AAHE Bulletin* (June 1989): 8–13.

Simon, Roger I. "Work Experience." In *Critical Pedagogy and Cultural Power,* edited by David W. Livingstone et al., 155–177. South Hadley, Mass.: Bergin & Garvey, 1987.

Singmaster, David. *Rubik's Magic Cube.* Hillsdale, N.J.: Enslow, 1981.

"Skill Shortages Threaten Technological Prowess." *Futurist* 18, no. 1 (February 1984): 79–80.

Skovsmose, Ole. "Mathematical Education Versus Critical Education." *Educational Studies in Mathematics* 16, no. 4 (November 1985): 337–354.

Skovsmose, Ole. *Towards a Philosophy of Critical Mathematics Education*. Dordrecht, Netherlands: Kluwer Academic Publishers, 1994.

Smith, David Eugene. *The Teaching of Junior High School Mathematics*. Boston: Ginn, 1927.

Snyder, Robert. "The Patterson Jewish Folk Chorus: Politics, Ethnicity and Musical Culture." *American Jewish History* 74 (September 1984): 27–44.

Soffer, Susan. "I Got Behind The Wheel of Fortune." *Redbook* (January 1986): 26.

Stake, Jayne E., and Joan M. Singer. "Mathematics and Self-Esteem: Implications for Women's Career Choice." *Psychology of Women Quarterly* 10 (December 1986): 339–351.

Stake, Robert E., and Jack Easley, eds. *Case Studies in Science Education*. Urbana, Ill.: University of Illinois, 1978.

*Stand and Deliver*. Burbank, Calif.: Warner Home Video, 1988. Videocassette.

"Stand and Deliver." *Glamour*, May 1988, 215–216.

Stanley, Julian C., and Camilla P. Benbow. "Educational Policy Recommendations for Mathematically Precocious Youths." *Educational Researcher* (May 1982). Also published in *Educational Digest* 48, no. 3 (November 1982): 40–42.

Streibel, Michael J. "A Critical Analysis of Three Approaches to the Use of Computers in Education." In *The Curriculum: Problems, Politics, and Possibilities*, edited by Landon E. Beyer and Michael W. Apple, 259-288. Albany, N.Y.: State University of New York Press, 1988.

"Students' Hesitance to Study Science, Math Examined." *Los Angeles Times*, 7 December 1984, A-7: 1.

"Studying Math Development." *Children Today* 10, no. 6 (November–December 1981): 25–26.

Suydam, Marilyn N., and Alan Osborne. *Mathematics Education.* Vol. 2 of *The Status of Pre-College Science, Mathematics, and Social Science Education: 1955–1975.* Columbus, Ohio: The Ohio State University Center for Science and Mathematics Education, 1977.

Swinson, Ginny, and Peter Haines. "How I (And the Taxman) Won $27,000 In Prizes On Wheel of Fortune." Good Housekeeping, May 1987, 72.

The National Commission on Excellence in Education. *A Nation at Risk: The Imperative for Educational Reform.* Washington, D.C.: U.S. Government Printing Office, April 1983.

"The Odds are You're Innumerate." *The New York Times,* 1 January 1989, 1+.

Thom, Rene. "Modern Mathematics: Does It Exist?" In *Developments in Mathematics Education,* edited by A. G. Howson. Cambridge: Cambridge University Press, 1972.

Thompson, Alba Gonzalez. "The Relationship of Teachers' Conceptions of Mathematics and Mathematics Teaching to Instructional Practice." *Educational Studies in Mathematics* 15 (1984): 105–127.

Tobias, Sheila. *Overcoming Math Anxiety.* New York: Houghton Mifflin, 1978.

Tobias, Sheila. *They're Not Dumb, They're Different: Stalking the Second Tier.* Tucson, Ariz.: Research Corporation, 1990.

Tom, Alan R. *Teaching as a Moral Craft.* New York: Longman, 1984.

"United Negro College Fund. A Mind is a Terrible Thing To Waste." *The New York Times,* 17 October 1993, N.J. 14.

U.S. Department of Education. *What Works: Research about Teaching and Learning.* Washington, D.C.: U.S. Government Printing Office, 1986.

"U.S. Report Fears Most Americans Will Become Scientific Illiterates." *The New York Times,* 23 October 1980, A, 22, 3.

U.S. Senate Comm. on Governmental Affairs. Crisis in Science and Math Education: Hearing, November 9, 1989. Supt. Docs Y4-G74/9:S. hrg 101–561, 1990.

U.S. Senate Comm. on Governmental Affairs. Precollege Science and Math Education: Hearing, February 28, 1990. Supt. Docs Y4. Sci 2:101/94, 1990.

Ulstein, Stefan. "Great Teachers Rock the Boat." *Christianity Today* 32, no. 61 (2 September 1988): 61.

Usiskin, Zalman, et al. *Transition Mathematics.* Glenview, Ill.: Scott, Foresman, 1990.

Usiskin, Zalman. "The UCSMP: Translating Grades 712 Mathematics Recommendations into Reality." *Educational Leadership* 44, no. 4 (December–January 1986–87): 30–35.

Usiskin, Zalman. "We Need Another Revolution in Secondary School Mathematics." In *The Secondary School Mathematics Curriculum,* edited by Christian R. Hirsch and Marilyn J. Zweng, 1–21. Reston, Va.: NCTM, 1985.

Van Hiele, Pierre. *Structure and Insight: A Theory of Mathematics Education.* Orlando, Fla.: Academic Press, 1986.

*Visible Language* XI, no. 3 (1982).

Walden, Rosie, and Valerie Walkerdine. "Characteristics, Views and Relationships in the Classroom." In *Girls Into Maths Can Go,* edited by Leone Burton, 122-146. New York: Holt, Rinehart & Winston, 1986.

Walden, Rosie, and Valerie Walkerdine. *Girls and Mathematics: The Early Years.* London: University of London Institute of Education, Bedford Way Papers 8, 1982.

Walker, James. "Rebels With Our Applause." *Journal of Education* 167, no. 2 (1985): 63–83.

Walkerdine, Valerie, comp. *Counting Girls Out.* London: Virago Press, 1989.

Walkerdine, Valerie. "It's Only Natural: Rethinking child-centered pedagogy." *In Is There Anyone Here From Education? Education after Thatcher,* edited by Ann-Marie Wolpe and James Donald. London: Pluto Press, 1983.

Walkerdine, Valerie. "On the Regulation of Speaking and Silence: Subjectivity, class and gender in contemporary schooling." In *Language, Gender and Childhood,* edited by Carolyn Steedman, Cathy Urwin and Valerie Walkerdine, 203-241. London: Routledge & Kegan Paul, 1985.

Walkerdine, Valerie. "Sex, Power and Pedagogy." *Screen Education* 38 (1981): 14–21.

Walkerdine, Valerie. "Subjectivity, Discourse and Practice in Mathematics Education." In *Political Dimensions of Mathematics Education: Action & Critique,* edited by Richard Noss, Andrew Brown, et. al. London: Department of Mathematics, Statistics and Computing, Institute of Education, University of London, 1990.

Walkerdine, Valerie. *The Mastery of Reason: Cognitive Development and the Production of Meaning.* New York: Routledge, 1987.

Waller, Willard. *The Sociology of Teaching.* New York: John Wiley, 1932/1965.

Waters, Harry F. "What a Deal!" *Newsweek,* 9 February 1987, 62–68.

Weber, Max. *On Charisma and Institution Building.* Shmuel Noah Eisenstadt (ed.). Chicago: University of Chicago Press, 1968.

*Webster's New Collegiate Dictionary.* Springfield, Mass.: G & C Merriam, 1977.

Weiler, Kathleen. *Women Teaching for Change: Gender, Class & Power.* South Hadley, Mass.: Bergin & Garvey, 1988.

Weinstein, Matthew. "Robot World: Crossing the Borders Between Official & Popular Culture." Paper presented at the annual meeting of the American Eduational Research Association, New Orleans, 1994.

Weiss, Iris. *Report of the 1977 National Survey of Science, Mathematics, and Social Studies Education.* Research Triangle Park, N.C.: Research Triangle Institute, 1978.

Weis, Lois. *Working Class Without Work.* New York: Routledge, 1990.

Welker, Robert. "Expertise and the Teacher as Expert: Rethinking a Questionable Metaphor." *American Educational Research Journal* 28, no. 1 (Spring 1991): 19–35.

Wexler, Henrietta. "The Man Who Loves Junior High." *American Educator* 18 (July 1982): 29–31.

Wexler, Philip. *Social Analysis of Education: After the New Sociology.* London/New York: Routledge & Kegan Paul, 1987.

White, Vanna. *Vanna Speaks.* New York: Warner Books, 1987.

Whitty, Geoff, and Michael Young, eds. *Explorations in the Politics of School Knowledge.* Nafferton, Driffield, England: Nafferton Books, 1976.

"Who Is Really Better at Math?" *Time,* 22 March 1982, 64.

Williams, Dennis A., and Patricia King. "Do Males Have a Math Gene?" *Newsweek,* 15 December 1980, 73.

Williams, Dennis A., Marsha Zabarsky, and Barbara Burgower. "Bait for Science Teachers." *Newsweek,* 14 February 1983, 79.

Williams, Raymond. "Base and Superstructure in Marxist Cultural Theory." In *Schooling and Capitalism: a Sociological Reader,* edited by Roger Dale, et al. London: Routledge & Kegan Paul, 1976.

Williams, Raymond. *Marxism and Literature*. Oxford: Oxford University Press, 1977.

Williams, Raymond. *The Long Revolution*. London: Chatto & Windus, 1961.

Willis, Paul. *Learning to Labor: How Working Class Kids Get Working Class Jobs*. New York: Columbia University Press, 1981.

Winnett, Susan, trans. "L'age de Hegel." *Glyph Textual Studies I*. Minneapolis: University of Minnesota Press, 1986.

"Women in Math: A rising trend." *Los Angeles Times*, 17 April 1980, V-28: 1.

Worrill, Conrad W. "Teaching Math and Science." Chicago Defender, 9 May 1990, 10:1.

Young, Jacob William Albert. *The Teaching of Mathematics in the Elementary and Secondary School*. New York: Longmans, Green & Co., 1907, 1914, 1931.

Young, Michael F. D., ed. *Knowledge and Control*. London: Collier-Macmillan, 1971.

Young, Michael F. D. "An Approach to the Study of Curricula as Socially Organized Knowledge." In *Knowledge and Control*, edited by Michael F. D. Young. London: Collier-Macmillan, 1971.

Young, Michael. Foreword. In *Towards a Critical Alternative to Internationalism and Monoculturalism in Mathematics Education*, by Andrew Brown and Paul Dowling. London: Centre for Multicultural Education, Institute of Education, University of London, Working Paper No. 10, 1989.

Zalewski, Donald L. "A study of Problem-solving Performance Measures." *In Problem-Solving Studies in Mathematics*, edited by John G. Harvey and Thomas A. Romberg, 67–91. Madison, Wisc.: Research and Development Center for Individualized Schooling, 1980.

Zaslavsky, Claudia. *Africa Counts: Number and Pattern in African Culture.* Boston: Prindle, Weber & Schmidt, 1973; paperback, Chicago: L. Hill, 1979.

Zoglin, Richard. "Game Shows Hit the Jackpot." *Time*, 24 February 1986, 78.

Zoglin, Richard. "Multiple Fun on Square One." *Time*, 23 February 1987, 86.

# INDEX